GAZETEER OF SLATE
QUARRYING IN WALES

Gazeteer of
Slate Quarrying in Wales

Alun John Richards

ISBN: 1-84524-074-X
978-1-84524-074-5

Cover design: Sian Parri

Published by
Llygad Gwalch, Ysgubor Plas, Llwyndyrys, Pwllheli,
Gwynedd, Wales LL53 6NG.
℡ 01758 750432
✆ gai@llygadgwalch.com
Website: www.llygadgwalch.com

Books by Alun John Richards

Gazeteer of Slate Quarrying in Wales
ISBN 0-84524-074-X / 978-1-84524-074-5
Slate Quarrying at Corris
ISBN 1-84524-068-5 / 978-1-84524-068-45
Slate Quarrying in Wales
ISBN 0-86381-319-4
Slate Quarrying in Pembrokeshire
ISBN 0-86381-484-0
The Slate Regions of North& Mid Wales
ISBN 0-86381-552-9
The Slate Railways of Wales
ISBN 0-86381-689-4
Fragments of Mine and Mill
ISBN 0-86381-812-9
Cwm Gwyrfai   (With Gwynfor Pierce Jones)
ISBN 0-86381-987-8
A Tale of Two Rivers (With Jean Napier)
ISBN 0-86391-989-3
Welsh Slate Craft
ISBN 1-84527-029-0
Crefftwyr Llechi
IBSN 1-84527-034-7
Slate Quarrying in Wales (Revised Edition)
ISBN 1-84527-026-6
Slate Quarrying in Corris (Revised Edition)
ISBN 1-84524-068-5

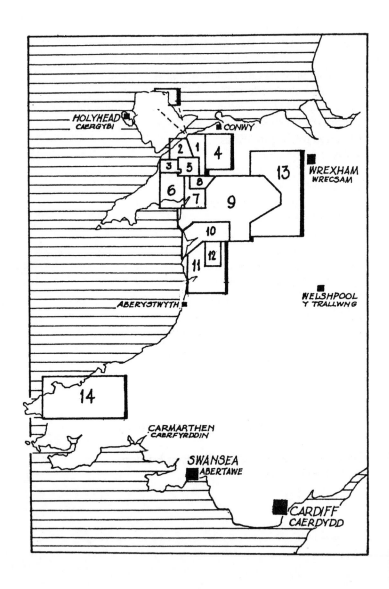

This book sets out to be a revised guide to the various sites in Wales where slate was worked, with some emphasis on their transport arrangements, since good transport was an integral part of the Industry.

It does not set out to be more than a superficial framework for fieldwork study. Nor is a detailed history attempted, dates and outlines being included merely to aid putting the sites into context. These are being increasingly provided by an increasing number of published works dealing with particular sites and various aspects of the Industry.

It cannot be entirely up-to-date as 'landscaping', infill, bulk extraction and decay are constantly changing sites, as is ongoing work at those quarries still operating. Neither can any claim be made that it is complete, as even the most exhaustive research and fieldwork cannot, with certainty, account for every place where slate may, at some time, have been extracted.

The diagrams in each section are not accurate maps but sketches to show the locations, and to indicate the importance of the various sites

Acknowledgements

I am grateful for the assistance and encouragement of, Myrddin ap Dafydd, Twm Elias, David Gwynn, Eleri Jones, Griff Jones, Gwynfor.P.Jones, Michael Lewis, Dafydd Roberts, Merfyn Williams, Richard Williams, my wife Delphine and many others including the Staff of Plas Tan y Bwlch.

Contents

Section 1 – Bethesda 20

Section 2 – Llanberis 37

Section 3 – Nantlle 59

Section 4 – Dyffryn Conwy 80

Section 5 – Cwm Gwyrfai 114

Section 6 – Pennant/Gest 132

Section 7 – Glasllyn 147

Section 8 – Blaenau Ffestiniog 171

Section 9 – North Meirionnydd 206

Section 10 – Mawddach 221

Section 11 – Dyfi 233

Section 12 – Corris 255

Section 13 – North-East Wales 280

Section 14 – South & Mid Wales 308

Remembering in gratitude the late Gwyndaf Hughes, Lewis Lloyd, Dafydd Price and Tony Rawlings

What is Slate

Welsh slate is almost exclusively sedimentary rock that, due to the heat and pressure of volcanic action, has become grain-orientated so that it readily splits into strong, thin sheets.

Generally, Caernarfonshire slate and some isolated occurrences in Meirionnydd is of the hard Cambrian series.

Slate in most of Meirionnydd and across to the English border, and also in south Wales, is of the less brittle Ordovician series

Slate in the northeast is Silurian that can be less durable.

The Background

Slate has been worked in Wales at least since Roman times, mainly for vernacular requirements. From the late 1700s, fuelled by world industrialisation and aided by the development of railways, Welsh slate enjoyed almost a century of unbridled bonanza up to the late 1870s, Although amalgamations and rationalisation enabled the industry to reach new peaks by the late 1890s, the 20th century brought a rapid and inexorable decline that reached a nadir in the 1960s, with happily something of a rebirth during the 1980s.

Quarrying Methods

Slate quarries are essentially of three basic patterns, dictated by the occurrence and dip of the vein.

1.**Hillside** workings as in the usual stone-quarrying manner, either a face on a single level, or in a large quarry, by a series of terraces.

2.**Pit** workings where the vein was followed downwards. Where the lie of the land permitted, a cutting would be made and/or tunnels bored, to avoid having to up-haul material and to obviate pumping. Large pits might be terrace worked

3.**Underground**, where open working would involve the removal of large quantities of overburden, the vein would be reached by tunnelling. It would usually be worked by driving a "roofing shaft" upwards along the top of the vein and working across and downward to develop a chamber. Typically, when a chamber was 70' wide another would be started leaving an intervening "pillar" some 30-40' wide to support the roof. This chambering could be repeated on many levels.

Most quarries are a combination of two or three methods. E.g. A hillside quarry may have been deepened into a pit and then further exploitation made underground.

Quarries originally were often only worked when a local need arose either by a landowner as a part of the exploitation of his land or by slaters who dug and made their own slates. Many quarries never progressed beyond this stage and today all that remains is a digging, waste heaps, a working area with possibly the ruins of a shelter and perhaps a track along which finished product was carried away. Some developed into full-time partnerships and, after the later 18th century into formal businesses

At its most basic, slate quarrying consisted of attacking rock exposures, hacking and levering out likely rock and breaking it into manageable and hopefully usable blocks, by the use of a big oak mallet (*Rhys*), "Plug and Feathers (expanding wedges), and so on.

From the late 18th century rock began to be won by blasting with black powder packed into shot holes, usually slowly and laboriously bored by repeated impact with a weighted iron rod (*Jwmpar*). Later some use was made of hand-powered rotary drills and from around 1880 compressed air drills. Mechanically drilled holes can be recognised by the rotation marks. For development work where the shattering of bad rock was of no account, high explosives replaced black powder. The absence of shot-hole borings in a working does not imply antiquity as small-scale operations continued to use (and still do) "crow-barring" methods.

The usable blocks, that at best represented 10-15% of the won rock, was split by chisel to a suitable thickness and dressed to size by holding the slate over a fixed blade (*Celfi*) and striking it with a knife-like tool (*Cyllell*).

By the 18th century saws were being used for slab work such as gravestones. Originally these were sand saws, i.e. toothless saws cutting by the action of wet sand in the kerf. Such saw cuts are recognisable by the possibly irregular horizontal cutting marks, and the fact that the saw was not taken right through to the full depth, leaving a slightly rough edge where the slab was broken off. "Carpenters type" handsaws were widely used in south Wales.

Waterpower was being used to drive sand saws the early 19th century. Often they stood on readily recognisable slate bases and their cuts go right through the slab. They might or might not, be housed in a building.

More efficient circular saws were introduced slightly later and were commonplace by the 1840s, there were originally several types but the industry standard became the moving table, with under-table iron (later steel) blade, invariably of the Greaves pattern based on the timber industry saw-bench. The saw marks are obvious and distinctive. Occasionally in small quarries circular saws were hand cranked.

The other notable saw was the fearsome Hunter saw which normally had an over-table circular blade with inserted, replaceable teeth. Its marks are recognisable by their depth and coarseness of feed.

During the 20th century diamond circular saws came into use and have, for some time been universal. Their blades can be up to over two metres in diameter and they exhibit a distinctively fine cut. They invariably have saws moving over a fixed table and can be in multiple gangs. (Very occasionally multiple-ganged reciprocating diamond saws have been used).

Mechanical dressing came in at about the same time as circular saws. Several types of machines were used but the industry standard became the Greaves Rotary Dresser, originally driven by hand or foot, powered versions becoming the norm sharing a mill with the saws. Despite many attempts to mechanise it, splitting has generally remained a hand operation.

Structures

In all but the tiniest workings, blocks were split and trimmed into slates in open-fronted dressing sheds (*Walliau*). Other buildings would include a smithy, for sharpening tools, a powder store, perhaps an office, stabling and probably weighbridges. These latter were mainly used for weighing rubbish to assess "rubblwrs" pay and the presence of them in a very small quarry is evidence of the existence of an employed workforce. The remoter sites would have barracks for the workforce and possibly cottages that formed a quasi village. Most would have a manager's house screened by trees, (coniferous to maintain cover in winter).

Powered sand-saws might operate in the open air, but circular saws other machines called for buildings. Thus every quarry of any consequence had a mill that might contain anything from one to a score or more of saws. From the mid 19th century when saws began to be used , not just for slab work, but also to pre-saw blocks to give the slate makers a rectangular work piece, there were dressing machineas in the mill as well. In these Integrated Mill, usually had one dresser to each saw, with a splitting area between them and often also had ancillary machines such as planers, polishers or lathes. In a big mill the power source was located in the middle of the building to minimise the length of the drive shaft that ran the whole length either on overhead hangers or, less commonly, in an under-floor trough.

In order to be clear of future extraction or tipping, and more importantly, to be near water, mills often had to be some distance, from the actual quarry.

Mechanisation, sophistication and increased size called for a wide variety of buildings. Maintenance shops, engine and boiler houses, compressor houses, stables, locomotive sheds, carpenters shops, electricity sub-stations, stores of all kinds shelters to dry or moisten blocks and mess rooms, joined the more basic structures. Some quarries had enamelling, writing slate and other speciality departments.

Besides barracks there might be houses, on or near the site – even schoolrooms and chapels, and in the case of the largest units, hospitals.

In spite of the depredations of scrap-men and magpie visitors, fragments of plant or equipment can help to identify otherwise anonymous structures.

Mills remote from their quarries and independently owned slate factories (Other than those within towns) are separately identified.

Waste

A constant problem was the disposal of waste as only a tenth, or less of the rock extracted became finished product. So that rubbish heaps are the main, and indeed sometimes the only substantial remains on a site. The waste, in five types, often provides valuable evidence to the working of a quarry. **Development waste**, consisting of "country rock", often in very large pieces, removed to reach the slate vein. **Quarrying waste**, irregular pieces of slate discards or trimmings from the working face or from the hand reduction of blocks. **Sawn Ends**, found either in dumps or used as building material, which give useful indication of the type and location of saws. **Dressing Trimmings**, fine pieces of slate from the final squaring of roofing slates which indicate that this product was made and where the operation was carried out. **"Fancies"**, fragements from the on-site making of "Downstream" products such as chimney pieces, were produced.

Power

The basic and almost universal power-source for pumping, winding, and driving machinery was water, usually with **Overshot** wheels where water poured forward over the top of the wheel to rotate it forwards. Where there was not quite enough head to direct the water over the wheel, slightly less efficient **Back shot** wheels that rotated backwards were used or if the head only allowed the water to impinge a little above axle height **Breast shot** wheels were used. Sometimes to maximise head, a wheel driving a mill might be installed below the building, transmitting power by belt, or for pumping it might be remotely sited, driving via flat-rods.

The wheel pits, to be seen on so many sites, and the overhead launders (or at least their supporting pillars), their reservoirs and the often extensive and ingenious leat systems are worthy of study.

Later to make more efficient use of water, turbines or Pelton wheels were used, calling for a piped supply rather than an open launder or leat.

In at least one instance wind power was tried.

Since water froze in winter and reservoirs dried out in summer, steam was widely used as a standby back up. In intensively worked, but sparsely streamed areas, steam was in permanent use. Later oil engines and coal-fuelled producer-gas engines were used. From the later 1890s some quarries hydro-generated electricity, from the early 1900s somewhat meagre public supplies were available in some areas. Later Diesel generators became widespread.

It was the 1950s before public Grid supplies were universal.

Transport

The basic means of transport was by water, either in coastal or ocean going vessels creating slate quarrying's great partner-industry, seafaring and ship building.

However carrying the product to the coast or a navigable river by pack animal or cart could exceed the cost of production. Hence the building of so many quarry-to-coast railways, some of which now constitute the "Great Little Trains of Wales". In addition these lines themselves had feeder lines, plus a great deal of standard gauge route mileage in both northwest and southwest Wales was laid down purely to meet slate needs.

Besides these external lines internal rails were vital to quarry operation. These could vary from a short length to move rubbish in a tiny working to fifty-mile networks in the largest. Three kinds of truck were used, open fronted wagons for rubbish, flat wagons for carrying blocks to the mill and fence-sided trucks for finished product.

Rail formations can show how blocks were conveyed to the mill from the quarrying faces and waste to the rubbish runs. Also, how mill waste was taken to the tips and finished product to the stocking yard. Most interesting are the inclines that conveyed trucks from one level to another. For upward movement they had to be powered, but usually movement was downward so they could be gravity operated, the weight of down going loaded wagons serving to raise empty ones. The ruined survivors of the several hundred drum houses at their heads, is an all-pervading characteristic of slate areas. The variation in design of these inclines and drum houses makes a fascinating study in itself.

Those quarries without rail connection usually had to build their own roads. Some of these are most elaborately engineered, and they also make an interesting study.

Site Visits

A few quarries are open to the public so access is no problem. Often the serious visitor, on making his interest known may be taken to parts not normally on view. Owing to insurance constraints, entering working quarries is not allowed but prior application may result in a conducted visit being arranged.

Sites though abandoned, are still private property so **PERMISSION MUST ALWAYS BE OBTAINED**. The same applies where land has to be crossed to reach a site. Such permissions are usually freely given once it is established that ones interest is serious, that one abides by the Country Code and that one has no dog.

For visiting remote sites, the usual precautions for mountain walking apply- suitable clothing and footwear, spare clothing, compass, whistle, map, food and an up-to-date weather forecast.

The importance of a site's archaeology is denoted by stars

****	Exceptional
***	Notable with unique features
**	Notable
*	Great Interest

Quarries having a maximum manning of over 100 (Ignoring brief or untypical expansions) are classified as follows -

A	3000	B	1500	C	500/600
D	400/500	E	300/400	F	250/300
G	200/250	H	150/200	I	100/150

Do not scorn the small sites, pathetic little scratchings though they may be. Each one represents toil and dedication, hope and disappointment, hardship, disease and early death, endured for scant reward.

All sites are dangerous. Slate waste is slippery when even only slightly wet, rock falls are prevalent, buildings are generally unsafe and concealed shafts and openings may be unguarded.

Going underground is particularly hazardous. Three persons is the minimum desirable party, one, experienced in mine exploration, being designated leader, who must brief any inexperienced members of the party before entering.

Never remove anything from a site, if an artefact is moved or uncovered for examination or photography, replace and recover it.

Section 1
BETHESDA
Plus Anglesey, Ynys Fôn

General

This section covers the Ogwen valley, centred on the village of Bethesda and dominated by PENRHYN quarry, that throughout its existence has supplied a quarter (and later much more) of the entire Welsh output. Working the near vertical veins of finest Cambrian rock, on the flanks of Mynydd Elidir; its huge workforce being accommodated by its pioneering terrace working.

Since it is a working quarry archaeological remains are constantly vanishing as modern work advances, but if permission can be obtained to visit, there is much to be seen, and on a scale that, DINORWIG apart, is not found elsewhere. Although the quarry built houses and leased land for self-build on small holdings, many workers avoided quarry tenancy by living on non-Penrhyn land, where they were free from the employer's Anglican-centred dominance and could build non-conformist chapels such as Bethesda, and develop the settlements around them that came to epitomise Welsh quarry communities.

The other quarries, situated to the north of the Ogwen valley, off of Penrhyn land, were, with three of four exceptions, extremely small and ephemeral affairs. The tiny workings were either optimistic trials attempting to share the riches of Penrhyn or "unofficial" workings by men made jobless by the Penrhyn stoppage of 1900-03. The trials were mainly investigation tunnels bored to assess the rock, but some, almost uniquely for north Caernarfonshire, actually worked underground. Some

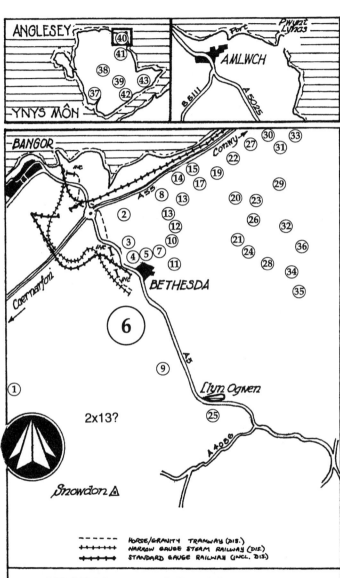

SECTION 1: BETHESDA AREA

were made viable by the occurrence of coloured (red & green) material, and some prospered briefly during the 1900-1903 and other Penrhyn disputes.

Anglesey, Ynys Fôn

For convenience, the Anglesey quarries are included in this section. Only two have remains of any significance, the community of Pwllfanogl, site of the Britannia Works is interesting,

Transport

Traditionally slates were carried by pack animals, often tended by young girls and shipped either at Hirael (SH589727) or at Aberogwen (SH613723). The Penrhyn quarry proprietors made considerable road improvements towards the end of the 18th century to facilitate cartage to the mouth of the river Ogwen (where traces of the staithes remain) and after the 1790s to the purpose built Port Penrhyn at the mouth of the river Cegin.

In 1801, having sensibly abandoned the idea of a canal, a horse-drawn 2' gauge railway was built linking Penrhyn quarry with Port Penrhyn. This was the first of a number of such lines that so dramatically reduced the cost of transporting slate from the quarry to the coast.

The civil work was good and the even spacing of the three inclines facilitated efficient working. Although the original round bar rail and semicircular wheel profile was unsuccessful, re-laid in conventional rail it served the quarry for 75 years finally carrying daily tonnages far in excess of its designed capacity.

In 1876 this line was replaced by a steam railway (also 2' nominal g.) that closed in 1962.

In 1852, a branch was made to the harbour from the London & North Western Railway's Chester to Holyhead main line, enabling any slate brought down to the port to be transferred to the main line railway.

Since the Penrhyn railway and port were closed to them, other quarries reached Aberogwen or Bangor by cart or pack animal. After the Bethesda branch of the L&NWR was opened in 1884, rail transport became available, although no quarry had direct connection.

The original horse-drawn Penrhyn line left Coed y Parc to cross a minor road on the level at SH614666 from where it can be walked (traces of slate sleepers) to the head of the Cilgerraint incline. From here there is little trace for several miles other than the head of an archway where the Dinas incline went under a minor road at SH607685. Close to the Landegai roundabout a lane defines the route which is from there on lost under the Llandegai Industrial Estate. The passage under the main road at SH594714 is still open. From there the route is defined by the curved wall of the Penrhyn Castle estate. At the head of the Marchogion incline the drum house and stables are in reuse as a dwelling. Near the foot of that incline there is a single arched bridge over the river Cegin, the route then passes under the later steam railway (see below) to re-cross the Cegin by a fine three-arched bridge and so on to Port Penrhyn. From the port to beyond the top of the Marchogion incline the 1801 line took over the track bed of an earlier (non-slate) line. This tramway passed through what is now Landegai village to an incline down to flint mills near the river Ogwen. This incline (severed by the Chester to Holyhead Railway near the eastern portal of Llandegai tunnel) is traceable.

The 1876 steam line left Coed y Parc by a similar route but at a higher level, its slate embankment being still extant. The route is readily traceable curving around

Tregarth, virtually interlacing the Standard Gauge line. The viaduct at Felin-hen has vanished and beyond there the track is much overgrown. From near Maesgeirchen, where it passed under the main road, it is clearly defined to the nice little span over the track of the old tramway and on to cross the Cegin by sharing the London & North Western Railway Port Penrhyn branch's steel bridge, and on though an arch to the dockside.

This branch (closed 1963) is readily traceable including the bridge across the Cegin that was widened on its south-eastern side to accommodate the Penrhyn steam line.

The port itself remains relatively undisturbed, apart from the lifting of track. There are several buildings of interest, including, an engine shed, offices, a unique, circular lavatory and the remnants of a pioneering writing slate factory.

Much of the L&NWR Bethesda branch, (closed 1963), is readily traceable from the site of the terminus, at SH619558 (the site of the Coetmor quarry tip). via the fine Ogwen viaduct and the Tregarth tunnel, to its junction with the main line near Llandegai.

1]	SH589645	Chwarel Robin Jones	
2]	611696	Chwarel Las	
3]	613677	Dôl Goch	
4]	617673	Coed	
5]	619672	Coetmor	
6]	620650	Penrhyn ***	A
7]	623671	Pant Dreiniog	
8]	624704	Bronydd Isaf	
9]	626638	Cwm Ceunant	
10]	626679	Moelfaban *	
11]	628677	Ty'n Ffridd	

12]	628683	Tan y Bwlch **
13]	631693	Bryn Hafod y Wern ***
14]	631708	Bronnydd
15]	633702	Ffridd
16]	634657	Braichmelyn
17]	636701	Dôl Pistyll
18]	637648	Cefn yr Orsedd
19]	640706	Nant Heilyn
20]	642697	Cwm Glas
21]	643672	Dr Hughes *
22]	645709	Crymlyn
23]	646688	Gyrn
24]	647667	Y Garth
25]	648604	Idwal
26]	648680	Galt y Mawn
27]	648715	Yr Ogof
28]	652668	Afon Gaseg *
29]	657698	Pant y Darren
30]	658723	Brechiau
31]	662720	Bontnewydd
32]	670675	Bera Bach
33]	675721	Bod Silin
34]	678663	Afon Wen *
35]	683655	Cwm Bychan *
36]	683664	Ochr Fwsoglog *

Anglesey, Ynys Fôn

37]	340890	Bodegri
38]	347892	Llanfflewin *
39]	450736	Llangristos
40]	481932	Llaneilian ***
41]	487921	Ogof Fawr
42]	490665	Trefarthen
43]	530709	Britannia (Works)

AFON GASEG SH652668
Pit working. **Remains.** Collapsed tunnel to pit, some rubbish runs several dressing sheds windowless building with iron door. Working at 647668 may be associated. [28]

AFON WEN SH678663
Underground possibly operated 1900s by 6-10 ex-Penrhyn men.
Remains. Adit, rails, tram axle etc etc, vestiges of buildings. [34]

BERA BACH SH670675
Trial? **Remains.** Run-in adit. [32]

BOD SILIN SH675721
Trial. **Remains.** Run-in adit some work done at 674721. [33]

BONTNEWYDD SH662720
Tiny undergound working. **Remains.** Vestige of adit and shed. Run-in adit at 664710 may have been associated. [31]

BRAICHMELYN SH634657
Trial. **Remains.** Traces only. [16]

BRECHIAU SH658723
Unsuccessful working? **Remains.** Traces in forestry. [30]

BRONYDD SH631708
Trial. **Remains.** Small pit. [14]

BRONYDD ISAF SH624704
Trial. **Remains.** Ground disturbance? [8]

BRYN HAFOD Y WERN SH631693 ROYAL BANGOR SLATE

Pit.that owing to unavailability of land downhill, could not be made self-draining and all material had to be up-hauled to the mill and waste further uphauled to lengthy tipping runs. Also the need to reuse a limited water supply (which had to be brought from Llyn Caseg) meant a less than ideal layout of the mill area.

Established around 1780, it was operated by the Pennants of Penrhyn, but abandoned by them in 1845 probably due to excessive working costs. Re-opened by the Royal Bangor Slate Co in 1845 (who built the mills) it closed in 1884 when the Pennants cut off the water supply.

Rock was raised from the 200' deep pit to a landing platform by a water powered incline, (the same wheel also pumping?), that may have replaced a water balance. Rubbish was further raised by a further water-powered incline driven by the tailrace of the first haulage.

Good slate was lowered from the landing platform by a short self acting incline to a small mill, with a further incline to a second, lower mill the mill wheels being driven in tandem from water from the haulages. Thus water was four times used. Product carted to Bangor.

In 1882, shortly before closure output was 2198 tons pa with 65 men employed, probably about half the number of the previous decade.

Remains. The pit is now flooded and the buildings are ruinous but otherwise it is relatively undisturbed. The foundations of buildings, incline formations and tramway layout are clear, also vestiges of the anchor of the chain incline that was the final means of raising from the pit. There is evidence on the prominent landing platform of a horizontal sheave. The upper mill may have been turbine powered. Both circular and sand-sawn ends are on site.

The financial constraints are shown by the traces of wagons having run on slate ways. There is a pleasing pointed arch providing access to the upper mills area under the landing platform. Bryn Hall, the owner's house, has a fine arched entrance gate and is still in occupation.

The leat from the river Caseg to the two reservoirs may be traced, the launder pillars and underground supply relief pipe are prominent. [13]

CEFN YR ORSEDD SH637648
Possible Trial. **Remains.** Trace of excavation. [18]

CHWAREL LAS SH611696
Pit, very small. **Remains.** Rubbish runs only. [2]

CHWAREL ROBIN JONES SH589645
Trial. **Remains.** Excavation. [1]

COED SH617673 CLODDFA Y COED, COED UCHA
Hillside quarry, very small. **Remains.** Building ruins. [4]

COETMOR SH619672
Used by Pantdreiniog, for tipping after 1870s closure, its own tip was levelled to carry the railway station.
No remains. [4]

CRYMLYN SH645709
Small, underground.
Remains. Collapsed adit in a gully Irony waste. [22]

CWM BYCHAN SH683655
Underground possibly part-time, possibly as trespassers. The two men working here in 1905 faced a long and daunting journey to move out the product.

Remains. Run in adit, building remains, possible powder house. [35]

CWM CEUNANT SH626638
Trial. **Remains.** Traces of excavation. [9]

CWM GLAS SH642697 LLEWLLYN , MOEL WINION?
Underground, very small, circa 1890.
Remains. Collapsed adit, trimming waste, some finished slates. [20]

DÔLGOCH SH613677 COED Y DDÔL
Small pit, operated for few years after 1836.
Remains. Depression in ground. Tip on far side of road. [3]

DÔL PISTYLL SH636701 FRIDD FEWD
Pit, very small.
Remains. Rubbish runs , trimming waste and building vestiges. [17]

FFRIDD SH633702
Putative quarry. **Remains.** Possible ground disturbance. [15]

GALT Y MAWN SH648680 CHWAREL PARRY
Underground trials, worked occasionally from about 1865, possibly slightly larger than the other tiny workings in this area.
Remains. Two small slits in ground. [26]

GYRN SH646688
May have been old metal trial re-investigated for slate.
Remains. Ground disturbance. [23]

DR HUGHES SH643672 LLIDIART Y GRAIANYN
Underground, very small. **Remains.** Run-in adit, Rubbish runs. [21]

IDWAL SH648604

Hone quarry. **Remains.** Some waste tips, rebuilt as Youth Hostel. [25]

MOELFABAN SH626679 Y FOEL Also outlier trial 633682

A small underground quarry producing speciality red slate, opened in mid 19th century. Adits, on three levels with incline connection, generally little chambering, good rock, red at first, then green coming from tunnels.

Like TAN-Y-BWLCH and PANT DREINIOG, it was operated co-operatively following the 1900-03 PENRHYN stoppage.

Originally material was lowered by a second incline, possibly to a small mill, and carted out via Rachub village, but later a tramway connection was made to TAN-Y-BWLCH mill. Closed c1910.

Remains. Little other than the adits, (two penetrable for a short distance), some traces of buildings, the impressive grass covered upper incline formation, tramway formation to TAN Y BWLCH and, nearby a nice row of cottages. Lower incline and any mill etc obliterated. [10]

NANT HEILYN SH640706

Trial. **Remains.** Disturbed ground. [19]

OCHR FWSOGLOG SH683664

A small and extraordinarily located working, may have been worked with Afon Wen. **Remains.** Working face and unusual revetment, remnants of a possibly turf-roofed hut. [36]

PANT DREINIOG SH623671 CILFODEN

Pit/Underground. Opened around 1850, expanded during the 1860s – 70s, but declined sharply in the late 1870s Steam haulage & locos at one time used, records of a water balance, closed in 1911 after having been run as a worker's co-operative (North Wales Slate Quarries) with MOEL FABAN and TAN Y BWLCH, from 1903 when up to 100 men found work. Unsuccessfully re-opened in 1920's to produce slate powder. **No remains.** Site landscaped, but nearby quarry housing is of interest. [7]

PANT Y DARREN SH657698 AFON GAM, BRACHIAU)
Doubtful if any saleable product was ever actually won.
Remains. Run-in adit. [29]

PENRHYN SH620650 (Incorporating CAE BRAICH Y CAFN, DOLAWEN, FRON LLWYD, and other diggings).
Working quarry do not enter.

Open quarry, worked from at least the 16th century, the present undertaking dates from 1782 when Richard Pennant bought out the leased workings. Within 10 years its 5 figure tonnages dominated the industry and by the latter part of the 19th century tonnages of around 100,000 pa were routinely produced. (In 1882 11166 tons with 2089 men). Apart from Dinorwig, it was several times the size of almost every other quarry.

By 1798 the problem of enabling a large number of men to work simultaneously was solved by the gallery system whereby the working face was terraced out at 65'/70' intervals. Ultimately there were 21 such galleries, each with its own rail system. Movement downwards was mainly by self-acting incline and upwards by water balance lifts, of a unique type. Latterly some use was made of Blondin aerial ropeways.

Originally all dressing was done by hand on the galleries, machine sawing was introduced in the 1830s and by the 1850's work was centred in several large mills, water, steam and latterly electric powered. As was usual in Caernarfonshire machine dressing was never as

31

widespread as in, say Ffestiniog, and it was 1912 before roofing slate was sawn, so that there were virtually streets of wallia for hand dressing adjacent to the mills.

Steam locomotives were introduced in 1876, and i.c. power in the 1930's, all locos were replaced by lorries by 1964. There was extensive electrification in the early 20th century.

Prior to the establishment of Port Penrhyn, as a harbour and a site for a writing slate factory in 1790, slate was carted to Bangor for shipment.

In 1801 the horse/gravity Penrhyn Railroad replaced the 140 men and 400 wagons by then employed in cartage. This was in its turn replaced by the steam Penrhyn Railway in 1878.

After the opening in 1852 of the Port Penrhyn branch from the L&NWR main line, an increasing tonnage was transferred to rail instead of being shipped coastwise.

Quarrying still continues with all movement being by dedicated transporters and fork trucks. The old office continues to be used, but everything in the mills area is entirely new.

Remains. The whole quarry is much disturbed by modern bulk working and by road construction, but a few inclines and drum houses and a number of other buildings remain. Little old is extant on the vigorously worked southern section, but separated by a great bank of modern waste, the currently disused, partly flooded, northern section has much of its precipitous terracing, as well as some structures, intact.

One of the unique water balance lifts is preserved near the main office and one or two others remain on site.

The present mills complex, on the site of the old Red Lion mill are equipped with the latest machinery, including an "all-sawing" production line, that obviates splitting and all manual handling, that once more makes Wales the world leader in slate-working methodology.

At Coed y Parc, (615663) which was a concentrated industrial complex, there are several buildings in fair condition and the remains of waterwheels fed by inverted siphons. This was the terminus of both the Penrhyn tramway and the later Penrhyn railway and apart from workshops etc there were slate mills, the first dating from 1803. On the other side of the road the Ogwen Tile Works, later a slate mill, is now in industrial re-use. On the hillside above and to the west is an extensive water supply layout.

There are many items of peripheral interest in the area, such as paths, steps, stiles, cottages (with long allotment like gardens) and the model village of Landegai. Also at the upper end of Bethesda (that was on Penrhyn land) unique workers housing such as Tai Berllan. [6]

TAN Y BWLCH SH628683 BANGOR SLATE

The sole underground working of any consequence in Caernarfonshire. Established around 1805 it continued in sporadic use, including a period as a co-operative, until 1911.

Rock was up-hauled from a pit and reduced in a small mill. Later some underground working from the pit with vertical shaft haulage. Two steam engines were used, (to the detriment of profits!). A constricted site made tipping a problem. Stated to have had a drainage level emerging near Llanllechid church. Tonnage unlikely to have exceeded about 500 pa.

Material was carted, latterly via the exit incline at MOELFABAN when they were worked in common.

Remains. Some buildings, (in re-use) one with a slate sign "Bangor Slate Co", much tipping, squeezed into a restricted space, the abutments of two rubbish run bridges and a stack of finished product.

The pit is partly run-in obliterating any adits and any up-haulage arrangements. There is an unusually large engine house with an adjacent shaft (filled) some 4 x 4 m, stone lined. Presumably for up-haulage but run-off arrangements are unclear. It is not obvious where the second engine, presumably for saw power, was sited. There are the abutments of two rubbish-run bridges and much finished product lies in the stockyard. [12]

TY'N FFRIDD SH628677
Very small, operated in early 19th century. **Remains.** Virtually none. [11]

Y GARTH SH647667
Trial? **Remains.** Traces of two adits. [24]

YR OGOF SH648715
Small open working.
Remains. Shallow pit with traces of adits at 646716, and one at 645709 which may have been investigations on the same sett. [27]

Anglesey

BODEGRI SH340890
Putative working. owned by LLANGRISTOS proprietors.
Remains. Possible excavation. [37]

BRITANNIA WORKS SH530709
The Welsh Imperial School Slate factory. Originally slate and timber was brought in and finished product taken out exclusively by sea, later a multi-horse wagon could take output to Llanfair PG station. Two waterwheels (One

for timber machinery, one for slate circular saws?) with two steam engines as back up. Closed c1890 when the dam burst.

Remains. Site overgrown, manager's house, corn mill and pub survive, but much housing now lost. [43]

LLANEILIAN SH481932 POINT AELIANUS, CHWAREL SGLAETSH
The only one of a series of 17th century cliff face workings that included YNYS-GOCH 476925m PORTH YR YSGAW 479930 &. RHOSMYNACH (unidentified) to be seriously developed. The North Anglesey (Point Aelieanus) Slate & Slab Co, employed about 10 men from 1870-77. It was planned to create a shipping point (Porth Dinorben) directly below the quarry, in the Cornish manner. In the event their trifling output was carted to Porth Elian.

Remains. Small working faces, traces of buildings. At the main site an unique sloping shaft (with wagon jammed in it) enabled product to be lowered to a quay inside a sea-cave. This "dock" was also accessed by a most extraordinary flight of steps cut into the cliff. Tunnels emerge from the cliff face to enable rubbish to be tipped into the sea. The tunnel near the high-tide mark was a search for copper. [40]

LLANFFLEWIN SH347892
Pit working owned by the LLANGRISTOS proprietors, unsuccessfully developed by the 1874 Llanfflewin Slate & Slab Quarry Co.

Remains. Deep sloping cutting to access pit, fine quarry-waste formation intended to carry a tramroad across Llyn Llygeirian. [38]

LLANGRISTOS SH450736

Series of pits but product was poor. Mechanisation planned of 1875 never proceeded with.

Remains. Large overgrown pits, cut by A55. [39]

OGOF FAWR SH487921

Possible very early cliff working. **Remains.** Nothing found. [41]

TREFARTHEN SH490665

Alleged 18th century. Land owned by Vaynol estate.

No evidence on ground. [42]

Section 2
LLANBERIS

General
A continuation of the Bethesda Cambrian veins were
worked on either side of the lakes, virtually all by open-
air pit and hillside quarrying. As at Bethesda, slate
working was almost monopolized by one "Superquarry",
DINORWIG and one estate, Vaynol. However unlike
Bethesda this monopoly was far from exclusive, the non-
Vaynol workings on the southern side of Llyn Padarn
were extensive and long established, producing a
significant proportion of the area's output. Thus although
nowhere could one escape DINORWIG quarry's
glowering presence, Vaynol's influence on Llanberis was
far less than that of the Penrhyn's on Bethesda. Also
whereas Bethesda was very much the focus of
neighbouring villages such as Rachub and Tregarth, the
elevation of Deiniolen (Neé Ebenezer) and Dinorwig,
separated them from Llanberis and Cwm y Glo.

Transport
The traditional transport route both for slate and copper
ore was along Llyn Peris and Llyn Padarn. Following the
opening of Port Dinorwig in 1793, Vaynol did a great deal
of road building that, for their own quarry at least,
obviated perilous pack-animal carriage and the use of
boats along the lakes. It was 1824 before the 2'g. Dinorwig
Railway to Port Dinorwig was opened, but due to
landholding problems it started halfway up the quarry,
calling for up hauling to reach it, and resulting in a much
great fall than its Penrhyn counterpart and the uneven
spacing of the inclines hampered efficient working. The
gradients were variable and the use of slate sleepers

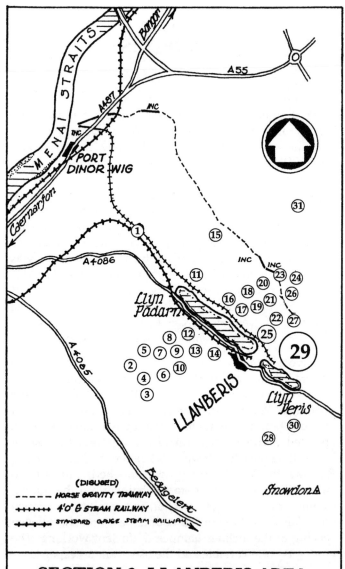

SECTION 2: LLANBERIS AREA

caused maintenance problems.

After only a few years it became obvious that complete replacement was called for. The new line, the Padarn Railway, although not originally steamed, was laid out in 1842 for steam operation. Its gauge of 4' suited the then minimum size of locomotives, and fortuitous land availability alongside Llyn Padarn enabled an almost gradientless run to an incline head above Port Dinorwig.

Although this railway gave an initial competitive advantage to Dinorwig quarry, the trouble of loading and unloading wagons and crewling them down to the port remained burdensome right up to the 1962 closure.

As at Port Penrhyn, a branch of the London & North Western Railway to Port Dinorwig was opened in 1852 to enable slate brought down the Padarn line to be trans-shipped to the main line.

Being both a private line and the wrong side of the valley, the Padarn railway could not be used by the quarries on the southern side, and they had to cart to Caernarfon, the lower ones via Llanrug, the upper ones via Wernfawr. This dramatically changed in 1869 when the L&NWR standard gauge Llanberis branch opened. This line, enabling these quarries to reach wharves at Caernarfon or Deganwy, or to distribute on the national rail network, transformed their fortunes.

Both GOODMAN'S and the GLYNRHONWY quarries had direct connection and most of the others could reach it via the magnificent Ffridd incline system. Interestingly the near mile-long lower pitch of the Ffridd incline had to be powered (by a steam engine that replaced a water-turbine), due to the weight of the rope preventing gravity operation.

Of the 1824 Dinorwig horse-line, the quarry end has

been lost in subsequent workings, but it is defined by the road through Dinorwig village to the head of the Upper Cwm incline at SH579624. This is now a steep footpath that continues via a manoeuvring loop down the Lower Cwm incline to stables at the lowest part of Deiniolen village. Present streets define its route towards Clwt-y-bont before it swings right across fields. At SH565656 is the rebuilt smithy/stables that served the line (and which continued as a smithy until about 1930).

The line is lost beyond here but can be traced where it departs right from the B4547 along a lane through trees to the head of the Garth incline near Garth Fach farm. The incline itself is largely lost in forestry but slate sleepers can be found. The line is again lost by road works but the western portal of the tunnel that carried it under the A487 is visible in a field. The short stretch into Port Dinorwig is obvious.

The steam line started from Gilfach Ddu, where the 2' gauge. quarry wagons were loaded in 4s onto carrier trucks and where the modern Llanberis Lake Railway begins. This 2' gauge line re-uses the Padarn track bed along the lakeside past the miniscule LADAS & BOUNDARY quarries and, via a curve (later straightened), past the foot of VANOL quarry incline. .

At Brynrefail, (the terminus of the Lake Railway), the track bed briefly becomes a road before passing under a road bridge, continuing on as a footpath to Pontrhythallt where there is an engine shed. It again passes under a road from where it runs alongside the formation of the standard gauge, Llanberis branch. Between the two lines are the long, narrow sites of the CRAWIA & PONTRHYHALLT slate works.

The track bed yet again passes under a road and swings right near Penrhyn farm. It may be followed with

40

varying difficulty to a footbridge with high clearance to suit the original locomotives (one of which, together with some quarry artefacts, is displayed in Penrhyn Castle). Nearby is a fine carriage shed, for workmen's carriage stock.

The B4366 was crossed on the level at Bethel and after a mile the formation swings left under a byroad to become a lane where there are railway cottages still in occupation. This lane led to the large drum house/unloading shed destroyed during the construction of the Port Dinorwig by-pass. From this drum house, wagons were lowered by chain down the 2'g Penscoins incline to Port Dinorwig, where the incline emerged from a tunnel. An engine/carriage shed, further railway housing, and a nice little hut partly constructed of stone sleeper blocks, survive near the site of the drum house. These stone blocks, used during the six years the line was horse-drawn, can be seen used for construction purposes at several places.

The standard gauge Port Dinorwig branch (closed 1960) is partly traceable. The main dock is now a housing estate but the original dock is largely unaltered despite marina development. Several buildings are in re-use including the dry-dock workshops.

Much of the Llanberis branch (closed 1964) is traceable from its junction to the south west of Caernarfon, but the seven river crossings render it very discontinuous. From near Cwm y Glo to Llanberis much has been taken for road improvements and part makes a pleasant walk alongside Llyn Padarn, passing under a pretty accommodation bridge. The Llanberis terminus buildings are is in re-use.

1]	SH536643 540641	Crawia (works) **	
2]	552600	Chwarel Fawr *	
3]	555597	Donnen Las	
4]	555598	Brynmawr *	
5]	555604	Cefn Ddu **	G
6]	560600	Bwlch y Groes *	
7]	560605	Cook & Ddôl **	
8]	560606	Glyrhonwy Upper *	F
9]	561602	Twll Goch	
10]	562601	Caermenciau	
11]	563622	Pen Llyn	
12]	565607	Glyrhonwy Lower *	H
13]	566603	Cambrian *	
14]	572606	Goodmans *	
15]	572632etc	Glan Dinorwig (works) *	
16]	574613	Boundary *	
17]	578610	Ladas	
18]	578615	Vaynol **	
19]	579613	Chwarel Isaf *	
20]	579617	Fronhyfryd	
21]	581617	Chwarel Goch *	
22]	582607	Alltwen	
23]	582619	Lloc *	
24]	584619	Frondiron *	
25]	586605	Vivian ****	
26]	588645	Parc Dryscol	
27]	591610	Allt Ddu *	
28]	594576	Arddu *	
29]	595603	Dinorwig ****	A
30]	601583	Galt y Llan *	
31]	602628	Marchlyn	

ALLT DDU SH591610 Including ADELAIDE & CHWAREL FAWR, CHWAREL (CLODDFA) GRIFFITH ELLIS

Pit/hillside working. Operating prior to 1771, in 1809 absorbed into Dinorwig, but operated as a separate department. The mill was not used after 1870, all material being railed to the adjacent DINORWIG mill.

Remains. The main excavation to the east of the road and the substantial mills area with buildings, inclines and rubbish runs haas been completely landscaped, save for a reconstructed powder house. Several quarry houses are occupied and the rail connection to the DINORWIG mills is clear. [27]

ALLTWEN SH582607

Putative site. **Remains.** In trees, possible ground disturbance. [22]

ARDDU SH594576 GWAEN Y GLO, GWAEN Y TY

A tiny undertaking consisting of two tandem cuts.

Remains. Ruins of a dressing shed and other small buildings on upper level. The stocking area has several thousand finished slates, mainly doubles and small doubles and parts of a rubbish truck. [28]

BOUNDARY SH574613

An ancient small open working on the lakeside, independently operated tight up against the boundary of Vaynol land.

Remains. Dressing shed against a rock face. Trace of a wharf. [16]

BRYNMAWR SH555598

Small open working,, operated intermittently in the 1860s & 1880s. Taken over by CEFN DU in 1886. Steam was used for pumping and hauling. Product was carried by tramway to the head of the Ffridd incline. Output only a few hundred tons pa. (1883 160 tons).

Remains. Virtually nothing other than the pit itself, trace of a part bored access/drainage tunnel, rubbish runs and the tramway formation. [4]

BWLCH Y GROES SH560600
Small, open quarry/pit operated in the 18th century, developed during 1870s. Taken over by CEFN DDU in 1886. Product carried by tramway to the head of the Fridd incline. Output of a few hundred tons pa.

Remains. A surprisingly large pit with rubbish runs & a very degraded tramway formation. Ruins of a barrack building to the west. [6]

CAERMENCIAU SH562601 CAE'R BANCIAU
A small and entirely unmechanised quarry operated in 1870s & 1880s, on the site of a much earlier undertaking. No railed access, may have carted to the Ffridd incline. (1883 300 tons, 12 men).

Remains. Almost none, other than rubbish runs. [10]

CAMBRIAN SH566603 FFRIDD GLYN
A working operating from the mid 19th Century in conjunction with GOODMANS, both amalgamating with CEFN DU in 1878. Tramway to the Ffridd incline. Output around 1000 tons pa.

Remains. Pits, a network of tramway formations and rubbish runs and several collapsed tunnels. Some ruins of small buildings and a possible mill (Steam powered?). One pit produced red slate. [13]

CEFN DU SH555604 (CHWAREL HIR) Incorporating, (with CHWAREL FAWR) old workings such as CHWAREL HUW DAFYDD, CHWAREL MORGAN,

CHWAREL OWEN, CHWAREL Y MAEN, CHWAREL Y PIGIA.

Opened in the 18th century or possibly earlier, part of the Cilgwyn & Cefn Du Company of 1800. Consisted of a pit, with locomotive tramways on 2 levels, the upper one having tunnels to serve the various districts and connected by an incline to the lower level, which was in turn connected by a further incline to the integrated mill.

The 1878 amalgamation with CAMBRIAN and the Llanberis Slate Company rendered redundant both the Ffridd incline extension, and its tramway connection.

By 1879 there were said to be 4 steam engines, 2 waterwheels and a water turbine on the site. Latterly on-site generated electricity was used.

It was a substantial undertaking with an output (including associated quarries) of 5640 tons with 197 men in 1882. Closed c1928

Remains. The large pit, with tunnels much collapsed. There are several very ruinous buildings in the mills area including the large mill. The rubbish tips make a spectacular landscape feature. [5]

CHWAREL FAWR SH552600 HOLLAND'S

The uppermost of the contiguous line of 18th century (Or earlier) quarries on the northern slope of Moel Eilio. In spite of its name it was not a large undertaking, indeed, until the late 1860's was very small. Material was originally carted to Caernarfon, via Waun Fawr. Later it was connected by a tramway to the Ffridd incline but after amalgamation in 1883, this line was abandoned, material being taken by tunnel (that also served as a drain) to CEFN DU quarry for reduction.

Remains. A crater- like pit with rubbish piled up almost all around it. The tunnel which carried the tramway to the incline head is open and the tramway route readily traceable.(There is a stock of slates alongside the tram route but this is likely to be from later reworking) There are no buildings, possibly there were some in the pit area but they disappeared when the working was deepened and tunnel-connected to CEFN DU after the take over. The entrance to the tunnel is visible and there is also a collapsed tunnel which carried a rubbish run. There are vestiges of a short incline possibly associated with early workings. There are traces of a tramway connection to BRYNMAWR quarry. [2]

CHWAREL GOCH SH581617 TWLL GOCH
Hillside working, larger than others nearby. Associated with Chwarel Isaf.
Remains. Pit to north of road, accessed by two tunnels (blocked), tips to south of the road on several levels. Buildings adapted and in re-use as dwellings. [21]

CHWAREL ISAF SH579613 TY CLUB
Pit working, connected to VAYNOL by tramway.
Remains. Tramway formation, drainage tunnel. [19]

COOK & DDÔL SH560605
Amalgamation of two ancient workings, the easterly (Ddôl) was abandoned early, the westerly being developed with a tunnel to the mill area. Material carted to Caernarfon from the west of the site prior to the building of the Ffridd incline. Connection was made to the original head of that incline by a short self acting incline, later by a tunnel, After the Ffridd was extended access was via the head of the lower pitch of the extension. A later (1890s?) mill was reached by converting a gravity incline into an up-haulage powered from the mill engine.

Output is unlikely to have exceeded 1000 tons pa. (631 tons with 26 men in 1882) Closed during WW1.

Remains. The pit is divided by a causeway built to give later access to Ffridd incline. There is a large, ruinous mill and other buildings. At a lower level is a large working area with ruined buildings served by a tunnel from the pit, and several inclines including the up-haulage. Vestiges of a barracks. There is an interesting building alongside the Ffridd incline that has a heavy slab roof and a fine fireplace, possibly a Caban. Extensive rubbish runs and vestiges of tunnels and dressing sheds. [7]

CRAWIA/PONTRHYTHALLT SH540641/536643 **Slate Works.**

Three works sited on a narrow strip between the Padarn & L&NWR lines. Operated from 1880's to 1920's processing slate into writing slates and slab products from DINORWIG material brought to the eastern end of the site on the Padarn Railway. The shallow fall of ground, forced the wide separation of the works to enable waterpower to be used in tandem. Finished product was loaded onto an L&NWR siding.

Remains. At the eastern end some vestiges of buildings, one with a waterwheel axle. At the western end, several buildings are in re-use including a house and a mill converted into a dwelling. Most of the leat is traceable and some of the inter-works tramway. [1]

DINORWIG SH595603 (Incorporating Take Note workings and also districts such as ALLTWEN, BRAICH. BRYNGLAS, BRYN LLYS, CHWAREL MYNYDD, CLODDFA GRIFFITH ELLIS, CLOGWEN Y GIGFRAN, DIFFWYS, GARET, HAFOD OWEN, HARRIET, MILLINGTON, MORGAN'S, MURIAU, SOFIA, TURNER, WELLINGTON.

Hillside Terraces. Established in 1787 when a group headed by landowner Assheton-Smith took over the pre-existing Take Note workings.

By the end of that century operations were consolidated into a series (ultimately 13) of terraces each 60'/75' high. Although the first incline was built in 1789, sledge operations continued until 1816, after which all downhill movement was by self acting inclines, there eventually being 2 main incline systems, each consisting of many pitches. An unusual feature of Dinorwig inclines was the practice of one pitch connecting not 2, but 3 terraces, traffic from the intermediate terrace being hitched and unhitched "on the run".

From the 1830s there was a tramway system on each terrace, laid out so that material was generally conveyed in one direction to the incline and in the other direction to the tipping area, efforts being made to slant the terraces slightly to facilitate movement. Steam locomotives appeared on the terraces in the 1870's, and petrol locos in the 1930's. At one time track mileage was said to exceed 50 & compressed air piping to exceed 15 miles.

From the mid 19th century central mill working was used, the main mills area for the north-western side was on "Mills Level" (On a level with Dinorwig village), but there were numerous mills at various points on the site. Extensive use was made of both water and steam power, in 1905 electricity from Cwm Dyli was used. Several Blondin ropeways were installed in the 1930's.

Early dispatches went by boat along Llyn Padarn then by cart to the coast. (There are suggestions, but no evidence of an early tramway alongside the lake. Port Dinorwig was built in 1793, and shortly afterwards road building avoided the Padarn boating, but it was not until 1824 that the Dinorwig Railway was built. Since Vaynol land ended at BOUNDARY quarry, the tramway had to run at an inconveniently high level. In 1842 the acquiring of FACHWEN quarry enabled the Padarn Railway to be laid on a lakeside route.

The eventual scale of this quarry was such that its output of around 100,000 tons pa in the late 1890's, (87429 tons with 2757 men in 1882) was on a par with Penrhyn, and represented almost a quarter of the total output of Welsh Slate. It rode out the inter-war years better than most, continuing to employ well over 2000 men. Finally closed 1969.

Remains. There is a great deal on this vast site and although much is no longer accessible, some of the western part and the whole of the Vivian quarry (separate from, but operated in conjunction with the main complex) are open to the public. The pumped storage scheme has destroyed the area of Wellington mill and the workings and lower C series inclines. There has been some work and tipping on the upper part of the site, mainly in connection with the surge-vent, but generally re-use has ensured survival of many artefacts.

The workshops building at Gilfach Ddu houses the North Wales Quarrying Museum, apart from a unique display of artefacts and relics, there is the big water wheel and the turbine that supplanted it.

Nearby is the entrance to the Glan y Bala tunnel that provided a connection to the southeastern area, until tipping enabled the line to be re-laid around the bluff. This tunnel is now used as a cable route.

On the hillside is the hospital building (open as a museum) and behind can be traced the embankment of an abortive rail line. Adjacent is the arched entrance to Vivian quarry. A path partly incorporating steps made from slate sleepers climbs alongside Vivian to Dinorwig village.

In the woods above is a large powder house.

Behind and above Vivian quarry, near the end of the public road out from Dinorwig village were CHWAREL FAWR and ALLT DDU quarries. This road through Dinorwig village defines the route of the 1824 line. The private road that continues towards the main mills defines the later Village loco line, which connected these quarries to the main complex and also served as an outlet for rubbish tipping.

The main quarry was divided into 2 sides, the NW known as Garret, was served by the 9 pitches of the A series inclines. On the SE side, the Braich levels were served by the 10 pitches of the C series inclines. The various other inclines, around the middle of the quarry were designated B.

Gilfach Ddu is at the bottom of the A series inclines, the lower 4 pitches of which brought material down from Mills Level to the Padarn Railway loading platforms. These drum houses have a pair of contracting shoes instead of the usual strap brake and have stops and adjusters that are unique to this quarry, as are the double bar brake rods and finialled cast iron locking pillars. As was often Dinorwig practice, the drum house walls and roof extend forward and the backs are fitted with wooden pelmets to improve weather protection. Generally rails are still in situ, with cast check plates at the top and bottom of each pitch. The 2 lower pitches (A1 & A2) have commodious brakeman's cabins with fireplaces and the upper one has also a contiguous office with a "squint" window to view approaching trains of wagons. At this latter point a path is carried over the head of incline by a nice cast iron bridge and a wall bounding the track has heavy slabs cantilevered out to provide shelter for men handling the wagons. Nearby too, is the Anglesey barrack in the form of 20 dwellings, 10 on each side of a street, some having the late occupants initials incised near the doorway There is a sharp turn between A2 & A3 as the later A1 & A2 inclines replaced older ones that ran straight down.

The 5 upper pitches of A are spectacular, but 5,6 & 7 have been modified to carry cables and the drum houses demolished.

The topmost (A9) has a very non-standard drum house having a lean-to slab roof and two separate drums on a common axle, the drum barrelling being sheet iron. The brake too is curious, consisting of two curved wooden blocks on long timber uprights pivoted at ground level, but the control gear is standard Dinorwig. It is one of the few drum houses on site (apart from the table inclines) that is of the remote type. Above this there is a small isolated development, not served by any incline but which had a ropeway, the upper sheave, with massive anchor block, being still in position.

Of the C series inclines, the 4 tracked C1 & C2 have gone and C3, 4 & 5, up to Australia level are much degraded. The C6 & C7, table inclines, are unique in that the drums are under-floor in pits below the rails, the brakes being controlled, from cabins, by a sort of ship's wheel, operating a rack through gearing. (This form of brake mechanism is to be seen on some A & B inclines) At C7 the usual cast-iron/wood drum has been replaced by twin sheet-metal drums. C8 has a conventional drum house but curiously, C9 drum house that is a massive stone structure has gear almost identical with the rather exiguous A9. C10 incline which has massive embanking does not appear to have ever been completed.

There are several other inclines of the discontinuous B series, one notable table incline has a pair of standard drums on a common axle with the two brakes coupled together, the drum house is almost totally walled in with, unusually a jockey pulley for the under-wound rope. Another incline is four-tracked with a double width drum house having 2 co-axial, handed drums.

Several inclines can be seen as converted to single acting with rubbish filled wagons acting as counterbalances.

On the Garret side, some of the Village level mills are standing as are some compressor houses, weighbridges, loco sheds and other buildings but apart from rail (properly chaired on the 'main lines', but bar type, often with slate sleepers elsewhere) and some minor items there are few artefacts. The Garret mills, near the top, have been stripped out

On the Braich side the ruinous Australia mill still has remnants of its 36 saw tables. They carry Ingersol Rand plates but seem to be of Turner pattern. It is of note that this mill, used right up to closure, had no trimming machines, all trimming being done by hand. Nearby is a compressor house with big Ingersol Rand compressors, one vertical, and one horizontal, with D.C. control gear and, behind it, a large cooling water tank. There is also on this level a nice loco shed and a weighbridge complete with all mechanism.

In the central area, there is some pit working with tunnels. There is at least one compressor house with horizontal Ingersol Rand equipment. There is a nice cabin, with steel blast shutters containing a winch for a rope incline and partly demolished, an all-metal rope incline drum house. Lower down is the big pit, tunnels etc of Matilda. There are now no traces of Wellington mill, which was near the lakeside. [29]

DONNEN LAS SH555597

Tiny surface working with tunnel access, an outlier of BRYNMAWR.

Remains. Excavation, possible powder house, formation of tramway to BRYNMAWR. [3]

FRONDIRON SH584619

Early shallow excavation.

Remains. Some surface disturbance, a considerable amount of fine trimmings. Building remains nearby may have a connection. [24]

FRON HYFRYD SH579617 BRYNHYFRYD

Tiny early working. **Remains.** Pit only. [20]

GALT Y LLAN SH601583 HAFODTY

Hillside quarry. Opened about 1811, and operated intermittently over a long period on a restricted scale. Terrace working with central incline.

The ease of working and convenience to the road favoured economic working, but the product quality was poor. In 1882 90 tons produced, 3 men employed. Closed during WW2.

Remains. Stone built incline formation and ruins of several small buildings. [30]

GLAN DINORWIG SH572632 & 582631 **Writing Slate Factories.**

The two buildings at Clwt y Bont, were on opposite sides of the road, close to the original Dinorwig Railway, the third was in Deniolen.

Remains. Both the Clwt y Bont buildings are in industrial re-use, the southern one has an internal waterwheel still in situ. There are traces of the reservoir to the north of the northern building. The village Band Room occupies part of the site of the third factory. There are the bases of launder pillars behind. [15]

GLYNRHONWY LOWER SH565607 Incorporating (With Glynrhonwy Upper) old workings CHWAREL BACH, CHWAREL FANOG, CHWAREL HIR, CHWAREL ISAF, FAWNOG, CLODDFA Y FFORD, GLODDFA GANOL, GLAN Y LLYN, GLYN ISAF, GLYN UCHAF, GREAVES, TWLL CHWILL, TWLL GLAI, TWLL GLAS, TWLL GOCH,. WEN FAIN

Open pit amalgamating 18th century diggings. It was extensively developed in the 1870's, amalgamating a number of independent diggings. One big and several subsidiary pits, with a large mill and an extensive, locomotive worked, rail system on several levels. (This quarry having been one of the pioneers of internal rail systems).

Self draining, with all downhill working and the facility of dumping waste into Llyn Padarn made this an efficient unit achieving outputs of 40 tons per man-year. The largest undertaking on this side of the valley, producing 1789 tons with 70 men in 1883. later outputs were even larger.

Product was carted to Caernarfon until 1869 (latterly by traction engine,) when an incline connection was made to a loading point on the main line railway. At one time connected to the Ffridd incline. Closed early 1930's.

Remains. Site has been much disturbed by bulk reworking and re-use; as well as for bomb storage during 1940-43, (With an extensive standard gauge rail network). Used for bomb disposal to 1956, but the collapse of buildings meant it was 1975 before the site was cleared of explosives.

Progressive reuse of the area and development as an industrial estate leaves little archaeology but some railway and tramway formations are visible, including the combined tramway and drainage tunnel (now blocked) under the road to reach the mills and on under the railway (now the by-pass) to dump in Llyn Padarn. Where the Ffridd incline crossed the road on the level can be seen. The area between the road and the railway formation was the site of the 1823 water-powered sand sawmill, later both conventional saws and a Hunter saw were used. The present factory buildings on this site originated as a WW2 ordnance factory. The tipping area now forms a country park. [12]

GLYNRHONWY UPPER SH560606 CHWAREL FAIN GLYN GANOL, PREMIER GLYNRHIONWY
Contiguous with GLYNRHONWY UPPER, originally worked separately.
Mid 19th century development of pre-existing small diggings. Basically two pits in tandem with mills and a most complex partly locomotive worked internal rail network, with spectacularly located tracks including some cantilevered along rock faces. Produced 2181 tons with 90 men in 1882
Originally connected to Ffridd incline, but after amalgamation everything went out though GLYNRHONWY LOWER via a tunnel.
Tonnage around 3000 pa. Down to two men when it closed in 1939.
Remains. Impressive pits with rock cut tramway formations, some tunnelling, inclines and several buildings. A nice wooden bridge is extant and the abutments of a bridge that carried rubbish over the road. [8]

GOODMAN'S SH572606 CHWAREL Y PERSON, COED Y DDÔL, GREEN'S, POTTER'S, TWLL TOMOS LEWIS, TY DU

An early working developed in the 1870's & 80's with a small mill

In spite of its small size it had its own tramway connection to Llanberis station, this same line being used for tipping into the lake. Water power believed to have been used for pumping. Output of a few 100's of tons pa. Closed about 1890.

Remains. Site redeveloped, tramway partly defined by streets. [14]

LADAS SH578610

Early hillside working accessed from the lake.

Remains. Excavation, alongside Padarn track bed. [17]

LLOC SH582619

Pit working.

Remains. Pit and fine trimming waste, one building. Waste above pit and on other side of road suggests that the present road cut through the site. [23]

MARCHLYN SH602628

An unsuccessful interwar attempt by the Dinorwig company to redevelop on a "Green field" site with a view to winning slate at lower cost, the Dinorwig quarry itself having become expensive to work owing to its dispersion and to indiscriminate dumping of rubbish on slate reserves.

A further major investment was made in the 1950's, including an electric mill but at a time of poor prices and shortage of capital, it was not a success. Closed 1969. Such product as was produced, dispatched by motor lorry.

Remains. Little on site apart from remnants of spoil runs, most of these having been used to create the upper reservoir of the pumped storage scheme. Buildings were mostly of Steel/timber, solitary relic being the brick electricity substation. [31]

PARC DRYSCOL SH588645
Putative site, **Remains.** Ground disturbance. [26]

PEN LLYN SH563622
Trial. **Remains.** Excavation only. [11]

TWLL GOCH SH561602
Small pit working, exploiting a red slate occurrence. No mill on site, may have been connected to Ffridd incline. Possibly associated with CAERMIENCIAU.
Remains. Scarcely any apart from rubbish runs and tramway formations. [9]

VAYNOL SH578615 Was FACHWEN
Pit/hillside working, the buying of this by Assheton Smith (and re-naming it Vaynol) enabled the lakeside route to be taken by the Padarn Railway. Incline was built after 1888, served by Padarn Railway. Disused by 1912.
Remains. Tipping run for upper, older working, weighhouse, some small structures and a bridge over road. Access tunnel (blocked) to lower working. On the waste bank a fine run of 7 dressing sheds (in re-use), weighhouse and other buildings. Incline. Pre-incline road down towards lake traceable. [18]

VIVIAN SH586605
Open hillside quarry, operated on 8 levels, (Two now under water), sharing all services with Dinorwig, but classed as a separate unit.
Remains. A spectacular vertical gash in the hillside, with a flooded pit, accessed through a nice archway with

working levels off to the northwest. Adjacent to the pit is the engine house of the up-haulage. The hanging sheave replicates the "Semi-Blondins" that were used in the main area.

On the upper levels, connected by steep pathways, are a number of fine rakes of dressing sheds and other buildings, some with excellent slab roofs.

The main interest is in the inclines, in 5 tandem pitches, the lower 3 being table inclines with much of the track and gear intact. The lowest pitch has been reconstructed to working order, but is powered since it was found impracticable to replicate the original gravity operation.

The drum houses of the lower inclines are built and ornamented to an almost extravagant standard, the brake mechanisms being unusually interesting, of massive cast construction, operated via spur gears and "ships wheel" controls, with elaborate remote control crimp sprags. The 4-6 incline is most unusual in that there is a continuous run from 6 down to 4 with tracks alongside from 5 down to 4 (giving four tracks on the lower part) both sets controlled from a double drum house on level 6. A traverser enabled traffic using the 4-5 tracks to be aligned with the No 4 drum house. On level 2 there is a rubbish run turning out towards the lake near the hospital.

At the foot of the main incline system is a short pitch at right angles to the rest, notable for its under floor sheave gear and slate sleepers in situ.

Most of the site forms part of a Country Park. [25]

Section 3
NANTLLE

General

This area is notable for its numerous pits delving deep into the solid Cambrian slate of the valley floor. Slate was certainly worked here in the 13th century and until overtaken by Penrhyn in the late 18th century, was the principal source of north Wales slate.

Other than a few large units on the northern side, most were small due to the several landowners seeking to maximise returns by issuing as many leases as possible. The result was that most workings were on very confined sites with lack of waste-tipping space, adding to the problems of up-hauling and pumping the pits. With the notable exception of DOROTHEA, few ever made money. Had the land been in one ownership and the whole area exploited as one quarry then a vast and highly profitable undertaking might have emerged.

Technically the area is noted for the widespread use of Blondins and chain inclines (that replaced horse-whims and windlasses), and for the vast revetments, reminiscent of ancient Egypt, built to contain waste.

It is a difficult area for the archaeologist as quarries were worked and reworked, were in close juxtaposition, and were subject to amalgamation, split-ups, re-naming and changes of ownership. Since so many buildings had to be erected on waste runs, many have collapsed and there has also been much land reclamation that has obliterated all trace of some quarries and destroyed interesting relics in others.

Settlement was unusually widely dispersed and including a number of villages as well as many disparate

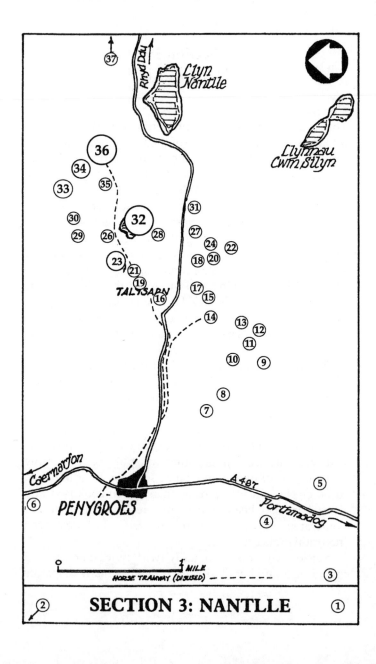

SECTION 3: NANTLLE

self-build mountainside homes (tyddynnod), a feature being the many tiny stone-walled enclosures that were the miniscule small-holdings that almost every worker cultivated.

Transport
Originally material was either carted to FORYD for loading into small craft for trans-shipment at Caernarfon, or carted to Caernarfon direct.

From 1828 almost all slate was carried by the horse-drawn Nantlle Railway to the quay at Caernarfon.

Unlike the Penrhyn railway of 1806 and the Dinorwig line of 1824 that were private routes exclusively serving their respective quarries, this 3' 6" gauge line was a full public railway, the first to be laid down to serve the slate industry. Modelled on the Turnpike roads, users supplied their own rolling stock and were charged tolls.

In 1867 the Nantlle Railway from Caernarfon to Penygroes was superseded when the London & North Western Railway's Caernarfon-Afon Wen branch, was laid substantially on the same route. In 1872 a sub-branch from Pen y Groes subsumed the line as far as Talysarn. The remaining rump to Talysarn survived until 1963 as the only British Rail horse-drawn line.

All the larger quarries had direct connection, whilst some smaller ones, on the southern side of the valley, reached it over the short but grandly named Caernarvonshire Slate Quarries Railway that joined the Nantlle Railway about half a mile west of Talysarn. This line continued as a feeder to the L&NWR line until about 1914. Those quarries with locomotives used 2' gauge internally, with 3' 6" for finished product dispatch.

The route (or at least the final route, as it was moved several times as quarrying encroached), of the Nantlle line is readily traceable from PEN-YR-ORSEDD to Talysarn, with a good run of slate sleeper blocks near the eastern end. The Talysarn-Penygroes section (common to both steam and horse lines) is now a road. (The short route of the Caernarvonshire Railway is partly traceable). In Penygroes itself, streets define the horse line, whereas the steam line ran to the south of the village.

From Penygroes to Dinas the standard gauge line forms a cycle track and on from there has been re-laid as part of the Welsh Highland Railway revival. A Nantlle Railway bridge at Bontnewydd (SH480599) and the Coed Helen tunnel (SH482616) were by-passed by the L&NWR and remain extant.

The Caernarfon slate quay below the castle that served first the Nantlle Railway and subsequently the L&NWR harbour branch is now a car park. The offices that served the harbour and the railway, survive nearby.

At FORYD (SH452586) the old shipping point may be identified by the slate waste and mooring posts, but the buildings post-date slate usage.

CAERNARFON PORT. All ports and creeks shipped coastwise, but like the much large Porthmadog; Caernarfon also became a deep-sea port By contrast material consigned from Port Penrhyn and Port Dinorwig for distant destinations shipped were often trans-shipped at Liverpool.

1]	SH454507	Foel Isaf
2]	454589	Foryd (shipping point)
3]	458506	Foel Clynog
4]	464513	Gelli Bach
5]	470508	Llwyd Coed
6]	470551	Inigo Jones (works) ****Visitor Centre

7]	477523	Bryn Castell	
8]	478521	Ty'n Llwyn *	
9]	485517	Tyddyn Agnes *	
10]	486518	Nant y Fron **	
11]	487519	Taldrwst	
12]	489517	Fronlog **	
13]	490518	Twll Llwyd *	
14]	490522	Singrig	
15]	490523	Tanrallt **	I
16]	490529	Coed Madog	H
17]	491522	Twll Coed*	
18]	491523	Plas Du	
19]	493532	Clodfa'r Coed	I
20]	494523	Ty'n y Weirglodd	I
21]	494533	Pwll Fanog	
22]	495524	Tŷ Mawr West	
23]	495535	Tal y Sarn **	D
24]	496523	Tŷ Mawr Green	
25]	496531	Cornwall	I
26]	496537	Allt Llechi	
27]	497524	Nantlle Vale **	
28]	498525	Twll John Ffowc	
29]	498535	Blaen y Cae ***	
30]	499535	Gallt y Fedw **	
31]	500525	Gwernor *	
32]	500532	Dorothea ***	C
33]	501540	Cilgwyn	E
34]	505538	Pen y Bryn ***	F
35]	506535	Wern Ifan	
36]	509539	Pen yr Orsedd ***	C
37]	535532	Talmignedd	

ALLT LLECHI SH496537

Pit working, closed 1880s, later part of TAL Y SARN, subsequently used by BLAEN Y CAE for tipping.
No Remains. [26]

BLAEN Y CAE SH498535

Small open pit working started about 1830. Material was raised by chain incline (later by Blondin) to a mill to the west of the pit. Finished product went down the lower part of the westerly CILGWYN incline to the Nantlle Railway. Some tipping was done on far side of that incline. Maximum of about 40 men employed, peak output around 800 tons pa. Later part of TAL Y SARN. Closed 1930s.

Remains. Dry pit. Traces of a mill and other buildings, tramway formations, remains of a steam Blondin winding engine (& collapsed masts). [29]

BRYN CASTELL SH477523

Tiny trial. **No remains.** [7]

CILGWYN SH501540 Including FAEN GOCH (VAINGOCH), GLODDFA GLYTIAU. Incorporating, CLODDFA EDWARD REGIOL,, CLODDFA EITHEN, CLODDFA GLANLLYN, CLODDFA LIMERICK, CLODDFA'R Y NANT, GLODDFA BACH, GLODDFA JOHN MORRIS, CLODDFA ROBERT ROBERTS, COCSYTH BACH, COCSYTH FAWR, GARTHEN, GLODDFA DWR, GLODDFA FACH, GLODDA GLYTIAU, GWAITH NEWYDD, HEN CILGWYN, TWLL CHEINIA, TWLL PEN Y BRYN, TTWLL Y CHWIL COCH, TWLL Y CHWIL GLAS

A number of individual workings, (dating from at least the 13th century) were brought together by the Cilgwyn & Cefn Du Company in the early 19th century.

In the 1840s it was idle and was much illicitly worked by trespassers. Restarted in the 1850s, it rapidly developed into a large undertaking in 4 pits with, in 1882, an output of 7430 tons employing 300 men.

There were two steam railway systems, one in the workings with tunnels connecting the pits, and a separate system around the south and east rim of the excavations. Steam powered the main mill to the east and the three other mills to the south as well as the chain inclines and Blondins.

An early (1900s) user of oil-engine generated electricity.

Waste disposal space downhill, towards the valley floor was non-existent so a long rubbish bank was established to the west. Later tipping was to the north, via a sinuous locomotive line.

Prior to the opening of the Nantlle Railway product was shipped at FORYD, for trans-shipment at Caernarfon. The Nantlle Railway was reached by an incline through TAL Y SARN quarry that was later extended to meet the Robinson Tramway that served quarries at Y Fron [Section 5]. In 1881 with tipping encroaching and the use of the North Wales Narrow Gauge Railway by the Y Fron quarries rendering the tramway redundant, a new incline was constructed some 200 yards to the east. This latter was abandoned in 1923 when CILGWYN itself connected to the NWNGR via the horseshoe tipping line.

Output declined steeply during the early 20th century. Closed 1956.

Remains. All buildings have been demolished and the pits are now the council rubbish dump. Some tramway formations and inclines are traceable. The massive tip to the west and, the 'Horseshoe" line and its tip are prominent features. The reservoir is partly dried out. [33]

CLODDFA'R COED SH493532 BANGOR & CARNARVON, WELSH SLATE, HAFODLAS.

Early pit working possibly 17th century. In the 1820s it was, with CILGWYN, TALYSARN and PEN Y BRYN, one of the "big four" who sponsored the Nantlle Railway. It failed to match the growth of the other three, all of whom were later eclipsed by DOROTHEA and PEN YR ORSEDD. Notable for having its pumping waterwheel replaced by a steam engine in 1807, the very first in the industry. Injudicious excavation caused its collapse into the pit in 1817.

Operated intermittently until WW2, doing well in the 1890s but its 1873 8 tons and 4 men was more typical, although there were 10 men at work in 1938. Had a small mill and direct connection to Nantlle railway.
Remains. Site landscaped. [19]

COED MADOG SH490529 GLODDFA GLAI.
Incorporating TWLL TYDDYN

Pit working opened early 19th cent, output in 1883 2879 tons with 135 men employed. The internal tramway system had 3 De Winton engines. Chain inclines were used. Closed 1908. The Nantlle Railway was reached via the CLODDFA'R COED quarry, but later was served by its own branch from the L&NWR. The only quarry in the district so connected.
Remains. Site completely landscaped. [16]

CORNWALL SH496531 SOUTH DOROTHEA
Pit working opened 1867, on site of diggings circa 1760, allegedly by Cornish copper miners from Drws y Coed. The mill was on a rubbish bank reached by a Blondin.

Output in 1882, 1040 tons with 70 men, increasing towards the end of century. Connected to Nantlle Railway. After 1899 tipped to south of the river Llynfi by a timber bridge, (collapsed 1927). Became part of TAL Y SARN., later incorporated into DOROTHEA 1921.

Remains. Flooded pit, several ruinous structures. [25]

DOROTHEA SH500532 CLODDFA TURNER. Incorporating GLODDFA BACH, GLODDFA GLANLLYN, HEN DWLL, PEN DWYLLT, TWLL BACH, TWLL COCH, TWLL GALLT Y FEDW (EX CAE YSGYBOR), TWLL TÂN (TWLL FIRE), TWLL UCHAF, TWLL Y WEITGLODD

Although not opened until 1820 it rapidly became the dominant undertaking in the area. By 1848 it was producing over 5000 tons pa with 200 men and by the 1882 its 533 men were producing 16598 tons pa. . There were ultimately 6 pits, the last being sunk in 1891.

Except when persistent flooding problems sapped profits, it consistently made money right into the 20th century, a most unusual record for a non-landowning slate quarry.

At least 8 waterwheels were eventually used, for pumping, haulage and mill power. Steam was introduced in 1841 to power the first of 8 chain inclines, including 2 double & 1 triple, replacing the horse whims and hand-worked turn trees hitherto used. These inclines served the mills at natural ground level so that further powered ramp-inclines, some of the transporter type, were needed to up-haul waste. Steam locomotives (De Winton) were introduced in 1869. The first of 4 steam Blondins sited on the rubbish banks was erected in 1900. Converted to electricity in 1959, they remained in use until 1965 when a road to pit bottom was built, eventually there were 8 mills with a total of 66 saws.

In 1906 a large Cornish beam engine was installed to pump the pit, which by this time was 550 feet deep. (Replaced by electric pumps 1951).

As the quarry expanded the old Talysarn village was engulfed, some of the buildings being used for quarry purposes and the Nantlle Railway had to be re-routed further north. There was an extensive loco powered rail system both at ground level and on top of the waste banks. As with the other large quarries there was 2'g & 3'6"g track on site, some wagons having double flanged wheels loose on the axle to run on either gauge. Final closure 1968.

Remains. The site is dominated by the lake formed by the flooded workings, (the depth of water is such that it appears as virtually a single pit). The rubbish banks with fine stone incline formations and magnificent revetments; make this a singularly impressive site. To the south are the ruins of the big integrated mill and many other buildings and remains of hoist gallows and haulage housings.

To the west is the Cornish Engine house, which still has the engine complete with boilers. To the northeast are some of the old village buildings including the ruins of what was the Commercial Hotel. On the old line of the Nantlle Railway is a notable inverted arch retaining buttress. Nearby is a fine flight of cantilevered steps. [32]

FOEL CLYNOG SH458506 CLYNOG, FOEL UCHAF
A mid 19th century pit working, pumped by water wheel.
Remains. Destroyed by reclamation and bulk working. [3]

FOEL ISAF SH454507
Trial. **No remains.** [1]

FORYD SH454589 Wharf

This was the original shipping point for Nantlle slate. Out of use by about 1810.

Remains. Mooring posts. Some buildings that remotely might be rebuilds of originals, much slate waste underfoot. [2]

FRONLOG SH489517 BUARTH FOTTY, VRONLOG GREEN

Small pit working dating from about 1840. Output 1642 tons, 98 men in 1882. Became part of NANT Y FRON. Closed during WW2 but reworked on a small scale in the 1980s for its green slates.

Remains. Two pits [12]

GALLT Y FEDW SH499535 ALEXANDRIA, VICTORIA, Y FOEL Incorporating CAE YSGYBOR, TWLL MÛG, OLD PEN Y BRYN

Open pit workings, arising during mid 19th century out of ancient diggings. Steam inclines raised material to a 6 saw-table mill, plus possibly some un-housed saws. Finished product went out by an incline, which crossed and then joined the Nantlle railway. A rubbish run bridged the easterly CILGWYN incline. Output only a few hundred tons pa with around 12 men employed. Some work continued until 1930.

Remains. A crowded site, several buildings including a small mill. One building, has the coloured patterned slate roof common in this area. Incline formations, including at least one powered incline engine house. Possible launder pillars suggest use of waterpower. There is a fine privy structure also a shallow stone lined pit about 30 metres diameter of unknown purpose. The vast retaining wall is in a poor state. [30]

GELLI BACH SH464513

Trial. **Remains.** Traces of a pit [4]

GWERNOR SH500525

Small open pit operated intermittently 1860-1915. Water (turbine?) powered mill. (2 saws & 2 planers) Water also wheel used for pumping and powering a chain incline. An oil engine drove the air compressor. Rubbish was tipped to the north of the public road. No rail connection, carted to Talysarn station.

Remains. Flooded pit. Ruins of mill and traces of rubbish-run bridge. [31]

INIGO JONES SH470551 SLATE WORKS Visitor Centre

Established in 1850s, on the Nantlle tramway, first for writing slates, later for enamelled work. Water powered by launder over main road.

Remains. Still in use producing high quality slab products. Besides the usual saws (modern) and planer it has an interesting, possibly unique sand-polisher. Visitors to the award-winning Visitor and Interpretation Centre are able to tour the workshops. [6]

LLWYD COED SH470508 CARNARVON, CARBARVON GREEN, GREEN ARFON, EUREKA. NEW LLWYDCOED, NORTH WALES GREEN

Pit working, in 1883 6 men produced 78 tons. Early user of producer gas engine generated electricity. **Remains.** site cleared. [5]

NANTLLE VALE SH497524 TY MAWR EAST

Opened in the 1860s as part of the original TY MAWR working, one of the largest on this southern side of the valley;

Prior to the use of steam, waterpower was possibly used for hauling and pumping, 20 men employed in 1882 only raising 150 tons. No rail connection. Closed c1910.

Remains. An interesting site. Several buildings including a nice rake of dressing sheds and an engine house with chimney. There is a stone-lined pump shaft about 2m square with pump-rods. Haulage ramp incline that may have been water powered. Alongside the engine house is the firebox and boiler of a semi-portable steam engine. Elsewhere on the site is a wheel pit and nearby a chimney for an engine and winder, now quarried away. These c1870 structures were replaced in 1890s by the now extant engine house. Near the pit are possible Blondin bases. There is well-engineered access road. [27]

NANT Y FRON SH486518 ERYRI, FRONHEULOG, (VRONHEULOG), Incorporating NEW FRONLOG, UPPER TYDDYN AGNES

Worked from about 1840. Tandem pits may have had water-wheel haulage with gravity inclines down to a mill, originally water-powered. Later a third pit was opened below the mill level, possibly served by a double acting water balance. Operated intermittently with tonnages, exceptionally, up to 2000 pa (1682 tons 1882) with a maximum of about 90 men employed. Connected to the Caernarvonshire Slate Quarries Railway.

Operated in conjunction with FRONLOG. Closed 1939, but some very small scale working in the 1970s seeking the rich green coloured product.

Remains. A number of buildings including a mill and a manager's house. Stone built inclines, one partly in a cutting. The lower incline has a curious tunnel through it for a watercourse and associated with it a stone covered leat. There are pillars that may be launder supports and blocks that could be chain incline anchorages.

In the mill area is an unusual structure of unknown purpose. [10]

PEN Y BRYN SH505538 Incorporating CAE CILGWYN Including HERBERT'S QUARRY & TWLL PENYBRYN, CLODDFA LÔN, DEW'S QUARRY, HEN DWLL, TWLL BALAST & TWLL MAWR, DAVID'S QUARRY, MIDDLE QUARRY, NEW PEN Y BRYN, OWEN'S QUARRY, TWLL ISMALIOD.

Opened around 1770. In 1882 employed 240 men producing 5083 tons. Eventually consisted of 4 pits adjoined by a mill area. Two waterwheels were used for pumping, later steam was used for pumping and winding, it being a. pioneer (1830) user of chain inclines. (Later supplemented by Blondins that remained in use utilised until the late 1930s). An incline, with an unusual drum buried under the crimp led down to the Nantlle Railway that terminated here before its extension to PEN YR ORSEDD. The Nantlle line was diverted to the south along its presently traceable route as work at this quarry encroached. After 1836 owned by DOROTHEA, who used part of their own site for tipping. Effectively closed in late 1890s, but some small scale working until the 1940s. Post WW2 the Dorothea Company made a road access in an unsuccessful bid to re-open.

Remains. Much of the eastern part of the site has been covered by PEN YR ORSEDD tipping burying HEN DWLL and TWLL MAWR & TWLL BALAST are partly filled with water & rubbish. On the older, southerly area, there are ruins of a number of buildings some of which, (apart from the 15th century Pen y Bryn farm), may date from the 18th century. On the newer, northerly mills area are the walls of long mill, a barracks and the chimney of a winding engine house. A tunnel, one of several that gave access to the upper pits is penetrable. Remains of incline formations, drum house (with some gear) and several artefacts such as flat rods, vestiges of a bucket pump etc are to be found. Some tramway formations are traceable with the abutments of the rubbish run bridge onto DOROTHEA property. Both the original and the diverted route of the Nantlle Railway are obvious with some stone blocks to be seen. [34]

PEN YR ORSEDD SH509539 NANTLLE. Comprising ARTHUR, ELLEN'S, EUREKA, GWAITH NEWYDD. Incorporating TWLL CALED, CUENANT Y CLAW, HEN DWLL, TWLL MAWR, WERN IFAN, WILLIAM
Developed from 1816 to, eventually, a four pit working, extending down to valley floor level, dewatered by a drain.

The first mill was opened in 1860 followed by an integrated mill in 1870. By 1898 there were four mills on three levels.

Output in 1882 was 8251 tons with 230 men but grew further in the 1890s. Even up to WW2 there were up to 350 men and almost 200 in the immediate post-war period.

The quarry was notable for its six Blondins that replaced chain inclines and a water balance. The Blondins were initially steam powered, but as a founder customer of the Cwmdyli Power station, all were eventually electrified, remaining in use until the 1970s when a lorry road was built into the then one working pit. It is said that Captain Idwal Jones the distinguished airman son of a quarryman, once flew under all six catenaries.
Amongst their saw-tables were some to a unique De Winton pattern with a hydraulic table feed. Although these machines seemed to offer clear advantages over the rack feed type, they were not a success.

Another unique feature was the driving one mill by another via a belt.

The first connection to the Nantlle Railway was via PEN Y BRYN. When this was blocked by tipping, incline connection was made to the extended railway. The 3 mills levels were connected by 2 incline pitches, with a third down to the Nantlle Railway. There were extensive tramways in 2' & 3'6" gauge, a De Winton loco surviving on the narrower gauge until 1960.

There was a proposal to abandon the Nantlle and up-haul to the North Wales Narrow Gauge Railway at Y Fron, but this would have been contingent on the NWNG building a loop to avoid the bottleneck of their Bryngwyn incline. Exit via Y Fron only occurred (by lorry) in 1963 when the Nantlle Railway succumbed to the Beeching axe.

Immediately prior to closure in the 1970s 12 men were employed with only the top mill being used. Its late 1980s re-activation was cut short by a big fall.

One of only a few Nantlle quarries to provide workers' housing on a generous scale, it was also notable for the scope of its maintenance workshops, these latter it is hoped will form the basis for an Engineering Conservation Training Establishment.

Remains. The pits being partly rubble filled do not now reach their full depth. There are several access/investigation/drainage tunnels.

On the upper level are the mill, the remains of Blondins, some with vestiges of quite complex pulley arrangements enabling the towers to be as working progressed, as well as other artefacts.

On middle the level there are various office and other buildings, remains of two mills, a 'specials' department and workshops

On the lower level are further buildings including a mill with shafting and other machine remains. Some buildings have signs of late renovation.

The drum houses and inclines are in fair condition with some track on the ground and have hinged wooden crimp sprags. There are pleasing 'sentry box' type brakeman's shelters. Drum gear is conventional except for the use of pulley & weight counterbalances for the brake levers.

At the Nantlle Railway terminus at the foot of the lowest incline are the line's stables amd a building with a building with a wheel pit alongside, where horse feed was prepared.

There has been some late reworking by its present owners PENRHYN.

The fine on-site war memorial has been re-erected in Nantlle village that is mainly made up of ex-quarry houses. [36]

PLAS DU SH491523
Small pit hived off from Tan yr Allt, part worked for a time by SINGRIG as DOLBEBI EAST
Remains. Tips, bridge abutments, and vestiges of buildings. [18]

PWLL FANOG SH494533
Tiny 18th century working,
Remains. Buried by waste from CLODDFA'R COED [21]

SINGRIG SH490522 DOLBEBI, (WEST). Incorporating DOLBEBI EAST
Very small open pit working, possibly never mechanised. Not rail connected although this was proposed.
Remains. Pit and dressing sheds. [14]

TALDRWST SH487519 CARNARVONSHIRE QUARRY, LLYN Y COED
Including TALDRWST ISAF (LOWER) 486524,

TALDRWST WEST 486517, TALDRWST UCHAF (UPPER) 487519, TWLL MELIA 483525, all worked as one or separately from time to time.

An assemblage ot tiny workings, active until the 1930s. May have been connected to Caernarvonshire S Q R. Stated to have had two waterwheels.

Remains. Pits filled buildings totally ruinous. [11]

TALMIGNEDD SH535532
Very small, hillside quarry.
Remains. Forestry and other work has left only incline traces. [37]

TAL Y SARN SH495535 CARNARVON AND BANGOR, TWLL MAWR. Incorporating ALLT LLECHI, BLAEN CAE, CLODDFA FAWR, CLODDFA'R ONNEN FACH, CLODDFA'R ONNEN FAWR, CHWAREL COCH, TALYSARN BACH, TWLL PENDITCH, TWLL PENUPARC, TWLL FFACTRI
Pit working, opened in 1790 and by 1829 a water balance and a Rag & Chain pump were in use. Steam powered by chain inclines, were later supplanted by Blondins. Became 3rd or 4th largest in the valley with a tonnage of 8210 in 1882 with (Including TY MAWR) 400 men with employed and locos in internal rail system. (Reverted to horse working before end of the 19th century). An incline connected to the Nantlle Railway, that was re-sited further south to allow for expansion of the working. Closed finally in 1946. Their policy of buying up neighbouring quarries as tips appreciably reduced operating costs
Remains. Flooded pit. Some ruinous buildings, remains of incline, several artefacts including a self-contained steam winch in excellent condition. Entering the property

from above are the formations of the 2-pitch incline that connected the John Robinson tramway with the Nantlle line. [23]

TANRALLT SH490523 CAERNARFONSHIRE SLAB. Incorporating CHWAREL OWAIN JONES, PLAS DU, TWLL COED, TWLL LLWYD.

Open in 1805 material was up-hauled to the north, and later a mill was built on waste on the far side of the public road. Worked intermittently, tonnage of 1000 with 40 men employed, recorded in 1873 was possibly an exceptional peak. Some very small scale working up to the 1980s. Was connected to Carnarvonshire S Q Railway, via FRON HEULOG, Stated to have had up to three waterwheels (one for pumping?) 11 men in 1938, only very small-scale working after WW2

Remains. Flooded pit. Some sheds from late working, up-haulage incline formation and vestiges of early buildings including a wheel pit, the abutments of a bridge across road and a possible barracks. [15]

TWLL COED SH491522 COCKLEBANK

Small hillside working producing green slate, was for a time, part of Tan y Allt, Operating in 1970s

Remains. Some modernised buildings, with an H Owen & Sons saw table and a Williams Portmadoc (Greaves type) dresser. [17].

TWLL JOHN FFOWC SH498525

Was part of TY MAWR EAST, worked independently in the 1890s by J.Ff.Williams.

Remains. None identifiable. [28]

TWLL LLWYD SH490518 NICHOLSON'S, TAN YR ALLT GREEN RUSTIC. **Working quarry, do not enter.**

Small hillside working, was part of Tan y Allt, still

operating on a small scale, using virtually pre-19th century methods of crow-barring rock.

Remains. Small modern building with locally made diamond sawing machine. Also an interesting "homemade" sawing machine on old lathe bed. Warehouse-type weighing machines. [13]

TYDDYN AGNES SH485517 NANTLLE UNITED, TALEITHIN.

Small pit working, active in 1860s/70s possibly used waterpower. Directly connected to C S Q R that passed though the site.

Remains. Some buildings including a possible mill, a dam and railway formations, tip filled with refuse. [9]

TŶ MAWR GREEN SH496523

Small pit working, a hiving off from original TŶ MAWR

Remains. Some small buildings. [24]

TŶ MAWR WEST SH495524, WELSH GREEN

Pit & hillside quarry also hived off from TŶ MAWR. Access to pit by an open cut. Later, as work progressed downwards, by Blondin. Active in 1860s with up to 40 men employed but tonnages well under 1000 pa. Material reduced in a mill with 3 saws driven by a Robey steam engine. Product taken to the road by a long, shallow incline. Closed 1930s

Remains. Pit, adit & shaft. A number of buildings, Blondin bases and concrete machinery base possibly for a late oil engine. Remnants of an interesting "lash up" cableway used in late re-working of tips. The fine, embanked incline is now much eroded. [22]

TY'N LLWYN SH478521

Small pit working. **Remain.** Two pits and vestiges of buildings. [8]

TY'N Y WEIRGLODD SH494523, VALE, WEST DOROTHEA,

Early 19th century pit/hillside working producing green and red slate. Mill to north west of pit. Haulage incline, may have been water powered. Successively, steam, gas engine & oil engine power used. The road was reached by incline. Immediately pre-WW2 had almost 40 men.

Remains. Site used for bulk fill, some vestiges of buildings and a house that clearly predates the quarry. Some concrete bases. Wheel pits and vestiges of haulage incline are much collapsed. The apparent tramway formation to NANT Y FRON is a road built shortly before 1953 closure. [20]

WERN IFAN SH506535

Small early working. Became part of PEN YR ORSEDD

Remains. Small depression (behind buildings at terminus of Nantlle railway). [35]

Section 4
DYFFRYN CONWY

General

In the valleys of the Conwy and its tributaries slate was worked in a number of small quarries, collectively making the area a significant source before being overtaken and eventually dwarfed, by north Caernarfonshire and other places. Downstream of Betws y Coed, there were exploitable occurrences in the hanging valleys to the west, but to the east the slate was poor and disparate. There was good slate in the Llugwy valley and at the head of the Machno valley. In the Lledr valley around Dolwyddelan the characteristic intensely black product was won in several places. Although the first Welsh slate to be worked underground was in this area (CLOGWYN Y FUWCH & PEN Y FRIDD), workings were generally open.

Dolwyddelan, Penmachno and certainly Rhiwddolion, can be classed as quarrying villages, and if one includes the boating element, Trefriw, but the quarries were mostly too small and too disparate to generate settlement patterns.

Few of the sites have much of great interest, but several of those around Dolwyddelan are notable and both HAFODLAS and RHOS have a lot to offer and CWM EIGIAU is well worth the long walk.

Transport

Apart from the London & North Western Railway Conway Valley branch, (completed to Betws y Coed in 1867 and Blaenau Ffestiniog in 1879) the area was totally dependent on the river Conwy that carrying material to Conwy for trans-shipment.

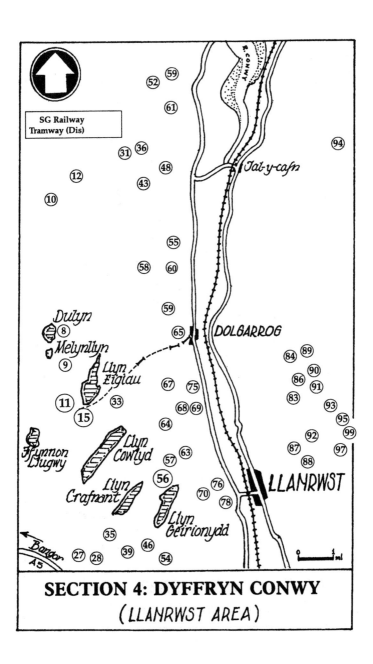

SG Railway
Tramway (Dis)

SECTION 4: DYFFRYN CONWY
(LLANRWST AREA)

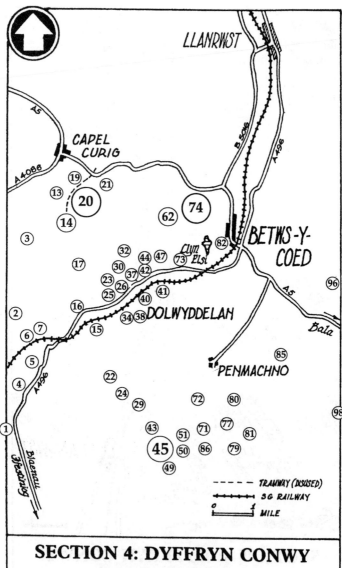

SECTION 4: DYFFRYN CONWY
(DOLWYDDELAN AREA)

The CEDRYN & CWM EIGIAU quarries reached the river at Dolgarrog by the 5-mile, 2' gauge Cwm Eigiau tramway, all the rest had to cart to Trefriw or Tal y Cafn. For the workings in the Llugwy, Lledr and Machno valleys this involved a long cartage. The L&NWR's route up valley from Llandudno Junction, being in the east side of the river was of no slate consequence until it reached Betws y Coed where it offered a much shorter cartage to the quarries in the three tributary valleys. HAFODLAS contemplated a tramway to Betws station.

When the line reached Dolwyddelan it was of even greater benefit to the quarrying cluster there, especially TYN Y BRYN that had a siding running right into their yard.

Such slate that did not remain on rail was shipped at the L&NWR's Deganwy harbour.

Most of the Cwm Eigiau tramway can be traced to the head of a 3-pitch incline at 765672 The road does not exactly follow the tramway route as it is on the bed of a standard-gauge steam line laid for the construction of the Eigiau reservoir making a diversion to avoid a short incline at 745664 near Pwll Du, where there are some excellent stone embankments. The winding house at the head of the incline is a later structure, built on the site of the upper drum house of the slate incline. This later incline, that up-hauled material to the Cowlyd water-works maintenance railway, made use of the upper 2 pitches of the slate incline, extended to form one straight run, whereas the lowest pitch of the earlier incline, turned slightly northwards. The bridge under the road of the more modern incline survives but the tunnel that took the earlier line under the road, and the track across the marsh to the riverside has been obliterated. The modern incline formation now carries pipes for the works hydroelectric plant.

Near CEDRYN quarry is Llyn Eigiau, now reduced in size following the 1926 dam collapse. The breached dam and the rock-strewn scour can be seen. This reservoir is connected to Llyn Cowlyd by a tunnel from where overground pipes run to the works. Llyn Coedty supplements the water supply and its pipeline joins the main pipes near the head of incline.

A further feature is the track bed of the narrow gauge railway that ran from the head of the incline to facilitate construction and maintenance of the Cowlyd dam, (lifted in the 1980s). The engine shed is still in use as a workmen's hut. There is a network of catchment leats that illustrate, on an enlarged scale the sort of leat work that was associated with the water supply for many quarries.

A shorter, but spectacular multi incline tramway, connected FOEL & RHOS quarries with the road at Capel Curig. Short but with a beautiful embankment and (replaced) bridge is the line that connected CHWAREL FEDWR quarry at Dolwyddelan with the PRINCE LLEWLLYN mills.

The ex L&NWR line to Blaenau Ffestiniog is still in use.

TREFRIW was an ancient port at the limit of navigation of the Conwy. handling agriculture, timber and wool from a wide area. Slate was (hand?) sawn in the village.

The 19th century expansion of slate, lead and other industries caused such congestion that slate awaiting loading had to be stacked at Betws y Coed, and forcing some shippers to use the poorer facilities at Tal y Cafn. Ocean-going ships of up to 100 tons could use the wharf, which eventually handled over 16,000 tons of slate p.a.

The railway caused its rapid demise although the passenger steamer service from Conwy continued until 1940

1].	SH683479	Cwm Fynhadog
2].	683520	Chwarel Owen Parry *
3].	685561	Cwm Clorod
4].	696496	Chwarel Gethin **
5].	697497	Moel Drongydd
6].	698512	Hendre
7].	700514	Coed Mawr **
8].	702663	Dulyn
9].	705654	Melynllyn
10].	706709	Nant Canolbren
11].	708635	Cwm Eigiau***
12].	715718 etc	Bwlch y Ddeufaen
13].	716569	Bryn Engan
14].	717556	Foel ***
15].	719635	Cedryn **
16].	721521	Chwarel Ddu
17].	722540	Penrhiw **
18].	726519	Pompren **
19].	727569	Cae Gwegi
20].	729564	Rhos ***
21].	729567	Adwywen
22].	730492	Chwarel David Hughes
23].	731528	Ystmiau
24].	732492	Cwm Penamnen
25].	734523	Llan
26].	735526	Chwarel Sion Jones *
27].	736594	Bwlch Geuallt
28].	736596	Clogwyn William *
29].	738495	Cregiau Geuallt
30].	738529	Adwy'r Dŵr
31].	738733	Tal y Fan
32].	740539	Fridd Bryn Moel
33].	741643	Siglen
34].	742521	Ty'n y Bryn **

35].	742601	Manod *
36].	743733	Ffriddlys
37].	744528	Prince Llewellyn
38].	746522	Penllyn *
39].	746602	Cornel *
40].	748525	Chwarel Fedwr *
41].	748528	Buarthau
42].	748723	Ffridd Ddwy Ffrwd
43].	749472	Glyn Aber (Tunnel)
44].	749537	Rhiwgoch **
45].	750471	Cwm Machno *** H
46].	751601	Cynllyd
47].	752539	Tyn y Fallen *
48].	755727	Coed Mawr *
49].	756464	Blaennant
50].	756466	Moel Marchyria.
51].	756474	Swch *
52].	756757	Llechan Uchaf
53].	757452	Foel Rudd
54].	757597	Tal y Llyn *
55].	757693	Pen y Gaer
56].	759618	Clogwyn y Fuwch ***
57].	759620	Hafod Arthen
58].	759687	Rowlyn
59].	759762	Waen y Fedwen
60].	760688	Penlan
61].	760745	Trecastell
62].	767558	Bwlch Gwyn *
63].	767630	Chwythlyn
64].	767639	Cefn Carwedd
65].	767672	Porthllwyd
66].	769464	Hafod Gwyrd
67].	770647	Ffridd
68].	773642	Ardda

69].	775642	Cae Rhobin *
70].	776612	Pen y Fridd **
71].	777477	Pen y Bont *
72].	779499	Moel y Pen y Bryn
73].	779533	Chwarel Glyn Lledr
74].	779562	Hafodlas ****
75].	779651	Cae Goch
76].	782618	Pont y Carw
77].	783483	Pen y Bedwr
78].	788610	Gwydir
79].	790469	Bryniau Dduon
80].	792498	Hafod Dwryd *
81].	793576	Afon Oernant
82].	797552	Beaver Pool
83].	811652	Penbryncaled
84].	817673	Pennant
85].	819509	Hwlfa *
86].	825654	Cae Madog *
87].	826634	Hen Ffridd
88].	827627	Henblas
89].	827666	Pennant Ucha
90].	829663	Gwern Bwys
91].	831651	Fridd Uchaf
92].	834637	Cefn Coch
93].	840646	Nant y Wrach
94].	841727	Gofer
95].	844642	Liberty
96].	849545	Brynhaul
97].	851658	Lydan
98].	862492	Rhyd Goch
99].	881635	Tyddyn Uchaf *

ADWY'R DŴR SH738529

Small underground working, possibly part of PRINCE LLEWELYN.

Remains. Collapsed working, flooded access tunnel. [30]

ADWYWEN SH729567

Probably an attempt to reach the RHOS veins and possibly even provide a low-level access to that quarry.

Remains. Adit. [21]

AFON OERNANT SH793576

Trial. **Remains.** Digging and run-in adit below. [81]

ARDDA SH773642 PEN Y CEFN, TYLCIA.

A tiny hillside working possibly from the early 18th century.

Remains. Pit & access track. [68]

BEAVER POOL SH797552

A very tiny scratching subject to speculation in the 1850s.

Remains. Possible vestiges in forestry. [82]

BLAEN NANT SH756464

Small hillside working. **Remains.** Traces of excavation. [49]

BRYN ENGAN SH716569

Open quarry with some underground, mid 19th century?.

Remains. Dressing shed, another building, tiny annexe with fireplace. Thomas Hughes bar rail on the ground. [13]

BRYNHAUL SH849545

Putative site. **Remains.** No evidence of slate working. [96]

BRYNIAU DUON SH790469

Trial. **Remains.** Two run-in levels. [79]

BUARTHAU SH748528

Possible trial site.

Remains. Ground disturbance in forestry. [41]

BWLCH GEUALLT SH736594

Small open working

Remains. Rock face with signs of hand drilling, some trimming waste. Vestiges of a building some distance away may have been part of it. [27]

BWLCH GWYN SH767558 EAST ARFON, CHWAREL RHIWDDOLION

Open quarry of moderate size operating late 19th/early 20th cent. Material trammed some 150 yards to a (water powered?) mill. Product almost entirely slab that was carted by road to Betws y Coed. The community outlasted the WW1 closure of the quarry, the quarrymen finding alternative employment mainly in Blaenau Ffestiniog, catching the train at Pony y Pant in the Lledr valley.

Remains. Site is now in forestry but some buildings are discernable including the old Bwlch Gwyn farmhouse that was reused for the quarry operation. Outside of the afforested area are the abandoned terraces and a chapel. of the quarry village of Rhiwddolion.

There is a delightful slate flagged path leading from the village to the chapel and quarry. Much of the access road is traceable. [62]

BWLCH Y DDEUFAEN SH 715718,720720, etc,

Tiny underground workings without surface shelter of any kind, probably worked on an as required basis.

Remains. Excavation only. [12]

CAE GOCH SH779651

Putative site possibly not slate. **Remains.** Excavation only. [75]

CAE GWEGI SH727569

Underground trial. **Remains.** Adit, some spoil. [19]

CAE MADOG SH825654 CEFN MADOC, CAE FFYNON

Shallow pit producing slab, with 2 saws & 2 planers with a 10-hp steam engine (installed 1860s?). The only mechanised unit this side of the valley.

Remains. Rubbish runs, tramway, mill building in re-use. [86]

CAE RHOBIN SH775642 CONWAY VALE

A small & primitive open quarry on a difficult site, with workings trammed to a mills area. Intermittently worked over many years with final closure in the 1920s. Present public road provided access.

Remains. Two buildings, one sunken with steps access and a stocking area in front, the other with engine holding down bolts possibly contained a saw. Much waste and trimmings, some tramway formations. Two small pillars of unknown purpose. Possibility of water power but no physical evidence of this. [69]

CEDRYN SH719635

A small and remote quarry, connected by an incline and bridge to a water powered mill on the opposite side of the valley. Sand and/or Hunter saws used. Opened early in the 19th century. Originally material was carted to Tal y Cafn but in the 1860s the 5-mile tramway, to a shipping point at on the river at Dolgarrog was opened. Closed about 1880.

Remains. Little on the site itself. A well engineered cart road rises past a rake of barracks to the original working.

The incline has a collapsed drum house part way down, where it was truncated to suit later, lower working. A third working is reached by a tunnel.

The embankment that carried a tramway to the mill is obvious but all trace of the wooden bridge over the river has gone.

The ruined mill has a wheel pit alongside and mountings, apparently subsequently raised up, for the drive shaft. There is an unusual rubbish trackway. Alongside the mill there is a small reservoir and some leat work. The 5-mile tramway can be readily traced. [15]

CEFN COCH SH834637 PEN Y GLODDFA
Possibly not slate. **Remains.** Pit at roadside. [92]

CEFN CYFARWYDD SH767639
Trial. **Remains.** Excavation. [64]

CHWAREL DAVID HUGHES SH730492
Small open working. **Remains.** Excavation only. [22]

CHWAREL DDU SH721521 CASTLE, BWLCH Y BEUDY, DOLWYDDELAN
A small unmechanised working developed into a pit on three floors with a trial underground. Late 18th century, sporadic working until the 1860s the few hundred tons output was carted to Trefriw. Revived briefly in the 1920s, when up-haulage was by i,c. engine.
Remains. Landscaping and road works in the 1990s destroyed what vestiges there were, but during this time remnants of iron sheathing for wooden rails also a Thomas Hughes 'Dog-bone' sleeper. It can still be seen how previous road building cut though the tip. [16]

CHWAREL FEDWR SH748525 Y FEDWR
An early open working. Material was brought down a

short incline and across the river Lledr by a causeway and bridge for cartage to Trefriw, (latterly reduction was done at PRINCE LLEWELYN). Closed circa 1890.

Remains. Site and incline now almost lost in forestry. The incline is cut by a forestry road and the rail underpass is blocked. There are drum house walls and vestiges of several dressing sheds. The causeway and (rebuilt) bridge are prominent and pleasing features. [40]

CHWAREL GETHIN SH696496 CHWAREL ANDREAS, CHWAREL IFAN LLOYD, CRIMEA
A small unmechanised underground working that Gethin Jones the railway contractor and builder of the Lledr railway viaduct, opened in the 1870s, taking advantage of the road he made to service the building of the railway tunnel. Originally material from the adits was lowered by a short incline for carting down valley to Dolwyddelan, but later work at a new, lower adit tipped over this incline. At one time a big future was predicted for this site.

Remains. On the upper level; the original open quarrying and subsequent underground working. On the middle level, chambering that breaks out to bank with a roofing shaft coming up from below. The lower adit is run-in. Tipped over incline may have had a horizontal sheave. Ground disturbance on the lower side of the track may have been trials. The sawn ends lying about are from re-working with an un-housed portable saw. [4]

CHWAREL GLYN LLEDR SH779533
Possible site. **Remains.** Lost in forestry. [73]

CHWAREL OWEN PARRY SH683520 (etc)
Three separate trial adits, the middle one may have yielded product.

Remains. Traces of a small building. [2]

CHWAREL SION JONES SH735526
Small open pit.
Remains. Possibly the nearby house may have been connected. [26]

CHWYTHLYN SH767630 (Also 737652)
Small diggings for flags. **Remains.** Excavations. [63]

CLOGWYN WILLIAM SH736596 CLOGWYN MAWR
Tiny working on a cliff face shelf. An abortive 1920s re-opening included an overhead ropeway
Remains. Dressing sheds with stock of 13 x 7 slates. A number of small slabs possibly intended for the production of hones. [28]

CLOGWYN Y FUWCH SH759618
An entirely unmechanised, 18th century underground working on 6 levels rising some 400' up a near vertical scarp.,. The series of large openings up the hillside and the use of a cut-and-cover entrance are redolent of Lakeland practice, but there is no evidence to connect this site with any particular Lakeland operator. Originally output sledged down, the table incline dates from the 1820s.

In spite of producing small, irony and perishable slates, was working in 1890 when O.E, Hughes' 3 men produced 155 tons. Closed early 1900s. Much was used locally but Trefriw could have served as shipping point.
Remains. There has been some disturbance at the foot of the site, but there is the ruin of a small building, a working area and a chamber going straight in from the hill-face, accessed through waste tipped from above by a cut-and-cover tunnel. Level 2 is a tiny working, clearly non-productive. Level 3, a considerable distance above

has a twisting strike tunnel leading to some pillared chambering that just breaks into level 4. Outside there are several dressing sheds, those beyond the incline reached by a bridge.

Level 4 is chambered in for some 300', at the far end there are footboards still in situ for a roofing tunnel development. There is small forge underground. On the surface there are several buildings including a small smithy and the remains of the remote type drum house at the head of the incline. Level 5 has been chambered out from level 4. Surface structures include the circular base of a powder house with a rock "bench" around the inside. There are possible traces of a slide way down to level 4. Level 6 has some traces of small buildings, underground it has been chambered though from below. All buildings are in poor condition. [56]

COED MAWR SH700514 TYN Y DDÔL
A small open pit, from, c1870. Haulage and pumping by waterwheel (water presumably by inverted siphon from a source to the northwest), by the end of the century a steam engine set on the rubbish bank was used. Output carted down valley (To Roman Bridge station?).
Remains. Several buildings including engine house and a forge. Curious small square aperture penetrates the retaining wall alongside the incline formation, possibly for the pump pipe. No evidence of sawing found. [7]

COED MAWR SH755727
Ephemeral 20th century working. **Remains.** Brick quoined building. [48]

CORNEL SH746602 MYNYDD DELWYN, COED Y FRON
A small hillside quarry worked successively downwards

into a pit Reduction in a small mill, which during an early 1920s revival had an oil engine driven diamond saw. Transport by cart down valley. Some product may have been converted to hones at HAFOD ARTHEN

Remains. The pit has been worked down to the level of the now collapsed access tunnel. A nice weigh house has been rebuilt, Office now a dwelling. Base for oil-engine. [39]

CREGIAU GEUALLT SH738495
Putative site. **Remains.** Possible scratching, not identifiable as slate. [29]

CWM CLOROD SH685561
Trial. **Remains.** Spoil. [3]

CWM EIGIAU SH708635 (Including CAERHUN an 1866 attempt to hive off part of the sett)
A small open quarry connected by an 1863 extension of the Cedryn tramway. Opened before 1830 closed by 1880. In spite of elaborate (and expensive) development, production cannot have exceeded a few hundred tons p.a. Some weekly barrackers walked from Bethesda!

Remains. Workings on 5 terraces with an incline to a mill, overlying an earlier incline. There is also a most unusual short incline that may have been a temporary up haulage balanced by down-going rubbish. There is some exploratory work above drum house level.

Apparent traces of four, (presumably successive) mills, the one alongside the massive leat embankment being the earliest, followed by the one in front of it. Curiously this latter had sand saws (with unusual external line-shafting) whereas the earlier had circular saws The third mill, at an angle to it, dating from the time of the tramway connection, had at least one Hunter saw and although possibly intended for steam power could have been driven from the second mill via a crown gear. The fourth mill on the far side of the pit from the 30' wheel possibly never completed. There are several small supply reservoirs and leat work. There is a barracks, workshop, powder house and several other buildings. During successive operating periods, undoubtedly redundant structures were robbed to build new ones, making it difficult to interpret the site. A cast iron Thomas Hughes sleeper and rails, have been found.

The cart road follows the tramway formation to Cedryn. [11]

CWM FYNHADOG SH683479

Open quarry, with underground trials. No sign of any production.

Remains. Excavation, run-in adits nearby. [1]

CWM MACHNO SH750471 MACHNO, PENMACHNO, RHIWFACHNO, TAN Y RHIW

Two hillside workings, the lower deepened into a pit with some underground extraction. Operated almost continuously from at least 1818 to 1962, employing upwards of 100 up to WW2, it only finally closed due to lack of skilled manpower. Three mills, successively waterwheel, turbine and IC powered.

There were ideas for dispatching by a water-balance incline up to the Rhiwbach Tramway, for using the RHIWBACH drainage tunnel and underground incline [Section 8] or for a branch from a proposed Corwen to Betws y Coed railway; yet this quarry survived without rail connection, carting, to Trefriw wharf, later to Betws y Coed station. A traction engine replaced horses, later a steam, then a motor lorry was used. From 1948 a diesel loco worked the MOEL MARCHYRIA rail link. Then having 75 men were almost the only quarry to have more than half their pre-war total (108).

Remains. The mills area has been landscaped, leaving only two small buildings and part of one mill. The remarkable crenulated boundary wall has gone and tips removed to fill the pit of the lower working obliterating its up haulage, which latterly was air-winch powered. The inclines that served the terraces of this lower working are much degraded, but one drum house and a fine revetted tramway formation survive.

The most prominent feature is the big slate-paved table incline which brought block to the mills from the upper working and due to lack of tipping space doubled as an up haulage for rubbish from the lower working. Near its head is the pit of the water wheel that originally wound it. Alongside is the formation that carried a balance tank after it was converted to a water-balance. This formation that is pierced by a fine accommodation arch, is twice as long as the actual running ramp suggesting that a sheave was used to increase mechanical advantage. At its head is a massive structure, with access steps that carried the header tank. As well as fabricated pipe, there are some wooden launders.

The four inclines connecting the levels of the upper working, are in good order some with drums etc., one having remnants of a wooden bridge. There are vestiges of several older inclines. On an intermediate level there are parts of a tripod crane and nearby a trial adit. There are several other buildings on these upper levels including a hydro-compressor house with piping. Above is the bed of Llyn Penrhiw that provided the water supply.

Much of the village, including several rows of single-storey cottages, some still in occupation, was quarry property. [45]

CWM PENAMNEN SH732492 etc CHWAREL DAVID HUGHES
Some extraction here, other diggings wereonly trials.
Remains. A rubbish mound at this point and, in the vicinity, traces of at least half a dozen trials, some in forestry. [24]

CYNLLYD SH751601
Trial. **Remains.** Excavation. [46]

DULYN SH702663
Possible trial for hones. **Remains.** Excavations. [8]

FFRIDD SH770647
Tiny underground trial. **Remains.** Run-in adit. [67]

FFRIDD BRYN MOEL SH740539
Trial. **Remains.** Traces of adit. [32]

FFRIDD DDWY FFRWD SH748723
Trial. **Remains.** Surface disturbance. [42]

FFRIDDLYS SH743733 CRAIG CELYNIN
Putative site. **Remains.** Possible ground disturbance. [36]

FFRIDD UCHAF SH831651
Tiny open quarry. **Remains.** Excavation only. [91]

FOEL SH717556 BRYN CYPLE, MOEL SIABOD, TREWYDIR
Open quarry, developed into pit. Opened c1835, operating on five levels with tunnel access to the pit on two. There were two mills on site, the upper one possibly with a sand saw being powered by a waterwheel, and a lower one, which may have supplanted it, having a turbine or Pelton wheel driving circular (?) saws. For a short time in the 1860s a mill at Pont Cyfyng (735570) functioned with sand saws, (possibly with circular saws

later). Annual tonnage rarely exceeded 500 with under a dozen men.

Material went out by an incline to a tramway that led via further inclines to the Pont Cyfyng mill. Later this was truncated and turned to serve a roadside loading point at 734572 from where product would have been carted to Trefriw. Closed in the 1880s following a big rock-fall but continued to trade, renting their inclines to RHOS .

Remains. At the lowest level there is a small mill building with vestiges of the turbine supply and some other structures including a possible barrack also a tunnel to the pit. Above, connected by an incline, there is another working level with ruins of a small mill with a wall screening the transversely-placed wheel from the winds at this height There are some other structures including launder pillars and a forge. There are a number of dressing sheds including the much-photographed rake of three with cantilevered slab roofs. There is a second tunnel that like the one below has been blocked, to keep the pit flooded up as a water supply for RHOS. At this level is a possible horse-whim circle. There are several much-degraded internal inclines, and a further two barracks.

There is some interesting leat work on the hillside above and a very small reservoir.

The main tramway is traceable past the vestiges of another barracks, past the RHOS reservoirs to the head of the upper incline with its conventional drum house. The next incline, steeper and shorter has a remote type drum house, the two pitches are connected by a neatly excavated swan-neck loop. The roadside buildings and dwellings at the foot of the incline are undoubtedly connected with the quarry.

Below the road is the ruin of the Pont Cyfyng mill with

a pit for a breast shot wheel. There are massive slate bases for the reciprocating saws. The old incline down under the road is not traceable. [14]

FOEL RUDD SH757452
A series of small open diggings. **Remains.** Shallow pits. [53]

GLYN ABER SH749472
Not a quarry but the drainage tunnel of RHIWBACH quarry [Section 8]. [43]

GOFER SH841727 & 838726
Shale/flag diggings. **Remains.** Excavations. [94]

GWERN BWYS SH829663
Hillside quarry, shale. **Remains.** Excavation and rubbish runs. [90]

GWYDIR SH788610
Building stone quarry, possibly it yielded slate earlier.
Remains. Quarry face, much overgrown. [78]

HAFOD ARTHEN SH.759620
Hone quarry with small saw mill possibly also reduced material from CORNEL
Remains. Quarrying site now obliterated, the mill is part of a house. [57]

HAFOD DWRYD SH792498 HAFOD Y REDWYDD, PEN Y BRYN
Small, used waterpower? **Remains.** Traces of buildings. [80]

HAFOD GWYRD SH769464
Tiny underground working.
Remains. Rubbish run and access track in forestry. [66]

HAFODLAS SH779562 BETWS Y COED, LONDON
A mid 19th century open quarry that was extensively, and expensively developed in the last quarter of the century. In 1883 11 men employed producing 289 tons, but tonnages were at time swelled to up to 2000 producing the sills and such seen in Betws y Coed buildings (some showing coarse Hunter saw markings).

Two contiguous pits worked on 6 levels, unusually, the upper levels do not seem to have been entirely abandoned as work progressed downwards. The main mill was on the fifth level down, blocks from the lowest level being raised by a most unusual power conversion of the main exit incline. Output was carted to Trefriw, latterly to Betws y Coed station. Despite a galaxy of distinguished railway engineers having interest at various times, the tramway to Betws was never built. Revived post WW1 by J J Riley it closed in 1929. One of the very few quarries to enamel on site.

Remains. Even though heavily wooded this is a most interesting site. The highest level has a tunnel taking a tramway to the head of an incline (with drum house) down to mills level. The hoisting derrick that survived for many years has collapsed.

At the second level down there is an access tunnel, (with a cutting diversion), leading from much collapsed workings, past a weighbridge to the head of another incline. Back from the head of this incline are under-floor horizontal sheaves with cable ducts leading towards the crimp where there are 2 levers that controlled by wires a band brake and a deadlock respectively. As this incline led almost directly into the mill, there is a pile of blocks at its foot to arrest runaways.

At mills level, there is a tunnel into the quarry and a cut-and-cover tunnel through waste, weigh-houses and other ruins and a most elegant mill. This main mill is in two parts of differing but equally elaborate architectural styles. The earlier (1862), eastern end has the roof-trusses the 'wrong way round' i.e. on the longer dimension. The later, (1867) western part has attractive doorways upswept to accommodate some kind of gantry. Between the two parts is a large wheel pit reconstructed to house a Pelton wheel and latterly an electric motor.

An under-floor shaft tunnel runs the full length of the two mills and in addition the newer mill has overhead line shaft mounts on its unusual steel gantry structure. Originally had Hunter saws, presumably the overhead shafting dates from their replacement by conventional saw tables. Sand saws also may have been used .

Close to, but out of alignment with, this newer section is an obviously much older drum house. This main incline drum house, like the one on the topmost level is larger but less substantial than is usual. Uniquely, it has been converted to power operation from the mill line shaft, with some of the gearing and control rods being still in place. This conversion enabled this balanced exit incline to double up as a powered up haulage incline serving the lowest level. A further unusual feature is the remote control for the crimp sprags. .In front of the main mill is the ruin of what may have been an earlier mill with a wheel pit alongside. At the back of the main mill the alignment of launder pillars and other ruins suggest a further wheel, presumably to augment the power of the original wheel.

Beyond the drum house is a forge and workshop, also on this level there is an extensive stocking area and the vestiges of enamelling kilns.

The lowest level has tunnel access to the quarry, a weigh house with much of the mechanism intact, several buildings including a stable and the incline landing stage.

At the top of the site is a quaint powder house. There are some small dressing sheds from an early date, but clearly product was mainly slab.

The nearby manager's house, has a slate lined food store cut into the hillside behind. Alongside this manager's house a flat area denotes the site of the wood and zinc-sheeting 1920s "London" mill.

There are traces of a watercourse from Llyn Elsi that originally supplied the wheels, and the 24" pipe that may have supplied the Pelton wheel or turbine and the public electricity plant, vestiges of which are near the foot of the main incline. Near the top of this run of pipe is a penstock with a curious slate gasket. Surprisingly for such an accessible a site there are many artefacts to be found. [74]

HENBLAS SH827627

Small flooring-flag quarry. **Remains.** Excavation only. [88]

HENDRE SH698512 CWM FYNNADOG, GLYN LLEDR

This small unmechanised pit worked from circa 1840. the same black slate as COED MAWR. A horse-whim raised rubbish, later water was used for haulage and pumping, afterwards steam. In the early years tonnages were 600 and mote but in 1882 6 men produced 120 tons. Closed early 1900s. Transport by cart down valley.

Remains. Traces of some buildings, two wheel pits, presumably from different eras There are launder pillars and behind the site, traces of a reservoir, dammed partly by natural rock. Traces of a unique horse-whim circle with a curved screening wall. [6]

HEN FFRIDD SH826634

Tiny open working. **Remains.** Roadside digging. [87]

HWLFA SH819509

Literally a cottage industry, worked on an occasional, as required, basis.

Remains. Shallow pit, cottage ruins, with a "workshop" alongside. There is a small turbuary nearby that supplied the big peat fireplace, [85]

LIBERTY SH844642

Very small. **Remains.** Slight traces of excavation. [95]

LLAN SH734523

Very small possibly only building block, **Remains.** Quarry face. [25]

LLECHAN UCHAF SH756757

Possibly very ancient site. **Remains.** Excavation only. [52]

LYDAN SH851658

Tiny shaley digging. **Remains.** Small pit. [97]

MANOD SH742601 CLOGWYN MANOD

Partly underground working, with a small mill, disused by 1896.

Remains. The upper level, subsequently worked out from below, some small buildings including a round powder house. On the intermediate level there is a large opening to an excavation that has a small tunnel leading off it and 2 dressing sheds. At the lowest level, a collapsed tunnel and the remains of a possible mill.

There are nice, well engineered tracks to all three levels. [35]

MELYNLLYN SH705654

Hone quarry producing sharpening stones from high-grade, close-grained slate. Worked in mid/late 19th century, revived in early 1900s, machinery removed and re-installed at PENRHIW 1908

Remains. Cave-lile adit, tramway formation to ruins of mill, part of crank of its one water-powered sand saw. [9]

MOEL DRONGYDD SH697497
Tiny scratching. **Remains.** Almost nil. [5]

MOEL MARCHYRIA SH756466 & 756468 FOEL OCHA, Y FOEL
Small hillside quarry later part of CWM MACHNO, reached by a short locomotive line that replaced an access track known to the quarrymen as the "Burma Road". **Remains.** Excavations and tips. [50]

MOEL Y PEN Y BRYN SH779499
Trial ? **Remains.** Excavation only. [72]

NANT CANOLBREN SH706709
Several small pits, trials only? **Remains.** Traces of digging. [10]

NANT Y WRACH SH840646
Very small. Shale? **Remains.** In forestry. [93]

PENBRYNCALED SH811652
Small flag digging. **Remains.** Excavation. [83]

PENLAN SH760688
Trial, associated with speculations in the 1860s, almost certainly never produced. **Remains.** Blind adit. [60]

PENLLYN SH746522.
Hillside quarry on three levels opened in 1875 as an extension of TYN Y BRYN output sent to that quarry's mill by incline and tramway.
Remains. Excavations, building traces. Sand saw blade fencing. [38]

PENNANT SH817673

Small roadside digging, building block? **Remains.** Excavation. [84]

PENNANT UCHA SH827666

Building blocks only? **Remains.** Excavation and rubbish runs. [89]

PENRHIW SH722540 MOEL SIABOD, LLWYN GRAEANIG

Hone quarry operated intermittently from mid 19th century to WW1. Usually less than about six men employed. Material taken by tramway for a water-powered mill that had a sand saw and possibly a polishing machine. Some machinery transferred here from MELYNLLYN in 1908, Output carted to Capel Curig.

Remains. Open working accessed by adit from below. Tramway formation with rail on ground to water-powered mill at 723542 that has a small forge hearth, and remnants of sand saw. In a room behind are plummer blocks that may indicate a drive for a polishing machine. The mill has two lean-to structures and there is at least one 7' long sand saw blade and fragments of others. The tip contains many reject hones. [17]

PEN Y BEDW SH783483 (Also 786481?)

Tiny hillside trial.

Remains. Collapsed adit, traces of two sheds, steep access track. [77]

PEN Y BONT SH777477

Tiny pit, possibly only a trial. **Remains.** Excavation only. [71]

PEN Y FRIDD SH776612 LLANRHYCHWYN

Open quarry, part underground, and operating late 18th

century (possibly much earlier). Tonnage was around 1000 pa, exceeding double this in the 1820s but their 50-man payroll declined to a handful, closing in 1865 Finished product carted via Llanrychwyn, to Trefriw quay.

Remains. Probably the oldest underground slate working in Wales. Site now forested, the only structure is a smithy(?) in fair conditions. Stated never to have had any railed transport but a set of wheels on axle were found on site. An eerie series of chambers in the original working face, dip down on 5 levels, pillars are so slender as to virtually form one vast cavern. Much fallen rock from old faces and from the roof. [70]

PEN Y GAER SH757693
Possible trials. **Remains.** Scratchings. [55]

POMPREN SH726519 PONTPREN FEDW, PONT Y BRON BEDW
Pit, a small (100 tpa?) and early (1840s?) working. Material left the two pits by a drainage adit, rubbish being raised by horse-whim. Later the renowned publisher Thomas Gee installed a "Hydrauilc Winch" to raise rubbish up an incline and also built a water powered mill with a sand-saw. Employment under a dozen , although the railway "passed the door" there was no connection. Closed before WW1.

Remains. Pits with adit access. Some vestiges of dressing sheds, smithy and a haulage incline. Lower down the site, are mill ruins with a wheel pit and launder pillars. Traces of a reservoir behind the site. [18]

PONT Y CARW SH782618 TAI ISAF
Trial. **Remains.** In forestry. [76]

PORTHLWYD SH767672 DOLGARROG
Small slab quarry. **Remains.** In forestry. [65]

PRINCE LLEWELYN SH744528 BWLCH, (CYNNUD), Y FOEL. CAMBRIAN
Opened in the 1820s as hillside quarry, deepened into a pit with some later underground working. A steam mill erected c1850 had 4 sand saws but power sawing may predate this. The mill also dealt with blocks from CHWAREL FEDW. The steam engine was replaced by a 30' water-wheel, but steam was retained for pumping. The 1890s mill that brought the total of machines to 9 saw-tables & 3 planers was water-turbine driven. Output in 1882 was 1685 tons (mainly slab) with 74 men, (may have been more in earlier years), making it the largest in the Dolweddelan area. Closed 1934. Product carted originally to Trefriw, later to Dolwydellan station. May have been the very last user of sand-saws.
Remains. Disappointingly little, the site having been used for bulk fill, cleared and afforested. The pit is flooded and adits are inaccessible. Some traces of inclines. A garage is on the site of the original mill. Quarry cottages are still occupied. There is a reservoir behind the site. [37]

RHIWGOCH SH749537 BRANDRETH
Hillside quarry, opened 1860s deepened into a pit on three floors, accessed by adits, with some limited underground working There were two water-powered mills, the later and larger one possibly was never completed. A water balance raised rock from the lowest level. Tonnage may have nudged 800, but by 1890 it was less than 100. Amalgamated with TY'NAFALLEN. Closed 1908
Remains. A large pit with some limited chambering off it.

A tunnel led to the original mill (now incorporated into a farm building). The big mill lower down the site (that allegedly latterly had a steam powered "shot saw", much used for stone but rarely for slate), only has walls remaining. There is further tunnel access to the pit at this level and another tunnel lower down with traces of a water balance incline. A tramway formation leads in from TY'NAFALLEN. Near the bottom of the site is a drainage adit, big enough to suggest that material removal was planned. There are several other buildings including a powder magazine. The exit road, which may have been intended to be an incline, crosses a stream by a nice bridge. The proposed connection to Pont y Pant station was of course never built. Above the site is a substantial reservoir. [44]

RHOS SH729564 CAPEL CURIG, RHOS Y GOELCERTH
A large pit working, with extensive use of water power, opened in the 1850s, developed 1870s. Produced 1285 tons with 45 men in 1882.

At first, material was trammed out of the working via a short tunnel, (later opened out as a cutting), to the nearby mill area.

As work progressed downward, a haulage system was powered by the 30' mill wheel. It is likely that this wheel also pumped. There was also an 18' wheel at the mill, which may have supplemented the larger wheel when the mill was extended to double its original size.

Later a drainage tunnel was cut permitting the use of a water balance and providing a ready route out for waste. This was consolidated into a platform incorporating a wheel pit as the intention was to construct a new mill at a lower level to avoid up-haulage.

Later the water balance was abandoned and a further

18' wheel (that may have come from Nantlle) was inserted into the mill wheel supply to operate a chain incline. In 1919 a 40' Wheel (ex Cyfty lead mine?) was installed working off the mill tailrace to power a compressor. At some time another tunnel was started from the pit bottom but never completed.

A De Winton locomotive was used in the mill area from 1898, replaced by diesel 1935. A tramway connection was made to the FOEL inclines, finished product being carted from Pont Cyfyng. Flourished in the 1930s under J J Riley with annual tonnages at a record 1500. Closed in 1952, having less than half their 50+ pre-WW2 manning.

Remains. The pit is of impressive size. The head frame of the water balance is in place, (a balance tank is on the opposite side of the quarry), but the incline itself has been quarried away. There are some traces of the later chain incline with its wheel pit inserted onto the main mill wheel supply, with associated sheave mountings etc.

The fine mill has the wheel behind, at right angles. This wheel has a mounting for some secondary duties, possibly pumping and winding. There are traces of the earlier, smaller wheel.

The mill building has a series of alcoves forming dressing sheds along one side in the usual Caernarfonshire manner, no trimming machines being used. There is an adjacent lavatory using the wheel tailrace. From this tailrace a well-built stone channel with penstock leads to the big wheel pit for the compressor.

On the commodious mill area is a big stocking ground and several other buildings including a workshop/forge and a weigh house with its mechanism pit converted to a locomotive inspection pit. There are some underground leats for the water pumped out of the pit. Nearby is a rake of barracks/dwellings, one of which latterly housed a diesel generator.

Immediately behind the uppermost wheel is a small holding pond and behind that the lower reservoir that has a three-ply dam reinforced by bridge rail and slate slab. The upper reservoir still holds water. The access tunnels of FOEL have been stopped up to provide further water storage.

At the lower end of the drainage/rubbish tunnel is the area intended for a new mill with the wheel housing towering up. [20]

RHYD GOCH SH862492
Putative site unlikely to be slate. **Remains.** Obvious quarry face. [98]

ROWLYN SH759687
Underground. Although a company was floated around 1860 to exploit this site it is unlikely that any, saleable product came out.
Remains. Blind adit accessed by a bridge, possible second adit, some building remains, spoil. [58]

SIGLEN SH741643
Possible trial. **Remains.** Excavation only. [33]

SWCH SH756474
A compact underground working operation, part of CWMMACHNO. Block from the adit was transported by a short incline to the mill.
Remains. Adit is barely traceable due to later tipping from CWMMACHNO. The incline is clear with a leat alongside. The mills area is in agricultural re-use. Traces of walls and a wheel-pit suggest that there were two mill buildings. The office and adjacent dwelling are in good order. Traces of launder pillars and possible up haulage for mill waste. [51]

TAL Y FAN SH738733
A tiny, primitive quarry, possibly 16th century, two small faces worked, plus an underground trial.
Remains. Vestiges of an adit, two dressing sheds, possible smithy and a powder house. There is evidence of power drilled holes, (portable compressor?) from the 20th century, small-scale reworking. In spite of its comparative insignificance, there is a well-engineered road to the site. [31]

TAL Y LLYN SH757597
A small, long abandoned open working, going into an overhang. Final access by a cutting.
Remains. Large trees growing out of rubbish runs, vestiges of one or possibly two dressing sheds, the access track is traceable. [54]

TRECASTELL SH760745
Open quarry, possibly not slate. **Remains.** Excavation only. [61]

TYDDYN UCHAF SH881635
Small pit working, slab? Sawing planned?
Remains. Flooded pit. Traces of attempt to use waterpower. [99]

TY'N Y BRYN SH742521 BWLCH Y LLAN, FRAITH, LLEDR VALE
Developed in the 1860s on the site of much earlier working. On five levels connected by inclines to a water powered mill that from 1875 also dealt with PENLLYN output. Despite having circular saws, possibly including a Hunter saw, some sand-saws were used right up to closure.

Originally material was carted to Trefriw for shipment, but later had a siding from the Blaenau branch of the L&NWR. One of only four quarries to have standard gauge on site (The others being GLOGUE & ROSEBUSH. [Section14] & COED MADOG [section 3]). .

Tonnage (including PENLLYN). may have neared 2000 tpa Closed 1924.

Remains. 4 inclines with and ruined drum houses, a number of dressing sheds and weigh houses, one with mechanism. Tips have been used for bulk fill leaving little in the mill area other than machine bases and a wheel pit. Vestiges of a tramway from PENLLYN. [34]

TY'N Y FALLEN SH752539 EAST RHIWGOCH, LORD & LADY WILLOUGHBY

Underground working, a small operation started by Joseph Kellow in the 1870s, combined with RHIWGOCH in the early 1900s.

Remains. 2 adits, the lower one has very limited chambering attempts, some rail on ground. The upper with adjacent dressing shed and drum house has several small workings breaking out to bank and a steeply inclined shaft downwards. Some rail in the tunnel. The incline formation is much degraded. The tramway to RHIWGOCH now partly forms the access road to the farmhouse. [47]

WAEN Y FEDWEN SH759762

Trial. **Remains.** Possible excavation. [59]

YSTUMIAU SH731528.

Trial probably by PRINCE LLEWELYN. **Remains.** Adit. [23]

Section 5
CWM GWYRFAI

Area served by the North Wales Narrow Gauge Railway

General

The quarries are in three groups, Cwm Gwyrfai, to the west of GR570 around Waunfawr and Betws Garmon. working the Caernarfon Cambrian slate; those east of 570 on the Meirionnydd Ordovician veins that created the village of Rhydd Ddu, and the Moel Tryfan workings that are contiguous with the Nantlle area [Section 3]. Their people made villages such as Rhostryfan, Rhosgadfan, Carmel and Y Fron, with many more in scattered, hillside mini-smallholdings.

The depredations of time, weather, tipping, clearance and re-working limit the extent of remains on most sites, but there are still interesting relics on many.

Transport

By the time the North Wales Narrow Gauge Railway opened in 1877 (final completion 1881) several quarries in Cwm Gwyrfai itself had given up the struggle of getting their product to market whilst development at for instance GLANRAFON had not even been attempted.

BRAICH and FRON had from 1868 been able to reach the Nantlle Railway but it was not until the Bryngwyn branch of the NWNGR opened that there could be serious development in the Moel Tryfan area.

The 2' gauge. 7 mile NWNG line ran from Dinas, near Caernarfon, where slate for Caernarfon port or for the main line network. could be transferred onto the London & North Western Railway.

Exclusively loco worked the NWNGR was never a

SECTION 5: CWM GWYRFAI

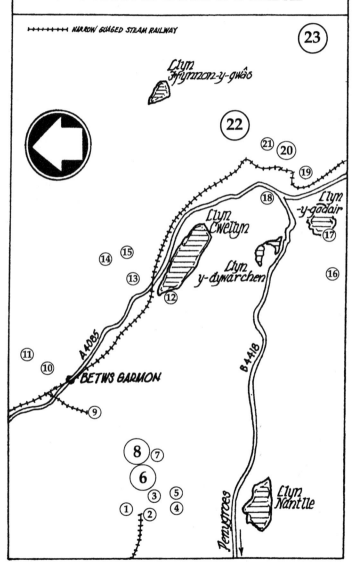

├┼┼┼┼┼┼┤ *NARROW GUAGED STEAM RAILWAY*

(23)

Llyn Ffynnon-y-gwâs

(22)

(21) (20)

(19)

Llyn y-gadair

(18)

Llyn Cwellyn

(17)

(14) (15)

Llyn y-dywarchen

(16)

(13)

(12)

A4085

B4418

(11)

(10)

BETWS GARMON

(9)

(8) (7)

(6)

(3)

(5)

(1) (2)

(4)

Penygroes

Llyn Nantlle

commercial success, it declined during the first years of the 20th century and was virtually moribund by the time it was incorporated into the Welsh Highland Railway in 1923. The short-lived WHR provided an extension to Porthmadog, but carried little slate traffic on its main line since it opened after the industry was well into its almost terminal decline.

The whole of the NWNGR main line (plus the Caernarfon-Dinas part of the ex L&NWR Caernarfon-Afon Wen branch) has now been rebuilt as the revived Welsh Highland.

The TREFLAN and HAFOD Y WERN branches are traceable whilst the course of the Bryngwyn branch wends its sinuous, overgrown way from Tryfan junction (SH502592) to Rhostryfan where the rails passed under the road (infill gives the impression of a level crossing) and on to the foot of the Bryngwyn incline. The incline up to Drumhead, the official end of the line, makes a fine landscape feature.

Traces of the four quarry branches diverge From Drumhead; the magnificent "Alpine" line to ALEXANDRA, the shorter lines to MOELTRYFAN and BRAICH and the line that wended its way through Fron village to FRON quarry. Also traceable is the 1922 link that connected the Cilgwyn "horseshoe" tipping line to the Fron branch, enabling CILGWYN quarry to use the NWNGR via the Bryngwyn incline. .

The "John Robinson's Fron" tramway can be traced from the southern side of BRAICH as a wide verge alongside the access track to Fron village, and on first as a road, then as a lane between the stone walls of quarrymen's small holdings behind CILGWYN, to where it dropped down through TALYSARN [section 3].

116

1]	SH510552	Braich	I
2]	512549	Braich Rhyd	
3]	513556	Crown	
4]	515548	Fron	I
5]	515551	Pretoria	
6]	515559	Moeltryfan	G
7]	518556	Brynfferam	
8]	519562	Alexandra	G
9]	530571	Hafod y Wern	
10]	538582	Garreg Fawr	
11]	539584	Treflan	
12]	552552	Castell Cidwm	
13]	552562	Plas y Nant	
14]	552587	Moel Eilio	
15]	553562	Bryn Manllyn	
16]	557508	Bwlch y Ddwy Elor	
17]	564519	Llyn y Gadair	
18]	570533	Cwellyn	
19]	573526	Ffridd Isaf	
20]	576530	Clogwyn y Gwin	
21]	577547	Bron y Fedw	
22]	581540	Glanrafon	F
23]	600521	Bwlch Cwmllan.	

ALEXANDRA SH519562 CORS Y BRYNIAU

A substantial multi-pit working with 3 steam powered mills, and an extensive loco worked internal tramway system. Opened in the 1860s, at its peak produced 6000 tons pa employing over 200 men. Finished product was sent down to Drumhead, by their spectacular "Alpine" line.

The mills were closed in the late 1930s, reduction up the 1960s being done at MOELTRYFAN. Some small-scale work continues.

Remains. The 1960s lorry road combined with bulk working has much degraded the now merged pits 1 & 2, and buried pit 3. Flooding up to floor 5 tunnel has drowned four galleries and the debris from MOELTRYFAN that engulfed them following merger.

There is almost nothing left of the old mill and just remains of the twinned new mills, the office, workshops and winding engine rooms. On the upper bank are more substantial remains of Blondin anchorages, six winder houses, weighbridge and the once-impressive electricity sub-station.

The outstanding feature is the spectacular 2-mile "Alpine" rail formation down to the head of the Bryngwyn incline. Part way along is an isolated tipping site at the end of the (run-in) floor 5 tunnel, 'Lefel Fawr'. [8]

BRAICH SH510552 BRAICH MELYN, NEW BRAICH. & BWLCH Y LLYN

An open pit, dating from the early 19th century and substantially developed from 1868 when a steam-driven mill was built, Steam also drove the chain incline and backed up the water-powered pump. One De Winton locomotive. Used the 1868 FRON tramway, prior to 1870s direct connection to Drumhead. Output 1882 2614 tons, 124 men. Closed 1911.

Remains. Mainly a near rectangular flooded pit, with vestiges of a pumping-engine house and traces of pump rod runs. There are the ruins of a large mill and winding houses, and the anchorages of the chain incline and the Blondin. The original short incline to the Fron tramway is obvious, crossing a very nice primitive bridge. The line of this tramway is defined by a verge alongside the lane down to Fron village.

At the northern end of the quarry the degraded bed of the upper pitch of the later exit incline (with steps alongside) drops to a lower working area, where there is secondary excavation by tip contractors, their little shelters and the anchorages for their light cableways. From the extensive lower rubbish runs, a further incline formation drops to the track bed of the branch line to Bryngwyn Drumhead. On the margins of an adjacent field to the north can be found the roofless powder magazine, the remnant of a small header reservoir and a very ruinous water-wheel pit. [1]

BRAICH RHYD SH512549 OLD BRAICH
An 18th century pit working entirely distinct from the newer and larger BRAICH quarry. Following the collapse in a storm of the 1827 wind power pump, steam was used for pumping and also for hauling. Used the NWNGR Fron branch to Drumhead Closed early 20th century.
Remains. Surrounded by tips, a road separates the narrow pit from the truncated, but largely complete 1904 mill, the only roofed slate mill in the district. In the pit a length of wire rope attached to a broken timber denotes the cableway system. Further to the west is the small red slate quarry and in the field below this is a party-in filled trial. [2]

BRON Y FEDW SH577547
Unsuccessful 1870s trial in anticipation of the opening of the NWNGR.
Remains. Excavations (Near GLANRAFON valve house). [21]

BRYNFFERAM SH518556
Small pit working consisting of two excavations accessed by tunnels. Opened 1825, suffered many vicissitudes and

speculations, output in 1883 252 tons, 18 men, but usually probably half this. Closed 1900s reworked in the 1920s and early 1950s. No rail connection, carted to FRON quarry

Remains. The upper (main) quarry is on three floors, the upper open cutting being the trial of 1825, its tips engulfing the ruins of the bleak Bryn Fferam smallholding. The pits of floors 2 and 3, accessed and drained by tunnel are from successive eras. The lower and latest (run-in) tunnel has a neatly walled cutting with, at its outer end, a hut with the concrete base of the oil engine for the 1920s saw; the building is within an earlier smithy. Nearby is the 19th century production area - a long wall having a cantilevered slab parapet set against the prevailing wind. [7]

BRYN MANLLYN SH553562 CAERGWYNION, DONNEN LAS
Very small hillside quarry, 1870s-1880 in conjunction with PLAS Y NANT.
Remains. Working face only. [15]

BWLCH CWMLLAN SH600521 WEST SNOWDON
Open pits operated over at least two separate eras. An early working, possibly dating from the 1840s had tunnel access to a small water powered mill. Probably in the mid 1870s, a fresh excavation was made at a higher level with a new mill. A chain incline system may have been used, with two inclines in tandem bringing material down to this mill. Later a third mill seems to have been built with a further access tunnel to the working. Tonnages were moderate (about 850 tons 1877), mainly slab, and cannot have justified the large volumes of overburden which had to be removed, let alone the investment on site and on the cart road to Rhyd Ddu. The planned inclines to Rhydd

Ddu NWNGR station were never built.

Remains. At the top of the site are two reservoirs in tandem, which with the small holding pond for the lower mill testify to the problems of water catchment near a summit. There are some trial workings including a short tunnel on the highest point. Just below is the upper working and associated mill, which has a fine wall that was the support for its water supply launder. Lower down there are vestiges of another mill probably a re-siting to avoid up hauling, and perhaps eliminating a chain incline by accessing the deeper workings via a tunnel.

The upper incline has a sheave pit set back from the drum house, which may have replaced it (or vice-versa?). The lower incline drum house had, unusually for Caernarfonshire, overhead horizontal sheaves.

There are traces of a weighbridge and a third mill and wheel pit, also the body of a rubbish wagon, which following the American troops exercises in 1944 might do duty as a colander!

At the lowest part of the site is a building, (barracks?) and traces of a possible stable.

Remote from the main site is a small group of unexploited workings and the run in adit of a trial level. There is evidence of rubbish wagons having been run directly on slate ways, rather than rail, suggesting that in the latter days, at least, this was a marginal enterprise.

There is a nice slate slab bridge on the access road that has been reinforced with 'T' bulb rail and with what may have been round bar rail. There is also some bullhead rail nearby. [23]

BWLCH Y DDWY ELOR SH557508

A small pit accessed by a cutting, unmechanised (?),

output in 1883 160 tons with 7 men. Carted to Caernarfon, may latterly have used NWNGR

Remains. Site disturbed by forestry. Vestiges of dressing sheds. Putative wheel pit. (?) [16]

CASTELL CIDWM SH552552 AFON GOCH, CHWAREL GOCH

A small hillside/pit working flourished briefly (with 18 men) during the 1870s when a steam pump and winder were installed. Small-scale re-workings up to the 1970s. Cart road access beside Llyn Cwellyn.

Remains. Very little owing to hardcore extraction and infilling of the water-filled pit. There are traces of buildings, an access track at the original level also a later track alongside the lake. Water available on site but no evidence that waterpower was used. [12]

CLOGWYN Y GWIN SH576530 RHOS CLOGWYN

Developed on the 1880s. A tunnel brought material to the substantial mills area. When connection was made with the railway, this incline became disused, make being trammed out on the level to a short incline to a siding on the NWNGR. During the small-scale 1920s revival a new lower tunnel was used, slate making being done inside the quarry with possibly a portable saw. From this lower tunnel finished slate was taken down to the railway by a short ropeway. Final closure in the 1930s.

Remains. The mills area has been completely cleared suggesting that the mill may have been a timber and sheet structure It possible that an up-haulage incline between the two levels may never have been completed. The course of the original exit tramway from the middle bank, and the distant incline down to the railway are obvious as is the later tramway formation to the head of the little ropeway down to the a re-located siding. Within the quarry pit are the remains of a dressing shed surrounded by trimming waste, where slates were made during the final era. [20]

CROWN SH513556 NEW CROWN

A 1930s development by MOELTRYFAN on the site of 19th century trials.

Remains. The main working has an enlarged cutting on the top floor, with a sink in its centre, accessed by a curving tunnel. There are investigative tunnels leading north-east on both floors.

A working to the south, is long and curved with a drain culverted under and the ruins of a weighbridge. To the west, is a run-in adit and around the site are several shallow trial cuttings probably all pre-1888

Most of the 1937 mill stands, there is a slab base for a saw drive-pulley mounting, plus the high-level mounting of the electric motor. At the base of the tip just southwest of the mill is a hefty anchorage that formerly held the inclined cableway (with clearance trench cut through an old tip to the north) that lifted the meagre output to the main MOELTRYFAN area. [3]

CWELLYN SH570533 BRYN CWELLYN, CLOGWYN COCH

Small pit working, one pit accessed by a cutting, the other by a tunnel. Tipping on far side of main road. Closed before the NWNGR arrived.

Remains. Much disturbed by bulk working; now no trace of the office that survived as a shop into the 1930s. [18]

FFRIDD ISAF SH573526 FFRIDD

Small open working dating from at least the 18th century, close to Rhydd Ddu station but was idle by the time the railway was opened.

Remains. A distinctive slot-like cutting close to a filled in pit. The relatively complete office has, due to excavation, an elevated aspect. Alongside the access track are vestiges of the 1863 smithy and carpenter's shop the upper floor of which was used as a barracks.

The water-filled approach cutting to the lower-floor adit lies to the north, a significant distance from the upper workings. The (run-in) tunnel initially heads at right angles to the vein, suggesting that there must be a sharp curve or T-junction. Outside, there are vestiges of a weighbridge. The fine powder store has now gone. [19]

FRON SH515548 VRON

Two pits joined by a short tunnel, opened around 1830. Possibly used waterpower for pumping, but from 1860s used steam for the mill and for a chain incline that replaced a water balance and also had a steam locomotive. From 1868 incorporated BRAICH RHYD, but even with 100 men (and up to 3 steam locomotives), peak output may not have exceeded 1500 tons pa, falling sharply in the late 1870s (1883 728 tons with 62 men employed). Some work continued until the 1930s.

In 1868 the Fron tramway superseded carting and , from 1881 was connected to the NWNGR Bryngwyn incline.

Remains. Large pit and extensive rubbish runs, the upper bank merges into the OLD BRAICH tips, and is now almost featureless due to tip reworking and modern landscaping, though the ramp for the exit tramway still remains. On the lower tips to the east, there are vestiges of the old mill and pump water-wheel pit. Lower down near the farm track, two crossed railway sleepers are remains of the cableway used during late re-working. The rail line to Drumhead is readily traceable. [4]

GARREG FAWR SH538582

A small pit possibly dating from the early 1800s. There was a separate, later, underground development. Operated sporadically until mid 1880s (1883 96 tons, 6 men) and occasionally on a small scale, up to the 1960's. Output carted to Caernarfon.

Remains. A NWNGR branch to the ironstone mine could have afforded connection but the quarry was a spent force by 1902 when the link was made. An incline was planned but never built, its drum house being adapted as two-storey office. There is also a possibly older office building with whimsically castle-like embellishment, reminiscent of the rectangular keep at Dolwyddelan Castle. There are dressing sheds etc, a modern brick and air-compressor house and sundry artefacts from the late working

The unique 1875 ex-HAFOD Y LLAN three-speed saw table by John Owen of Bangor that was on site for many years has been restored for display by the National Slate Museum. [10].

GLANRAFON SH581540 WEST SNOWDON

Open quarry, by far the largest in the district, serious work began with railway connection in the late 1870s, producing 1725 tons with 92 men in 1882. peaking with a workforce of over 400 in the mid 1890s, but rapid rundown followed and apart from late re-working, closed in 1915 . Consisted of one big and several subsidiary workings. As the main working deepened, material was raised by a water balance, (later turbine driven) incline.

The pit was pumped by flat rods from a remote water wheel. Material was originally taken by incline to the large mills area, (double mill with a central wheel), but later a tramway tunnel joined the pit to the mills. There were several locomotives on site. A short, followed by a longer, incline went down to make a triangular junction with a siding on the NWNGR.

Remains. At the head of the lower exit incline are the vestiges of the office with adjacent barracks and the old dining room (with collapsed brick kitchen-chimney stack) These barracks are unusual in that they are two rows one above the other. The upper row, facing into the hillside, had a tramway spur off the incline to deliver goods & coal to a small storeroom. The row below faced outwards to its own "ground level" The end room of the lower level had a bay window since it was it was used by a supervisor.

An upper, shorter pitch of the exit incline system (with abutments for a tip-run over-bridge) connected to the mills and stockyards. The drum house, like almost all the other buildings has been sliced into roofing slates; the office can be identified by its red tile floor.

The pillars of the water-launder for the mill water wheel, the brick-built water bypass chute, and the water wheel bearing stones, all survive. The original part of the mill containing some dozen saws has vestiges of the unusual brick pillars with mounting holes for the timber infilling. There is an external sunken tramway for waste from the dressing machines.

There are traces of brick construction of part of a mill and a partly buried stone foundation block with holding-down bolts (now upside-down) shows the location of the steam engine brought into use during droughts or frosts, nearby is the collapsed brick chimney of the smithy and also traces of the two-storey workshop where saw-sharpening and other maintenance was done. There has been much tip working.

The remains of two inclines are visible close to the east

end of the mill. The obvious gravity incline lowered slabs coming off the steam-powered aerial incline to the mills, and a second incline (a water-balance transporter?) might have raised rubble to the extensive floor 1 tips, where there are the foundations of a locomotive shed.

The formation of the water balance/water turbine incline from floor 'D' up to floor 2 is extant inside the quarry pit, and there are vestiges of the pipe run which fed it. The establishment of this floor as the main site for pit rubble required its expansion over the older floor 1 heap below. A high timber bridge, the massive ruined abutments of which remain, crossed the launder carrying water to the mill wheel.

The highest floor connected to the main transport system was No.3, which has few features other than a weighbridge, drum-house, and access to a supplementary pit beyond a 'post' of volcanic rock. The next floor up (No.4) was only an overburden tip, unconnected to the rest of the transport system. Vestiges remain of a similar tip-run to the south of the pit. The bed of the external steam-powered haulage incline down from the mill level to floors 'B' and 'C' is also obvious.

Further up the hill is the concrete-lined pressure header 'tank'. Beyond this is the site of the main collecting reservoir, fed from two lakes at the foot of Snowdon, which had low dams to increase their capacity. [22]

HAFOD Y WERN SH530571 VICTORIA
A small working developed with the coming of the railway into a relatively substantial undertaking. Originally a hillside working it deepened into three pits, accessed by tunnels. Material was brought down by incline to mills at valley floor level. Closed in the mid 1920s, following some years of very small-scale working.

A branch of the NWNGR ran to the mill.

Remains. The whole site is much overgrown and the mill area and tip have served as a modern aggregate 'quarry'. The outstanding feature is the long main incline, rising from mill bank into the woodland above. At its foot are vestiges of a tunnel that accessed the bottom of the 'Old Quarry' (not the oldest, but older than the adjacent 'New' quarry!). Part way up the incline is a very wet area representing the header reservoir for the mill water wheel. At its head is the ruin of a drum house. Latterly this incline was truncated, only the lower part being used. There is no trace of a drum house at the new summit, but the presence of a brake lever in the ground suggests that under-floor horizontal sheaves may be in situ.

The railway branch alongside the quarry road, and the site of the level crossing is obvious.

Some distance up the hill to the south at SH524565 are trials made in the 1860s Trials at SH32565 etc may be from the very early era. [9]

LLYN Y GADAIR SH564519 DRWSYCOED, GADER, GADER LAKE, with GADER WYLLT, HAFODDRUFFYDD

Two separate workings, the first named being the northerly but for archaeological purposes can be treated as one.

Various owners from late 18th century including an unsuccessful excursion into ownership by the North Wales Quarrymen's Union. After the opening of the NWNGR, slate could be loaded at Rhydd Ddu. The tramway to the road may not have been completed, a branch from the NWNGR was planned but never built Ceased 1928.

Remains. LLYN Y GADER, Several open faces with a

two-way incline to a mill built on top of an earlier structure. There are two wheel pits (pumping/haulage and mill drive?) fed by a massive leat embankment.

To the south (GADER WYLLT) is an open working with a small mill; Adjacent is a rubbish run with Hudson track in situ and a short incline down to a lower level with a relatively large, uncompleted mill.

Above this is a tramway route to a tentative underground working, where there are ruined dressing sheds and other buildings including an office. There is also a trial 200 yards further east.

Overlaying a rubbish run to the lake from early open workings is the exit causeway intended to carry a tramway. Part way along is a forge. At the northern end are the bridge pillars for the planned railway branch. [17]

MOEL EILIO SH552587 Trial. **Remain.** Possible disturbed ground. [14]

MOELTRYFAN SH515559 CLODDFA'R FOEL
A small site that, thanks to connection with the NWNGR expanded rapidly in the 1880s, very much against the then trend; employing up to over 200 men. Material was taken by tunnel to the mills area.

Finished product went down a long incline to the Bryngwyn drumhead. Latterly following amalgamation, ALEXANDRA, material was reduced in their mills. Survived into the 1970s
Remains. Five layers of tips dominate the site; the upper ones had 6ft-high storm walls to prevent the wagons becoming airborne! At the quarry edge of these upper banks are vestiges of massive rope anchorages of three Blondins. (replaced by a lorry road in 1966.

The main pit is now an enormous void contiguous with the Alexandra pits. Run-in entrances of access tunnels can be seen on the middle three floors, but the lowest tunnel is buried.

On the main floor at the original pit near the entrance road, are the ruins of the ornate office, and of two loco sheds, (De Winton locos), weigh-houses and smithy, but the mill has been flattened as a shooting-range.

The head of the fine exit incline is buried under modern-era tips, but its lower reaches are well preserved. Part of the way down are the ruins of the Floor 4 steam mills, with the remains of a crude cableway used by tip contractors still anchored into a gable wall.

The original, remote (water driven) mill at Glyndwr SH503558 is denoted only by waste and possible traces of its tramway link. [6]

PLAS Y NANT SH552562 PLAS ISAF, GATMON VALE
Three-gallery hillside quarry, opened mid 19th century, 28 men produced 672 tons in 1883. An incline led to a small mill. Used, but had no direct connection to, the NWNGR. Some work post WW2
Remains. Some traces of (possibly timber and sheeting) buildings, a nice powder house and the incline formation. Also a trial to the northwest. [13]

PRETORIA SH515551
Very small, opened in the 1860s in association with BRYNFFERAM. The west pit was abandoned early and little was done in the west pit except during the slate shortage of the early 1900s (Hence the Boer war name);.
Remains. The east pit with collapsed access tunnel and the west pit with a cutting. No buildings, but much. Tipping beyond the track to Betws Garmon. [5]

TREFLAN SH539584 Y DREFLAN
Two pits, at one time under separate ownership formerly

separated by the 'Factory Stream', but the water has long-broken its bank into the lower quarry. Was operating in the 1800s and possibly much earlier, most active mid to late 19th century. Probably a maximum of about 30 men employed producing around 7/800 tons pa. Material was brought from the pits by tunnels to an unmechanised dressings area. Finished product went by incline to a NWNGR branch. Closed in the 1920s

Remains. Two tunnels lead into the upper pit; near the top one is an office/workshop that was the ancient Treflan Uchaf farmstead. An incline connects the higher level of the north (upper) quarry to a surprisingly large working area, now almost totally cleared.

At the highest point of the tips associated with the lower quarry is a curious structure about 10 ft x 6_ ft and around 13ft high. It is open at the front at ground level and at the back at "first floor" level. Its purpose is unknown

There is water available on site but no evidence that it was ever used for power. What appears to be a leat is a ditch to keep water run-off out of the workings. The exit incline formation is an obvious feature, the upper part now in re-use as a farmer's track, but no drum survives. Where the incline bed crossed the access road to GARREG FAWR is a small smithy.

The incline continues (part as a public footpath) towards the river crossing, where a steel-girder bridge (of 1902) survived until the 1990s. Partway along are is the concrete base of an unsuccessful 1920s granite-crushing plant. Piled nearby are stones that still await crushing! [11]

Section 6
PENNANT/GEST
Cwm Pennant and the coast from
Porthmadog to Criccieth

General
In this area are many small quarries that operated on the tail end of the Gwynedd occurrences. Some are ancient quarries of convenience, but few lasted long and fewer enjoyed any degree of success.

Although most have left scant traces there are several sites with important remains extant. Both the equally unsuccessful PRINCE OF WALES and GORSEDDAU quarries have an exceptional amount to offer, particularly the latter, with its unique YNYS Y PANDY mill. Almost all working was in the open. Since the quarries were small or ephemeral, there are no significant settlements.

Transport
The ancient quarries carted or carried to the nearest point on the coast any product not used in their immediate locality. After the 1830s some may have used Porthmadog. But workings in upper Cwm Pennant such as PRINCE OF WALES used Caernarfon via Bwlch y Ddwy Elor.

There were plans to connect HENDRE DDU and possibly others on the western side of Cwm Pennant by a rail line to Criccieth.

The one railway actually built was the 8 mile, 3ft gauge Gorseddau Tramway opened in 1857 to connect GORSEDDAU with Porthmadog. It is notable as it was, apart from the Nantlle Railway, the only significant quarry-seaport horse-drawn line never to have used inclines, the one abrupt change of level being handled by a switchback.

SECTION 6: PENNANT/GEST

HORSE TRAMWAY (DIS)   SG RLY (INC.DIS)

In 1875 the then defunct line was re-laid in 2 ft gauge and extended via PRINCE OF WALES to a metal mine at the head of the valley. It did have one spanking-new De Winton loco, but it is said to have been out of use by 1878. The whole system (latterly hand-pushed!) was out of use by the early 1890s.

The line is readily traceable almost throughout its length from the foot of the Cwm Dwyfor mine incline to Penmorfa where the road crossing has been lost in road works. Through Penmorfa it is defined by a lane, before dropping down in front of the scarp behind Tremadog via a reversing spur. From there, crossing the main road, it used the track bed of the Tremadoc Ironstone tramway, now defined as an arrow-straight footpath alongside the Tremadog canal. In Porthmadog, the line, partly on an embankment, followed the present day streets to the port itself, this part of the route being utilized in the early 20th century by Moel y Gest granite railway.

1]	SH394407	Pont Rhyd Goch
2]	454407	Foel Isaf
3]	497378	Marine Terrace
4]	506428	Tyddyn Mawr
5]	507394	Mynydd Ednyfed *
6]	508407	Ymlych *
7]	510427	Ysgubor Gerrig
8]	516437	Dolwgan *
9]	518439	Prince Llewelyn
10]	519393	Pencraig
11]	519444	Hendre Ddu ***
12]	521451	Moelfre ***
13]	525461	Chwarel Y Plas
14]	532448	Isallt *
15]	534399	Garreg Felen *

16]	536397	Bryneglwys	
17]	538396	Coed y Chwarel	
18]	538495	Dolgarth **	
19]	541469	Cwm Lefrith	
20]	541505	Cwm Dwyfor	
21]	542398	Cloddfa Sion Prys	
22]	544390	Bron y Foel *	
23]	548483 etc	Moel Lefn	
24]	549498	Prince of Wales ****	G
25]	550409	Ty Cerrig	
26]	550433	Ynys y Pandy (Mill) ****	
27]	552408	Penmorfa *	
28]	553495	Princess **	
29]	554365	Ynys Cyngar	
30]	554406	Ty'n y Llan *	
31]	555372	Garreg Wen	
32]	559388	Moel y Gest	
33]	559393	Penrhynllwyd	
34]	561389	Tu Hwnt y Bwlch	
35]	562372 etc	Penybanc	
36]	562386	Tyddyn Llwyn	
37]	564406	Cwm Bach *	
38]	566382	Garth	
39]	567386	Morfa Lodge	
40]	572385	Ynystywyn	
41]	573453	Gorseddau ****	G

BRON Y FOEL SH544390

Dating from at least from the 18th century, it may have been a very early shipper of slate. Possibly closed by the mid 19th century. Material was pack-horsed to Ynyscyngar.

Remains. Little apart from actual excavation. Present house on the site probably associated with quarry. Access track survives as a footpath. [22]

BRYNEGLWYS SH536397
Putative site. **Remains.** Possible excavation. [16]

CHWAREL Y PLAS SH525461
Small pit working. material carted to road at Plas y Pennant.
Remains. Upper working with dressing shed. Lower working, accessed by tunnel does not seem to have produced. [13]

CLODDFA SION PRYS SH542398
Tiny scratching circa 1880. **Remains.** In forestry, obliterated. [21]

COED Y CHWAREL SH538396 CAMBRIAN RAILWAYS
Small, early working. **Remains.** Obliterated by forestry. [17]

CWM BACH SH564406 TAN YR ALLT
Abortive attempt to take advantage post WW1 boom.
Remains. Bases of temporary buildings, zigzag access track. [37]

CWM DWYFOR SH541505 BLAEN Y PENNANT
1870s trial. **Remains.** Adit and rubbish run. All the buildings etc pertain to the metal mine. [20]

CWM LEFRITH SH541469
Possibly trial only. (1870s?) **Remains.** Adit & rubbish run. [19]

DOLGARTH SH538495 DOL IFAN GETHIN, PENNANT VALE
Hillside working on 3 levels, the upper level almost certainly not productive. Opened in 1870s possibly closed by 1880. Material taken from the hillside workings by a

balanced incline to a water-powered mill on the valley floor. Finished product carted down valley.

Remains. Being situated on a steep slope, viewed from the opposite hillside it provides a "diagram" of a typical quarry layout. Two levels have tramway formations to the incline, which has a substantial remote type drum house. There are some dressing sheds on each terrace. Near foot of incline is a massive rectangular structure of unknown use.

The mill building is an extension of a pre-existing building, another building (dwelling?) is in agricultural re-use. Notable is the long, slate covered tailrace leat to the river. Reputedly copper was mined on this site. [18]

DOLWGAN SH516437
Early 18th century open pit working.
Remains. Virtually nothing other than the pits themselves. [8]

FOEL ISAF SH454407
Putative trial. **Remains.** Not definitely located. [2]

GARREG FELEN SH534399
Hillside quarry (1830s?) very small
Remains. Excavation, possible building, much overgrown. [15]

GARREG WEN SH555372
Tiny scratching (1880s?) **Remains.** On caravan site, barely traceable. [31]

GARTH SH566382 & 568383
Small open slab workings. **Remains.** Possible vestiges. [38]

GORSEDDAU SH573453

This small early 19th century site was in 1855 spectacularly and unsuccessfully developed on four levels, with extraction at one end and tipping at the other, with a fine central incline. A huge multi-storey mill was built at YNS Y PANDY with extensive watercourses, reservoir, workers housing and a railway to Porthmadog. By 1859 its 200 men were producing less than 1400 tons p.a., a derisory seven tons per man-year. Tonnage briefly peaked at 2148 in 1860. Closed 1867, with some subsequent sporadic working

Remains. At the quarry site there is a great deal of low grade rubbish and it is apparent that quarrying having failed on the four incline-served levels, there was abortive work on three higher levels. There seems to have been some work on a detached terrace served by its own short incline, with, near its foot, an underground investigation (collapsed). There are other, seemingly random trials frustrated by bad-rock intrusions.

Where the incline bridges the main terraces there are differing sized apertures to suit the two gauges, 2 ft gauge for moving block arounf the terrace or for rubbish disposal, and 3 ft gauge for block going to the mill and for dispatch of such few finished slates that they made. There are some 2 ft gauge 'sleepers' for Thomas Hughes rail, made out of scrap slate. There are several dressing sheds, blast shelters etc on the worked levels. There is a curious absence of weigh-houses and no obvious powder house, but there is a possible barrack block and a stable. In this latter is a slate slab with 1" dia. holes, possibly for testing a hand-cranked Dixon drill, invented by the eponymous manager. The shot holes of three inches and more about the site were made by these fearsome three-man machines.

The best-known feature is the curious overhanging curved wall preventing the huge tip from overwhelming the tramway. Beyond, the track bed passes a grove of trees, the site of the manager's house, behind are the vestiges of the 18 pairs of houses, (the village of Treforus) laid out in three streets, which were built for the workforce. One can trace the covered leats that brought water for these dwellings and to the manager's house.

This track bed continues to, and past the magnificent three-storey YNS Y PANDY mill. From the mill the tramway can be traced almost without interruption to Porthmadog. [41]

HENDRE DDU SH519444 PRINCE LLEWYLYN
Early 19th century developed during the 1860s with a steam mill and an incline to the road. Despite employing over 60 men, annual tonnage was well short of 1000. Unsurprisingly it failed. A restart was made in 1872 with a probably wooden, turbine-powered mill at the foot of an incline joined partway down by tracks from adits into the pit. In 1875 the reservoir dam collapsed. They stumbled on until about 1880. A fresh start in 1898 failed. The planned rail link to Criccieth was never built.
Remains. At the original, highest, level there are barracks with unusually tall windows, dressing sheds and a weighbridge. There are some short investigative tunnels about the pit, and several trials. Below, are vestiges of the mill and a weighbridge. The incline that has several adits leading onto it is in fair condition, with a small reservoir (created out of a trial digging?) alongside. Only the foundations remain of the roadside mill. On the old original access track is a nice powder house. [11]

ISALLT SH532448 CHWAREL Y LLAN.
Open quarry operating around the 1840s-50s. Material

lowered by incline to a working area where there may have been a mill. As working deepened, access was by tunnel. There may have been a tramway to the road.

Remains. Very little apart from the incline formation and some ruined buildings. At the higher level there is a surprisingly long and well-constructed tipping run. Tunnel into the pit has collapsed. The access track seems clearly intended as a tramway. [14]

MARINE TERRACE SH497378
Ephemeral working, probably only supplied the adjacent streets.

Remains. Quarry face behind houses. [3]

MOELFRE SH521451
Developed in the 1860s on the site of early slate workings and copper trials. Material was taken first by cutting, then by tunnel and finally by up haulage, to an adjacent mill. Finished slate being sent down to the valley floor by incline. Handicapped by high cartage costs it closed, reopening in the early 1870s when a new, lower tunnel provided access and drainage, finished product being taken out through this and down a new incline to a valley floor mill, supplied by a second reservoir. About 30 men employed producing around 600 tons pa. Closed about 1880, but sporadic work done up to the 1930s.

Remains. Two pits, (one water filled), linked part way down by a cutting and at pit bottom by a now blocked tunnel. One side of the dry pit is elaborately walled and has an unusual cantilevered slab stairway. At pit bottom is the later drainage/access tunnel. Traces of a gallery in this pit may have been from earlier copper mining. At the top of this pit are vestiges of a water wheel powered chain incline with iron fixing bolts showing where a launder may have fed the wheel. The slate-lined tailrace from this wheel leads down to a working area with a mill, weigh-houses etc. A nearby tunnel also connects to this same pit. Not far away another tunnel connects to the "wet" pit.

At a lower level are traces of the tipped-over original incline and the later reservoir which has a stone lined leat passing between the pillars of the drum house of the incline down to the lower mill. Launder pillars lead to the site of the overshot wheel of this later mill, now in reuse. In the river near this mill are the remains of a small undershot wheel, probably for agricultural use.

There are two disused water turbines on site that generated electricity in post-quarrying days. One, said to be from HENDRE DDU, was fed by a diversion of the water-wheel leat, the second by an iron pipe. A third generator, fed by plastic piping, is in use.

Above the site are a reservoir and a powder house and another building that predates the quarry operation. [12]

MOEL LEFN SH548483 & 550489 & 551488
Probably trials. **Remains.** Tiny buildings on '83 &'89. [23]

MOEL Y GEST SH559388
Small open quarry. **Remains.** Rockface. Not to be confused with later stone quarry near top of the hill (with incline). [32]

MORFA LODGE SH567386
Said to be site of a tiny 1870s working. **Remains.** Area built up. [39]

MYNYDD EDNYFED SH507394 CLODDFA
A pit working producing a poor product, (For local use?). Possibly 1840s, closed by 1880.
Remains. No buildings some pits and rubbish runs. The access track now forms the road to the Golf Club. [5]

PENCRAIG SH519393
Very small pit. **Remains.** Development now obscures the site. [10]

PENMORFA SH552408 ALLTWEN
Hillside quarry with incline that crossed but did not connect to the Gorseddau tramway. Operated from 1820s to 1870s.
Remains. Incline and excavation, remains of a mill etc, powering of which is unclear. [27]

PENRHYN LLWYD SH559393
Putative site, possibly not slate. **Remains.** Ground disturbance. [33]

PENYBANC SH562372/562374 BORTH Y GEST
Very small open workings. Possibly block for building, circa 1870s.
Remains. Slight depressions in ground. [35]

PONT RHYD GOCH SH394407
Putative slate site. **Remains.** Ground disturbance. [1]

PRINCE LLEWELYN SH518439
A small pit working, name also applied to the later, and much bigger HENDRE DDU whose access track it shared.
Remains. Pits only. [9]

PRINCESS SH553495
A small and remote hillside working of 1880s, with some attempt at underground operation. Operated as an outlier of PRINCE OF WALES, sawing being done in that mill.
Remains. Ruined dressing sheds and other buildings. At a lower level an adit from which apparently was a trial only. The track down to PRINCE OF WALES quarry is clear. Thomas Hughes rail remnants. [28]

PRINCE OF WALES SH549498 CWM TRWYSCWL

An old working, with some development in the 1860s when possibly three levels were worked. Vigorously opened in 1873 when the extension of the Gorseddau Tramway to the site obviated cartage over the pass to Cwm Gwyrfai. Four further levels were started, connected by extending the main incline. Some underground working took place on three levels.

A water-powered mill was built at the then new terminus of the Gorseddau Tramway, reached from the foot of the main incline by an elevated tramway and a second short incline. At the peak 200 men were employed producing 5000 tons pa. Closed 1886, but some small scale working up to 1920. All reduction of roofing slate took place on the terraces, slab only being dealt with in the mill.

Remains. A particularly interesting site whose layout (as well as its economic misfortunes) closely replicates GORSEDDAU. Work was on a number of levels with extraction to the northeast and tipping to the southwest with the incline in the middle. Also like GORSEDDAU, its short working life and elaborate infrastructure provide a plethora of remains.

On each working level there are a number of buildings including weigh houses and dressing sheds etc., one level having a particularly fine rake of such sheds and a barrack block without fireplaces (possibly portable stoves were used). It does differ from GORSEDDAU in that the workforce was mainly barrack based with no elaborate family accommodation.

The well-engineered incline has remains of its final, upper drum house and traces of the two earlier drum houses that were abandoned as it was extended upwards.

On the lowest working level is evidence of some

143

under floor leats. Adits, some open, lead to very limited chambering.

The building behind the reservoir was the workshop, possibly a re-use of a pre-existing structure.

The stretch of level tramway from the foot of incline, past the reservoir is a prominent feature as is the lower incline drum house. One can see traces both of work begun to raise the height of the dam and the formation of a little tramway to serve that work. At the foot of the lower incline is the compact mill having very pleasing archways and a wheel pit with a row of launder pillars adjacent.

The track bed of the tramway to the south has some interesting little bridges and embankments and immediately to the north, on the subsequent extension to the Cwm Dwyfor mine, is a deep, curved cutting. [24]

TU HWNT Y BWLCH SH561389
A small and early working with cart access. Not to be confused with the later stone quarry which was connected to Porthmadog by tramway.
Remains. Almost nothing, traces of retaining wall for cart track. [34]

TŶ CERRIG SH550409 ALLT WEN
May not have been slate. **Remains.** Excavation [25]

TYDDYN LLWYN SH562386
Flooring flags produced in 1830s-40s? **Remains.** Almost none. [36]

TYDDYN MAWR SH506428 DOLBELMAEN
Tiny open quarry. **Remains.** Excavation only. [4]

TY'N Y LLAN SH554406 CAE CRWN
Hillside quarry connected by incline to Gorseddau

tramway. Unlikely to have been slate. **Remains.**
Excavation and incline. [30]

YMLYCH SH508407 BRAICH Y SAINT
Small hillside working. 1840s? **Remains.** None identified.
[6]

YNSYCYNGAR SH544365
Traditional loading place and pre-Porthmadog anchorage
for trans-shipment of Blaenau slate brought down the
Dwyryd. Some extraction hereabouts but probably only
for building block.
Remains. Extremely small working faces. [29]

YNYSTYWYN SH572385
Tiny working around a little knoll.
Remains. One tiny face behind modern building. [40]

YNYS Y PANDY SH550433 Mill
This unique, cathedral-like structure follows the pattern
of many mid-Victorian industrial buildings (such as the
Cannons Road Gasworks, Bristol). Built in the mid 1850s
to serve as slab mill for GORSEDDAU quarry, it was idle
by the late 1860s, occasionally later acting as a public hall.
Remains. This impressive structure has been conserved
by the Snowdonia National Park. It had two main floors,
with attic (storage?) and a part basement (Workshop?). It
is unknown why such an expensive to build and difficult
to work, design was adopted.

It contains an internal pit for a large breast-shot wheel
and a deep shaft trench running the length of the
building, (extended outside to permit the shaft to be
withdrawn for maintenance). There is a fine water tunnel
linked by a traceable leat from Llyn Cwmystradllyn.
Besides traces of rubbish tramways on the ground floor,
both main floors are linked by tramway formations to the

Gorseddau tramway.

Contemporary accounts as well as examination of the small amounts of waste from its trifling output, suggest that saws, planers and polishers were used. Which floor the machines were on is disputed, but since it is unclear how the wooden upper floor could bear the weight of machines or how water would be carried to the saws and polishers or slurries drained, it is inevitable that the machines were on the ground floor, despite the absence of evidence of mountings.

The upper floor was possibly intended for hand finishing, but any reasonable quantity of slab items would itself present a considerable load.

A more tenable theory is that the upper floor was used for the making of writing slate frames, calling for comparatively light wood-working machines, and for the assembly of writing slates possibly from blanks prepared on the ground floor, and brought up by hoist or by truck using the two tramway levels.

It is ironic that so little hard evidence exists about this, the most iconic slate-related structure in Britain.

At the Prenteg turning $1/2$ mile away, a length of multi fish-belly rail acts as a gatepost. It has been suggested that this from the original track, discarded when the tramway was re-laid and extended. [26]

YSGUBOR GERRIG SH510427
Tiny scratching circa 1880
Remains. Possible ground disturbance. [7]

Section 7
GLASLLYN

General

This area comprises the quarries in or around the Glaslyn valley. Some were open workings but most were underground.

The majority of sites were small and many, particularly around Beddgelert, were tiny ephemeral undertakings, trial burrowings, searching for virtually non-existent rock. HAFOD Y LLAN was more substantial and has interesting remains, especially its incline system.

Some in the units in the Nantmor area were on a reasonable scale, but the most archaeologically important are the larger of those centred on Croesor and made that village a quarrying community.

Transport

Numerically, most of the quarries' output was too small to call for any system of transport. PORTH TREUDDYN and the tiny diggings at Llanfrothen were, up to the end of the 18th century, virtually on the shores of the Glaslyn estuary. Others could cart to the estuary, or later to Porthmadog. CROESOR carted down Cwm Croesor (below the modern road to the quarry), whilst RHOSYDD, PANT MAWR and MOELWYN [Section 8] carted down Cwm Maesgwm. .

Railways for the area had been mooted from before the mid- 19th century the slate quarry traffic that would arise from the Beddgelert area being often cited in proposals, but by the time the Welsh Highland Railway reached there in 1923 such quarrying as had been had long ceased.

The one rail link actually built was the 2'g. Croesor

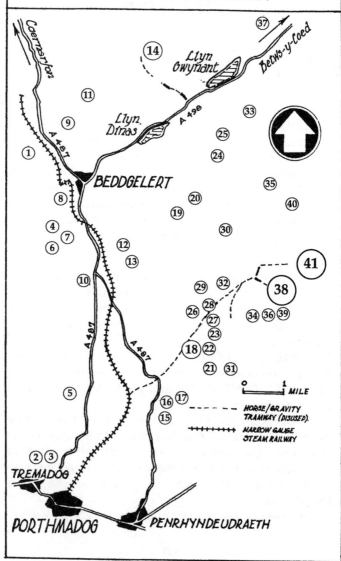

SECTION 7: GLASLYN

Tramway of 1864. Horse drawn, it linked to Porthmadog, the RHOSYDD, CROESOR, FRON BOETH, PARC and other minor quarries. It operated until the mid 1930s and never having been formally closed, unofficial use in Cwm Croesor itself may have continued into the 1950s.

The line is traceable throughout its length. It starts at the head of Cwm Croesor with the spectacular RHOSYDD and CROESOR inclines, the highest single pitch inclines in the industry. The former connected to its quarry by a magnificently engineered formation.

The Croesor line reached the valley floor via the Blaen y Cwm incline and part way along the valley floor it met the foot of the PANT MAWR/FRON BOETH incline. This incline was originally in two pitches, from the top of which it connected to PANT MAWR quarry by another finely engineered tramway.

In about 1886 when FRON BOETH was developed as a downwards extension of PANT MAWR, the upper pitch was abandoned and the lower pitch extended upwards some 100'. From this new incline head a line ran down valley to a tunnel (Now blocked near the north-western end), into Cwm Maesgwm. This tunnel is unique to the industry.

Shortly after passing over the third of three most attractive bridges, the Croesor line met the branch to PARC SLAB quarry, and further on a fine stone embankment led to the top of the two-pitch Parc incline. The upper drum house has been converted into a remarkable dwelling, The brake man's cabin at the ruined lower drum house has, like its Blaen y Cwm counterpart, a fireplace, an unusual amenity.

Near the foot of these inclines it was joined by the branch from PARC quarry branch, from there the formation runs across level ground to join the clearly defined route to Porthmadog, that was re-used by the Welsh Highland Railway.

1]	SH571485	Mellionen *
2]	573409	Porth Treuddyn *
3]	579411	Fron Oleu
4]	579472	Cwmcloch *
5]	582420	Aberdeunant **
6]	582466.	Cwm Cŷd
7]	583469	Bwlch Goleu
8]	584477	Goat *
9]	584496	Gwernlasteg *
10]	594453	Dinas Ddu **
11]	599514	Cae'r Gors *
12]	605466	Cwmcaeth *
13]	611458	Dolfrog
14]	613524	Hafod y Llan ***
15]	616421	Brondanw Isaf
16]	619426	Brondanw Uchaf
17]	620426	Brongarnedd
18]	626436	Parc **
19]	629481	Berthlwyd *
20]	631484	Gerynt
21]	632436	Hafoty
22]	632441	Garreg Uchaf
23]	632444	Parc Slab *
24]	632490	Blaenant
25]	632499	Castell
26]	634447	Bryngelynnen *
27]	635445	Llidiart yr Arian *
28]	637452	Croesor Bach *
29]	637457 etc	Criblwyd
30]	637463	Gelli **
31]	643434	Hafod Uchaf **

32]	643462	Cnicht *	
33]	645505	Nant Gwynant	
34]	646448	Cefn y Braich *	
35]	651485	Llyn Llagi	
36]	652448	Fronboeth **	
37]	656557	Pen y Gwryd	
38]	657457	Croesor **	H
39]	658446	Pant Mawr **	
40]	658476	Cwm y Foel	
41]	664461	Rhosydd ***	H

ABERDEUNANT SH582420

A tiny short-lived late 19th century, underground working, with about 12 men. Revived for a few years in the early 1900s with 4 men, making slab. This later work being close to the boundary fence, all material, including waste had to be up hauled to mill level, by an incline powered by an extension of the under floor mill shaft.

Remains. Wheel pit and mill with pit for the incline winder. The later and lower work chambers up through the original adit and out to daylight. Besides the incline up to the mill, a second, possibly uncompleted, up haulage incline runs up past a small rake of buildings. It was perhaps hand wound using a portable winch. [5]

BERTHLWYD SH629481 BLAEN NAMOR

A small unmechanised hillside quarry on two levels, which may reflect two separate periods of working. Operating c1840, then 1864-73 with 30 men, the output being under 200 tons p.a.

Remains. The upper level has a back to back dressing shed of a type normally only seen in north east Wales and the remains of another building, possibly a powder store. The lower level cuts into the floor of the upper working and at this level are a rake of three dressing sheds and an abortive opening. There are traces of access tracks, and of a leat that may have supplied water to drive farm machinery in post-quarrying times.

The 16th century house, after years of dereliction, has been the subject of an award-winning restoration. The farm servants' cottage may have accommodated quarry workers. [19]

BLAEN NANT SH632490 HAFOD BRITHION
Trial associated with HAFOD Y LLAN. c1861. **Remains.** Excavation. [24]

BRONDANW ISAF SH616421
Tiny, operated in the 1820's, said to have employed 10 men producing 60 tons pa Slate quality described as poor. Access direct to road. **Remains.** Quarry face, base of a shed. [15]

BRONDANW UCHAF SH619426
Said to have employed 5 men in 1836. Material taken down to the road by a sideway. **Remains.** Excavation and vestiges of slide. [16]

BRONGARNEDD SH620426
Said to have employed 10 men around 1820 producing 70 tons pa. Crude incline or slide to road. **Remains.** Traces of incline? [17]

BRYNYGELYNNEN SH634447
Small open pit, active from about 1860, 5 men employed. **Remains.** Quarry face, traces of dressing sheds. [26]

BWLCH GOLEU SH583469
Two tandem adits, almost certainly unsuccessful although an access track seems to have been built. **Remains.** Adits, the lower one non-productive. [7]

CAE'R GORS SH599514, 593516, 594512, 599514
DORLLAN DDU, WERN GASEG
A series of mid 1870s investigations that failed to fulfil the expectations that the Beddgelert area promised at the time.

Remains. All four adits are run in, the most westerly has vestiges of a tiny structure, and the next has a partly underground shelter. Next along is the most interesting having a "Keyhole" pattern powder house. I.e. a circular 8' diameter sub-surface chamber with inclined slate slabs forming a "vaulted" roof. It is accessed by steps into a 10' long by 18" wide, slab covered passage. Such powder stores were not unknown in the Ffestiniog area, but were all much larger and only one is know to survive intact [GRAIG DDU Section 8]. At the most easterly adit is a tiny shelter. Trimming waste suggests that the quality of at least some of the rock was good, but presumably insufficient to justify full-scale development. [11]

CASTELL SH632499
A mid-19th century underground working. Produced many writs and wrangles but little slate.

Remains. Adit is collapsed and the small pit is filled in, quite extensive rubbish runs on the opposite side of the road. [25]

CEFN Y BRAICH SH646448 BRAICH Y PARC
Hillside terraces, about 20 men employed and 240 tons pa raised, 1877/83. Product described as brittle. Became part of PANT MAWR/FRON BOETH, its open workings being designated Floors 19 & 20 of the combined unit.

Remains. Working faces, tramway formations connecting to the FRON BOETH incline system. [34]

CNICHT SH643462 CLOGWYN Y DARREN, DRWYS Y DARREN & DEUFAEN

A miniscule underground working, spectacularly located some 800' above the valley floor. Material was carried, possibly on men's backs down a pathway, but at some time a crude ropeway may have been used.

Six men, (part time?) produced around 20 tons p.a, in the 1860s. An attempt was made to develop in the early 1870s.

Remains. The adit is open bur is very short. There is a tiny dressing area with a double shed with fireplace, alongside is a stock of slates. Some 20' below is a substantial platform that appears to have been a stocking area and loading platform. The zigzag path is now much eroded. Below, almost at valley floor level near some (agricultural?) building ruins is a block that may have been the lower anchorage of a ropeway.

A few yards east is DEUFAEN, part of the unsuccessful 1870s scheme, abandoned before any serious digging was done. It is notable for the uncompleted formation (incline or slide way?) with a substantial loading platform at its foot, from where another zigzag path leads down. [32]

CRIBLWYD SH637457 & 639460

Abortive underground trials.

Remains. Both adits are open to dead headings, the southerly one ending in a face partially drilled for shot firing, possibly attempts to reach the Cnicht slate by an easier route. Also collapsed adits at 631454, 632457, and 634457. A building nearby may have been used with these trials. [29]

CROESOR SH657457

A medium sized underground quarry, unusual in never

having had any significant surface workings, in employing forced ventilation, in the number of, for its size, steam engines used, the ingenuity of its engineering and in the small volume of its rubbish tips (due to a vigorous policy of backfilling worked out chambers).

Working the western limits of the Blaenau Ffestiniog slate with mixed fortune from the 1850s, closing in 1878. Re-opened in 1895 under the energetic and innovative management of Moses Kellow, producing 5/6000 tons pa but declined rapidly during the early 20th century.

The water-powered mill, (28' wheel) with about a dozen saws was built in the early 1860's. An 1866 extension included a 39' wheel below the mill floor fed from the tailrace of the first, and a 13-hp steam engine back up. Shafting was under-floor with an under-floor rubbish tramway.

Kellow, replaced the water wheels with a Pelton wheel, driving through overhead shafting and after some late 1890s experiments electified, installing a full scale. Hydro station in 1903 The main output was 350 Kw, a.c with a small d.c. supply to charge the excitation battery and to light Kellow's house. One of the first ever a.c. electric locos was in use by 1905. Later two steam locos were used,

At the 1930 closures there were 18 saws (including Kellow saws, 18 dressers and a Kellow planer. The fearsomely effective but commercially unsuccessful Kellow patent drills were assembled on site

Underground working was arranged on seven floors. At the far end of the access tunnel (floor A) an incline went up the vein to floors B, C & D Up and another incline went down to floors B & C Down, with a further incline joining C Down with D Down.

Several steam engines were used for pumping,

ventilation and haulage and, at one time, a steam turbine (on level D Up). Much attention was given to ventilation, there were several vertical shafts out to bank, one being used to experiment with water blast ventilation. A Guiblas fan was installed in 1866 in a most impressive stone fan-house.

Apparently one of these vertical shafts was at one time used, via ropes and pulleys to water-balance the A-C Down incline and the other to mass balance the A-D Up incline.

An attempt was made to drive a second adit, lower don the hillside direct into floor D Down. A hydro compressor was specially built to power the air drills for this development and a short external incline laid down for a counter balance to haul out spoil from the downward-sloping tunnel.

Finished product was originally carted to the Ffestiniog Railway at Penrhyndeudraeth, but after 1864 output was taken down to the Croesor Tramway by an unusually long incline. (Reducing the carriage cost per ton to Porthmadog from 7/10_ (39p) to 2/6_ (12.5p).

Remains. Save for the tattered drum house and the ruins of the barracks, the whole site (including the remarkable fan house), has been levelled.

Immediately below the tip can be seen the small tip of the abortive second tunnel and near it the outline of the counter-balance track. Near where the tramway bed at the foot of the fine incline is joined by the RHOSYDD incline, there are the traces of the small compressor house with some sign both of the water-pipe run to it and the air-pipe run from it.

Above the adit, on the hill there are traces of the vertical shafts, an extensive leat system, the later Pelton wheel pipe, the washed out dam, and at 659458 the trials known as Upper Croesor.

Underground the 440 yard long access tunnel is of unusually large bore, intersected part-way along by two of the vertical shafts. At the far end it widens into a large marshalling area. There are several buildings and artefacts associated with the later explosive storage. The down incline is flooded up to adit level and the massive masonry of the haulage winch installed for explosives handling, hinders access to the up incline. The third vertical shaft that drops into this up incline has remnants of the counter-balance pulley system in situ.

To the right is a large flooded chamber, with a collapsed bridge to workings beyond. To the left are two blind tunnels.

Near the foot of the Blaen y Cwm incline of the Croesor Tramway, Moses Kellow's 1903 power station has been revived, still fed from Llyn Cwm y Foel. No trace has been found of the quarry-owned Blaen y Cwm cottages. [38]

CROESOR BACH SH637452

A small underground working and although quite late (1866/8) was unmechanised, hand dressing being done in shelters adjacent to the adit. Said to have employed 12 men but only produced 40 tons p.a. A cart track led to the Croesor Tramway at nearby Pont Sion Goch. (636450)

Remains. Adit collapsed, ruins of dressing sheds, slate waste on ground at Pont Sion Goch. Three trial adits are on the hillside above. [28]

CWM CAETH SH605466 ABERGLASLYN, NAMOR

An ancient working developed in the 1870s, when a water-powered mill was built (But not equipped?). Employed about 12 men 1876-79. Like so many small workings, it failed to survive the late 1870s depression.

Remains. Tunnel into pit, adit to one chamber. Several buildings, but these have been much altered for agricultural re-use. [12]

CWMCLOCH SH579472
Tiny underground working, 1860s-70s. Minimal product. **Remains.** Collapsed adit, ruins of a small building, access track. [4]

CWM CŶD SH582466
Remote trial. **Remains.** Collapsed adit. Also adit at 579465. [6]

CWM Y FOEL SH658476
Small underground working on an inaccessible site. Said to have been employing 5 men in 1820s producing 20 tons pa. Finished product possibly man-carried down Cwm Croesor. **Remains.** Collapsed adit. [40]

DINAS DDU SH594453
Small partly underground quarry 1860s-1880s. It had a small tramway network and a water-powered mill. Slate was carted to Porthmadog.
Remains. A house occupies what was possibly the site of the office. The Mill with its wheel-pit has been used as a source of stone for nearby farm structures. There is some leat-work. A nice stone cutting leads to the working area. Adit open, but only goes a short distance. [10]

DOLFRIOG SH611458 TY'N Y CHWAREL.
Open pit. Open by 1811, active 1865 with 10 producing a derisory 40 tons. **Remains.** Virtually nothing, site in forestry. [13]

FRON BOETH SH652448
Underground, a costly and ambitious 1886 enterprise to develop and extend downward the PANT MAWR

workings, although never successful up to 50 men were employed into the 1900s. Three adits to chambers were served by a short single acting table incline that brought material down to a steam-powered mill. Finished product was taken along a contour-chasing route to the head of a long, stone-embanked incline. From the foot of this incline (647446), a 500-yard tunnel led to Cwm Croesor, where the line turned up valley to a point above the head of the lower pitch of the PANT MAWR incline that was extended to meet it, the upper pitch being abandoned.

In the early 1890s a further mill was built at the tunnel entrance possibly to deal with CEFN Y BRAICH material, rock extracted from the tunnel itself and perhaps in anticipation of downward development. This mill was nominated as Level 22 (in a continuation of the PANT MAWR and MOELWYN [Section 8] numbering sequence).

Remains. There are various buildings on site including the upper mill (Level 18) that has evidence of 3 saw tables and 3 dressing machines having been installed although the building is large enough for twice this number. Alongside the mill is a large Lancashire boiler that must have been originally taken up via the PANT MAWR inclines and possibly was originally installed in the PANT NAWR mill, and re-used here for water storage.

The single acting table incline seems to have been a water balance; presumably to raise material to the PANT MAWR incline-head before the tunnel route was built. A slate lined water channel runs alongside it.

There are a number of adits, some blocked, some wet, leading to chambering working rather poor rock. There is much backfilling, including some in the adits.

Part way along the tramway, are the foundations of an elevated office structure. The drum house and incline, (which also served the CEFN Y BRAICH workings) down to the lower mill are in good condition but the lower mill itself is very ruinous.

The tunnel is unique as, although tunnelling is implicit in many slate quarrying operations, this is the only one outside an actual quarrying site and is one of the longest tunnels ever cut for horse drawing. It is penetrable from here as far as the collapse near the northern end. Most curiously, there is some chambering inside. Over the hill at the north end, the tramway up the Croesor valley can be followed to the head of the extended ex-PANT MAWR lower incline. There is brake gear in the drum house and some rope-rollers on the ground. [36]

FRON OLEU SH579411
Trial, associated with PORTH TREUDDYN?
Remains. Excavation. [3]

GARREG UCHAF SH632441
Tiny Pit possibly never produced.
Remains. Slight excavation. [22]

GELLI SH637463 CRAIG BOETH, BWLCH BATAL
A compact and isolated underground working based around one barrack/workshop, all purpose building. Finished product was carted to Croesor village.
Remains. There are some small ruined buildings on the site, and some distance away a small dwelling that may have been connected with the quarry. However the main feature is the substantial house with workshops, including a smithy, in a lean-to at the rear. The workings are on two, apparently separate, levels. Above and behind the site is an adit that seems to have been only a trial. The cart track is traceable. [30]

GERYNT SH631484 GELLI IAGO

A moderate sized open pit working usually operated in conjunction with BERTHLWYD. A gravity incline led down to a water-powered mill. Active around 1870 producing 200 tons pa. Estimates of manning vary from a surprising 30 down to a more probable 12. The high figure quoted by Bob Owen may well reflect part-time labour) Product may have been loaded at the Croesor Tramway siding at Pont Garreg Hyldrem (615431),

Remains. There is a fine stone-built incline ramp, unusual in a pit working as such a structure would inhibit future work, presumably it was assumed that all extraction would be on the opposite side of the pit. The power source is unclear but it could have been by hand-cranked windlass. There is an incline formation down to the site of the mill, which was a fine structure with a central wheel pit. Regrettably due to its closeness to the public road of it and the wall-retained tip, all had to be cleared and landscaped in the 1990s. [20]

GOAT SH584477

Small underground working 1870s. **Remains.** Four collapsed adits, vestiges of buildings, site now heavily overgrown. [8]

GWERNLASTEG SH584496

Open quarry, possibly opened in 1840s closed by 1880.
Remains. Excavation, rubbish runs, traces of buildings, access track. [9]

HAFOD UCHAF SH643434

A compact underground working with several adits in a little valley. Operated in late 1870s with 12 men employed producing 60 tons pa. Material removed by cart.
Remains. Adits on 4 levels, the lower ones collapsed.

There are traces of a dressing shed at the highest level, below is a neat smithy with a dressing shed backing onto it. At the bottom of the site are ruins of a mill, but it seems unlikely that machinery was ever actually installed. The sawn ends on site suggest the possible use of a hand-cranked circular saw

There are trial adits to the east and west of the site. [31]

HAFOD Y LLAN SH613524 SOUTH SNOWDAON, CWM Y LLAN

An open working started in the 1840s as an offshoot of metal mining. A mill was built and several plans devised to establish rail connection with Porthmadog. In the meantime finished product was sent by a short tramway to the Cwm y Llan cart road that also served the copper mines

Considerable development in the late 1860s. The water-wheel powered mill was extended and converted to turbine operation and in anticipation of a railway being laid along Nant Gwynant, the uniquely heroic incline system was constructed down to Pont Bethania. Although it was the only working in the Beddgelert area to achieve more than nominal tonnages, output never justified the infrastructure and it effectively failed to recover from the late 1870s slump. Some small-scale reworking in the 1960s.

Remains. There are a number of workings on several levels and traces of tramways connected by an incline to a mills area. There is an interesting archway where one tramway was carried over another. Pieces of drilled slate may be tramway sleepers.

In this mills area are as well as the ruins of the mill, two houses, a barracks, and a weigh bridge whose presumably wooden housing has long since vanished. The launder pillars to the mill are standing (just) and at the opposite end can be seen the route of a feed pipe laid on the formation of a redundant incline when the water wheel was replaced by a turbine.

The bed of a short tramway to the cart track now forms the path between the site and Gladstone rock.

The main feature is the exit tramway with its quite magnificent inclines. On route it cuts an earlier tramway (which brought ore from the Braich yr Oen copper mine to the Llywedd Bach Mill), on which is to be seen the finest run of stone block sleepers in north Wales. From the site is gradually descends for $1/2$ mile, via impressive stone embanking, cuttings and a rock-cut shelf to the head of the upper incline.

The precipitous upper incline has a ruined drum house with brakeman's hut. Part way down are the abutments of bridge over the cart road. From the foot of this incline the line runs for $1/4$ mile to a further drum house with hut at the head of the lower incline. The lower incline is shorter and also has traces of a bridge over the cart road and at its foot are the stables and sheds (now incorporated into Hafod y Llan farm) for the carts used to convey slate down Nant Gwynant. [14]

HAFOTY SH632436
Open quarry operating around 1875/76 with 17 men producing 100 tons pa. Possibly had a water powered mill. There was a proposal in 1904 to incorporate this into PARC by a tunnel from PARC Floor F
Remains. Almost nothing, possible mill foundations. [21]

LLIDIART YR ARIAN SH635445
This early underground working was the precursor of Parc Slab quarry and for which this name was locally used. **Remains.** Almost nothing. [27]

LLYN LLAGI SH651485
A small and remote underground working apparently operating in the mid-19th century, without any buildings or shelter of any kind. **Remains.** Collapsed adits. [35]

MELLIONEN SH571485
Small underground working, intermittent working from 1812 until the late 1870s, for a time ten men were employed.
Remains. Site now in forestry. Vestiges of a small building at collapsed adit. It is possible that a formation down the hillside was an incline. [1]

NANTGWYNANT SH645505
From the 1860's? Nothing known possibly sharpening hones produced
Remains. Excavation and spoil heap. [33]

PANT MAWR SH658446
Underground, sited some 1500' amsl. Operating in the 1840s with chambers under, and floors numbered later sequentially with, the MOELWYN quarry on the other side of Moelwyn Mawr [Section 8]. Finished product was taken down on pack animal via Cwm Maesgwm to be loaded on the Ffestiniog Railway at Penrhyndeudraeth. A small mill was built with incline connection. In 1863 a fresh incline to the mill was built and, partly using a pre-existing track, a spectacular tramway was constructed on a rock-cut shelf to the head of a two-pitch incline down to the Croesor Tramway.

Closed 1878. Re-opened in 1886 merged with FRON BOETH
Remains. Several adits on various levels are penetrable to chambers in the steeply dipping vein. The inclines from the adits and the compact mill with its impressive

retaining wall and other buildings are extant, but the main feature is the tramway gently climbing round the shoulder of the hill to the top of the 1000 ft incline, the highest two pitch incline in any slate quarry system. The drum house is ruinous but the upper pitch can be traced down to the embanked inter-pitch manoeuvring loop that led to the lower pitch before it was extended to serve the FRON BOETH tunnel line. The lower pitch (re-sited) drum house is in fair condition with some of the gear in situ and there are rope-rollers on the ground. [39]

PARC SH626436. CEUNANT PARC
A compact underground operation in a narrow valley opened around 1870 with up to 50 men. When Moses Kellow's took over, many innovations were introduced, and had not his energies been diverted to CROESOR in 1895, there might well have been others.

Chambering was on 2 floors above the adit (A&B), worked southwards and 4 below the adit (D-G). Floor C, (adit level), E, F & G were worked northwards, D to both north and south. H was not worked. The ambitious 700 yard tunnel eastwards from Floor F to HAFOTY was never bored.

The H to C underground incline was powered by an 80-hp hydraulic engine. Hydraulics were also used for the Kellow drills and for the injector pumps. There were two water-powered mills that housed 6 saws 3 dressers and 3 planers.

Although output was modest (350 tons with 15 men in 1883), specialities such as "Parcro" patent ridging, brought good returns.

Finished product was taken by a short incline to a bridge across the Afon Croesor, then by a further short incline to make a junction with the Croesor Tramway at the foot of the Lower Parc incline. Closed 1920.

Remains. Several buildings are in re-use or in good condition and the office (with Parcro ridges) is now a dwelling. The river is so extensively bridged by massive slabs as to be virtually culverted.

At the north eastern end of the site is the raised "Specials" mill with a wheel pit and a slate bedded incline (powered off the mill-wheel?) with a flight of stone steps alongside. Inside is the base of a later air-compressor base and around are off-cuts of the patent ridging.

Opposite is the collapsed adit near which are lavatories and the ruins of the main mill powered by a launder from the tailrace of the upper wheel. The leat that fed the mill before the "Specials" mill was built, is traceable. The rubbish runs are extensive, but save for drum house vestiges the tramway branch is almost untraceable. .

Above the road is a blocked adit (FloorA?) that seems to have served purely for rubbish disposal. [18]

PARC (SLAB) SH632444 GARTH LLWYNOG, HEN DWLL

Open pit working operating in conjunction with. PARC In 1870 20 men employed almost exclusively on slab. Finished product taken out via a branch line that joined the Croesor tramway at Croesor village.

Remains. Flooded pit. The mill site is not obvious since it was cut through by the Llanfrothen road leaving on one side of the road vestiges of one end of the mill and on the other side, the pit of the water-wheel said to have been the largest in Wales There is no trace of the wooden launder that fed the wheel from the pond (now a children's pool).

The short incline down to the mill appears to have also raised finished product up to the Croesor tramway, presumably powered by the mill wheel. Although an injector pump was latterly used, the size of the wheel suggests that it also pumped. Nearby is a tiny building with what appears to be a small wheel pit that may have been a compressor house.

There is a nice cutting for the connection to the Croesor tramway. [23]

PEN Y GWRYD SH656557
Small hone working certainly in existence in the 1880s – curiously there was another hone working that may have predated this, possibly immediately west of Pen y Pass.
Remains. Excavation and spoil heap. The second site is unidentified. [37]

PORTH TREUDDYN SH573409 PANTILLIAN
Open quarry, 18th century, took slate, probably mostly slab, perhaps by horse sledge, to a shipping point near the present main road that represents the limit of the tidal estuary in pre-Cob days.

In the mid 19th century operations moved to 578408, possibly going partly underground. Material was taken by incline to a water-powered mill near the road. Later owing to restricted water supplies, steam was used. The product that was actually Tremadoc Grit, a very hard rock used for slab esp. steps and thresholds, was carted to Porthmadog. Closed c1870.

Remains. On the 'Old' site, shallow pit and rubbish runs, building that may not have been part of the quarry. On the 'New' site, there are an excavation, some walling and a possible adit. The incline is much collapsed but at its foot is an unusual mill building, with a wheel-pit and stone lined leat, now in re-use. Of the other agricultural buildings, one may have been the steam mill. [2]

RHOSYDD SH664461

Opened in the 1830s it was developed underground from the 1850s, the surface works, mills, dressing sheds and so on following down the northward slope to match the underground levels as far as Floor 9. The half-mile long tunnel on 9 providing the main access and drainage, and was in the final phase, the site of the major surface works such as the main mill, barracks and so on. The adits above remaining to provide subsidiary access.

Above Floor 9 were 5 levels (Floors 1 to 3 being in effect the early open workings) and further 5 below Floor 9. There were finally 70 chambers making it one of the largest underground quarries outside Blaenau Ffestiniog itself, 192 men producing in 1883 5616 tons with 24 saw tables and 24 dressers, the first saws having been run in 1854.

Much use was made of waterpower for pumping and up-hauling levels below 9 (and indeed along 9 tunnel itself) as well as for electric generation, air compression and mill power. A poor catchment meant using an extensive leat system with several reservoirs and some stopped-up chambers used o store water.

The floors above 9 were served by single acting table inclines running up the dip of the vein, balanced by a weighted trolley running under the table on a track between its rails. This arrangement together with vertical head-sheaves enabled trucks to be moved two at a time in a comparatively narrow tunnel The floors below 9 were original served by a water-balance, the balance tank running in an inclined shaft above Floor 9 (drainage level), and connected to the carriage running below Floor 9 by a rope and pulleys). Later this incline was widened to three tracks and powered by Pelton wheels.

Some use was made of stationary steam engines, but it could be the largest quarry never to have used locmotives.

The site being remote meant that many of the men (and families) lived on or near the site (with their own chapel).

At first transport was by packhorse via Moelwyn and later by cart or sledge via Cwm Orthin. After 1864 the finely engineered tramway to the head of Cwm Croesor and the splendid incline down to the Croesor Tramway was used. Final closure in 1930.

Remains. From the two pits to the south (the surface near the eastern one showing signs of the 1900 collapse) the dressing sheds, other buildings including mills, inclines, adits, shafts and so on follow a chronological order northwards. In the West pit is a winder. Immediately northward is 2 Level adit and an early mill and workshops. Beyond, at 3 level, is the "square" mill, above which can be seen the depression for the flat rods that carried motion from this No. 3 mill to a pump in East pit. There is also the pit of a haulage wheel. Further on are 4 mill, offices, workshop etc.

Inclines lead down to the big mill area at level 9. Like the other 3 mills, the big main mill here has now almost vanished. From its wheel pit part of the culvert that led away the tailrace under the working area is traceable. There are numerous other buildings, some with exceptionally nice windows and other detail. The 'street' of barracks is notable.

Near the level 9 adit is the pit for the pitch back wheel (and some fragments of the wheel), that powered the endless rope haulage system, which pulled wagons along the tunnel. Recent excavations have shown that the mechanism was complex). There are also parts of trucks including a gripper truck that towed the journeys of trams.

Regrettably, the westerly workings (as the appearance of a new void on the surface testifies), now join the eastern workings as being classified as dangerous to enter, so the popular 'through trip' from west pit is no longer advisable. Fortunately some of the incline and other mechanism has been removed for safekeeping. Amongst the prominent surface remains is a big structure alongside the track down to Cwmorthin, which is an unfinished wheel pit. Near the foot of this track adjacent to the CONGLOG MILL [Section 8] is a row of RHOSYDD dwellings and not far away, in trees, Plas Cwm Orthin, the manager's house. Part way down that valley is the severely ruinous RHOSYDD chapel.

the vicinity of the site, particularly to the north are a number of reservoirs and lakes with leat systems partly traceable, (a collapsed timber dam is notable). The old track via Moelwyn may be followed and the later route via Cwmorthin is obvious.

The most spectacular relic is the incline down to the Croesor Tramway and the well-engineered tramway to its head. At almost 700' it is the highest single pitch incline in the Slate industry. Lack of space at the incline head forced the drum house's siting 50 ft above, the brake remotely controlled through wires by a wheel in the brake man's shelter. [41]

Section 8
BLAENAU FFESTINIOG

General
In this compact area of abundant Ordovician slate, are some of the largest and most efficient workings in the industry, producing in the latter part of the 19th century almost one third of Welsh output. Due to the steep northward dip of the five great veins, virtually all work was underground.

Sited at the last bleak outreach of Meirionnydd, where the Bowydd and the Barlwydd coalesce; glowered over by the Moelwyn and Manod mountains, the quarries form an amphitheatre with at their feet Blaenau Ffestiniog and its outliers Manod and Tanygrisiau.

Extraction still takes place at OAKELEY, BWLCH Y SLATERS, GRAIG DDU and LLECHWEDD, by modern untopping methods much to the detriment of historical relics; but sadly only LLECHWEDD makes finished product, and then almost as an adjunct to the its fine visitor centre.

Apart from the quarrying sites themselves the town, dominated by glowering cascades of waste, shows in the detail of many of its buildings, some fine examples of the slate workers' craft. The "Slate Workers" window in the parish church, being a unique tribute to that craft.

Happily or sadly, according to one's viewpoint, much of the cascades of waste that dominate the town are to become hardcore.

Transport
Prior to the 1836 opening of the Ffestiniog Railway, product was famously boated down the river Dwyryd. Like the railway, the boats have been extensively written

up; and the quays identified, but how the slate reached the quays has been less well publicised.

The route to the river from Llan Ffestiniog to Tâl y Bont (SH685416) was via the present-day road that had been rebuilt in the later 18th century to ease the gradient (The old road is traceable immediately to the south). The present bridge at Tâl y Bont dates from the 1860s, before that traffic took what is now the "back road" to Maentwrog, crossing the river to take up the line of the present road by a bridge that still exists in a field at SH684416. But to reach Llan remained a challenge.

In 1801 DIFFWYS built the present road from the quarry past PANT YR YNN mill to Tan y Manod (SH708452) and along the line of the now main road to join a pre-existing road to Llan Ffestiniog just beyond Congl y Wal (SH705442). This latter road is still the main road although it then went though Pen y Bont (SH706429), a diversion that can still be followed.

A year later BOWYDD built a road (now defined by a street) directly down to Four Crosses (SH704458), there it picked a pre-existing route over the river at Pont Fron Goch (SH703453) then on to Congl y Wal, (still traceable).

In 1804 MANOD built their fine road from the quarry to the pre-existing Cwm Teigl road at SH724435 (later diverted at SH721459) to join the Blaenau – Llan road at 706433. Apart from a few hundred yards at about the halfway point, this road is in good condition. The lower part of this route later provided access to GRAIG DDU's Lefel Dŵr Oer (SH717455)

In about 1819 Samuel Holland of RHIWBRYFDIR, built a road to join a pre-existing road at 697465 using that road (now the main street) to reach Four Crosses and join the BOWYDD route. Carts could now replace pack animals, but in winter it took two prodded and beaten horses in tandem harness to move a mere half ton (500 Kg) to Congl y Wal. There, the lead horse could be unhitched and the load augmented from a roadside dump to some 13 cwt (650 Kg). Only at Llan Ffestiniog, could the load be made up to the cart's one-ton capacity. Things were eased in the mid 1820s when Four Crosses was linked to the DIFFWYS road at Tan y Manod (the present Blaenau-Manod road) avoiding the steep drop down to and climb from Pont Fron Goch

The great leap forward came at the end of the 1820s when DIFFWYS, built the "Hen Ffordd Casson" that is defined by the present road from Congl y Wal via Cwmerau (SH695432) to RHYD Y SARN where it met the existing road to Tâl y Bont. This road and a road down to Cwmerau from the Orthin valley formed the Ffestiniog turnpike. With the increasing volume of traffic the formation of the Ffestiniog Turnpike Trust must have seemed appropriate but it soon lost its traffic to the Ffestiniog Railway.

There was no road from Blaenau Ffestiniog to Tanygrisiau until the mid 1850s when the present (back) road developed along the line of the Ffestiniog Railway
. Quarrying to the east of Llan Ffestiniog had to make do with the roughest of tracks to Llan Ffestiniog until 1818 when the Bala-Ffestiniog turnpike was built. From 722423 it dropped down to Llan by the present road obviating the previous, but still traceable, steep track.

(With acknowledgments to Mr. G.R.Jones M.A.)

The first quarry to have a connection to the Ffestiniog Railway was the WELSH SLATE COMPANY (Later part of OAKELEY). The incline now comprehensively tipped over, joined somewhere beyond the original Dinas terminus station (694464). Today, all that remains of that station, Rhybrifidr farm and a number of houses, un-engulfed by a million tons of waste; are the vestiges of the engine shed. Dinas was the original settlement, and the line to Duffws that became the main Blaenau FR station was considered a mere quarry branch. The incline adjacent to Dinas is comparatively recent, the stile crossing the main line marks the site of the level crossing on the route established by Samuel Holland. On the far side of the main line is the track bed of the narrow gauge line from the long-gone GLAN Y DON tip to the ex London& North Westernm ex-LMS station at Glan y Pwll.

Moving north on the FR trackbed alongside where the present railway is stilted above the Barlwydd, are two further incline vestiges, on either side of the pillar, the sad remains of the PEN Y BONT viaduct, fashioned by the OAKELEY carpenters in emulation of the great Brunel timber lattice spans. The nearer incline joined the FR while the further one turned north to cross the Lefel Dwr outfall to exchange sidings close to the mouth of the tunnel. The GLAN Y DON connection made these sidings redundant The FR track bed continues under the main line and on to the foot of the LLECHWEDD incline. On the far side of the main line is PANT YR AFON, the site of the temporary station when the L&NWR burst free of the mountain in 1879, later becoming the trans-shipment exchange for LLECHWEDD's loadings onto the L&NWR, as well as their (still working) power station.

At Glan y Pwll there are vestiges of the fine ex-L&NWR terminus and marshalling yard. In addition to Glan y Don link from OAKELEY a narrow-gauge link from the FR Duffws station enabled either loading into L&NWR wagons for rail distribution or the quarry wagons to be entrained pic-a-back to the wharves at Deganwy. On the other side of the road was the FR Glan y Pwll station that acted as a passenger exchange with the L&NWR.

The main line has now been extended to make common cause with the FR and to join end-on with ex-Great Western metal. This joint station is the site of the terminus of the GWR branch from Bala, that had a platform that enabled passengers to transfer from the FR to the GWR. Most of the GWR station has been lost but here curving off to the south; a lane marks the route of the FR branch to the Newborough slate factory .

The bridge that took the FR under the main street has been lost and the site of the Duffws station is now a car park. the passenger building surviving as a convenience. The DIFFWYS/BOWYDD incline survives as a public path and the No.1 incline of the Rhiwbach tramway is still extant.

The GWR (mostly on the track bed of the Festiniog & Blaenau Railway) now terminates at Trawsfynydd, but in its heyday it could, pick up GRAIG DDU wagons brought down on the 4-pitch incline at Manod and carry them pic-a-back to Blaenau, either for transferring their loads to GWR wagons or for shunting along to the FR.

At Tanygrisiau, reached past houses built by Holland along the FR line in pre-road days, the FR is joined by the Cwmorthin Tramway and the precipitous WRYSGAN incline, and near the power station the unique multi-pitched MOELWYN incline

SECTION 8: BLAENAU FFESTINIOG

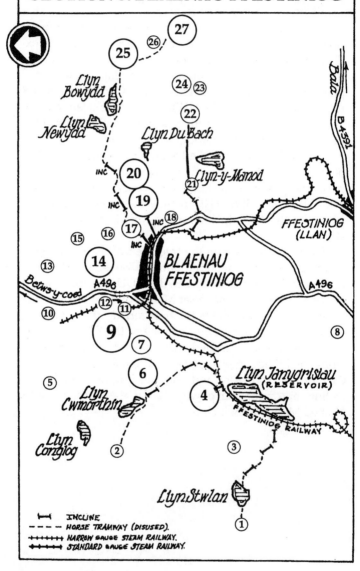

INCLINE
HORSE TRAMWAY (DISUSED).
NARROW GAUGE STEAM RAILWAY.
STANDARD GAUGE STEAM RAILWAY.

PORTHMADOG. Slate from Blaenau was always known as "Porthmadog Slate", appropriately so since from circa 1820 both places were inextricably intertwined. Unlike cosmopolitan Caernarfon, the other deep-sea port of north Wales, Porthmadog was almost exclusively used by ships crewed by local men. Thus whilst Caernarfon abounded with pubs and brothels, Porthmadog had a dearth of the former amenity and a complete absence of the latter.

1]	661442	Moelwyn **	
2]	670467	Conglog **	
3]	671446	Chwarel Twm Ffeltwr	
4]	676458	Wrysgan ***	I
5]	680493	Cwm Fanog	
6]	681459	Cwmorthin *	C
7]	689462	Nyth y Gigfran **	
8]	690421	Rhyd y Sarn (Mill)	
9]	691470	Oakeley *	B
10]	693483	Ffridd y Bwlch	
11]	697467	Glan y Don (Tip & Mill)	
12]	697469	Pant yr Afon (Sidings) **	
13]	699487	Bwlch Gorddinan	
14]	700470	Llechwedd **** Visitor Centre	C
15]	704473	Owain Goch (Pump site)	
16]	706465	Votty	
17]	708464	Bowydd **	D
18]	709454	Pany yr Ynn (Mill) *	
19]	712463	Diffwys **	E
20]	714465	Maenofferen **	D
21]	715455	Lefel Dŵr Oer	
22]	724454	Graig Ddu **	H
23]	726452	South Pole *	
24]	732455	Bwlch y Slaters *	

25]	734468	Cwt y Bugail ***	I
26]	735459	Blaen y Cwm **	
27]	740462	Rhiwbach ****	G

BLAEN Y CWM SH735459 736459 734464 FRIDD, PEN Y
FRIDD Including BWLCH CARREG Y FRÂN
Several distinct workings, the earliest dating from at least
1813. Much developed during the 1870s when the now
extant mill was built, with 5 saws and 5 dressers.
Although geographically extensive, output was small.

In pre-tramway times, output was carried via
Cwmmachno to Trefriw, later via Cwm Teigl to the
Dwyryd. Closed WW1.

Remains. The main feature is the mill with the large
wheel housing at one end accessed by cantilevered steps,
and with a fine tailrace tunnel. At the opposite end is the
coal store and house (with rope apertures) for the engine
that up hauled to the Rhiwbach Tramway. Nearby are
remnants of the portable engine boiler that replaced the
original and also the pulley support pillars for the
haulage.

The mill waste chutes along one side feed into a deep
rubbish wagon run that has neat slate slabs bridges.
There are weigh houses and other buildings and artefacts
include the upper sheave of the exit incline. This incline
was extended down towards an underground working
where there are some small buildings and an adit with
rail in situ leading to some chambering. Although rope
markings indicate use, this extension was apparently
never completed. Near the mill is a lavatory block built
over a large pit, undoubtedly the wheel pit of an earlier
mill. A little way off to the south is a powder-house.
Above the site is a small, now dry reservoir formed by
pounding behind the Rhiwbach Tramway formation.

The most obvious working is immediately to the south of the mill. This is a pit accessed by an adit. The formation of a balanced incline leads down into the pit to form a through route to the mill from BWLCH CARREG Y FRÂN when it was re-worked by BLAEN Y CWM. Here are vestiges of dressing sheds and an early mill. The small pit working to the south of the tramway was accessed by a short tunnel (now blocked).

Further to the south and immediately east of the BWLCH Y SLATERS branch of the Rhiwbach tramway is a further pit, the early FFRIDD workings. Adjacent are ruins of dressing sheds and a powder house. [26]

BOWYDD   SH708464   CHWAREL   LORD, NEWBOROUGHGH, PERCIVAL' S.

A late 18th century working one of the earliest quarries to have an internal rail system (2.2" g, 1825), and one of the first to use (hand) saws. Early user of Mathew's dressers and of. circular saws (1827?). Substantially developed in the 1830s, amalgamating in the 1870s to form VOTTY & BOWYDD quarry, producing at its end of the 19th century peak over 17,000 tons pa, employing nearly 500 men, with locomotives from 1878.

Ultimately there were three mills plus a writing slate factory. The three big mills A, B & C on massive terraces, had central wheels, (A & B 35' x 4', C 40' x 3'6") making successive use of water to drive a total of 50 saws (Including one Hunter), 50 dressers and 4 planers, through under-floor line shafting. Unusually, the track for the waste wagons was inside rather than outside the buildings. Latterly only C mill was used, diesel powered. Although electric power was brought in from Dolwen in 1899, its limited amperage forced the continued extensive use of water power including, in the 1930s, a hydrostat to raise water. Water balances were used (eg C-B & B-A) and there was a 3 track water-powered haulage incline. Diamond tipped saws, used in the early 1930s, the power supply by then augmented by the Maentwrog hydro-station.

It was not until 1854 that an incline made direct connection with the Ffestiniog Railway, shortly afterwards supplanted by the use of the No1 incline of the Rhiwbach Tramway. By 1880 most material was going out by a connection made partway down the DIFFWYS incline.

Taken over by OAKELEY in 1933 it was finally closed in 1963. Untopping operations were started by LLECHWEDD in the 1980s.

Remains. Due to untopping and landscaping much (including the mills) has been lost. There are extensive tramway formations, some with track on the ground. The big Tuxford haulage incline is just discernable. .

Alongside Rhiwbach No 2 incline are the fir-tree surrounded ruins of "Quarry bank", the manager's house. At this level are several other buildings including the remnants of the two-storey water powered writing slate factory. There are weigh houses, inclines etc The connection to the Rhiwbach Tramway near the foot of No 2 incline is obvious. In spite of clearance, the route from the lowest mill level to join the DIFFWYS incline is traceable. The Rhiwbach Tramway route to the head of No 1 incline down to Blaenau, is well engineered with cuttings and embankments. The No 1 incline itself is in good condition but the rock-cut remote drum house has largely collapsed. The lower end of the DIFFWYS incline, below the 'junction' is surfaced as a path. The drum gear is most unusual as its brake was located between the two halves of the drum.

There are numerous other buildings including offices and loco sheds and much substantial revetment work to retain terracing and to hold back rubbish from adits and working areas.

At the top of the site the old VOTTY pit is flooded as a water source. Nothing remains of the waterpowered writing-slate factory in the town at 699456. Burnt down 1912. [17]

BWLCH GORDDINAN SH699487, 700481, 701484 etc
Trials in conjunction with CHWAREL GETHIN [Section 8] Alongside the road to the east is 'Boot Hill' where a 'Gravestone' marks where un-repairable boots for the WW2 US Army boot-repairing factory in Blaenau Market Hall. were burnt.
Remains. Adits and ground disturbance. [13]

BWLCH Y SLATERS SH732455 (NEW) MANOD with NORTH POLE
Working quarry do not enter.
Dating from early 19th century, this mainly underground quarry was developed with a steam powered mill following connection to the Rhiwbach Tramway in 1866. In the early 20th century a subsidiary site was opened at 730458 connected by an incline. Annual tonnages varied considerably but never can have much exceeded 1000. As with all rock to the east of Manod mountain, winning is harder due to lack of foot joints.

The original route out was via Cwm Teigl, the same route being resumed in the 1930s to avoid tramway tolls. Present working benefits from road improvements in connection with art storage during WW2 and DoE occupation until the early 1980s. Shortly after de-requisition it became a centre for vigorous untopping work at GRAIG DDU. Blocks are sent to PENRHYN

[Section 1] for reduction

Remains. The site is much disturbed by current work including the cutting of roads, the 1900s incline having been virtually obliterated. The mill is new but the old office survives. There is a fine powder house with part of the original wooden lining intact.

The route of the connection to the Rhiwbach tramway, including the reversing loop, is visible. [24]

CHWAREL TWM FFELTWR SH671446

Very small. **Remains.** Traces of excavation, adit (gated) at 677450. [3]

CONGLOG SH670467 GLYN FFESTINIOG

A compact and delightfully situated underground quarry operating from 1854 to 1909 mainly producing slab. Latterly operated by a local syndicate whose initial output approached four figures, but for most of its output was a quarter of this. Employment rarely reached 20, finally falling to 2 Rhosydd workers working in their spare time.

Block was taken down an incline to a small water-powered mill, After 1875 finished product was taken out by an extension of the Cwmorthin Tramway.

Remains. Curiously situated, an "island" amongst RHOSYDD property. Plas Cemorthin, the stable. the row of houses and a little distance off, the chapel. all belonged to their larger neighbour

The blocked adit above the track is chambered out to bank, the drum house at that level has been extended in a curious manner. A leat, runs alongside the Rhosydd track. An open adit below the road has rails and contains trucks. A further, lower, adit is blocked.

The mill that housed 8 saws and 2 planers but only one slate-dressing machine has been substantially adapted for agricultural use but the wheel pit and launder pillars are extant. The tramway is readily traceable. [2]

CWM FANOG SH680493 & 681488
Possible site of trials. **Remains.** Traces of excavation. [5]

CWM ORTHIN SH681459 including TAI'R MURIAU .
A substantial underground enterprise notorious for bad working conditions, normal quarry perils being compounded by operating steam boilers underground, unventilated.

Started in 1810 as an open quarry it was worked sporadically until the early 1860s when the tramway connection to the Ffestiniog Railway, justified substantial underground development

Original chambering was above the water table with material being brought out by adits to mills at lake level. As work progressed deeper pumping and haulage were called for, at first by steam, later by electricity. Output in 1882 was 10376 tons, with over 500 men employed. The 3 mills, one steam, 2 water powered, had some 50 saws and 50 dressers.

After a serious collapse in 1884 production was much reduced. Incorporated into OAKELEY in 1900 and all surface works abandoned.

In 1925 there was a big, but unrealised scheme to develop open workings. In the 1930s there was a fresh period of activity and some further work in the 1950s. Subsequently worked on a small scale with machinery sited underground to combat vandalism, all transport both underground and on the surface being by an old Land-Rover. Extensively untopped in 1980s and a mill rebuilt in a short lived revival in conjunction with CROES Y DDWY AFON [Section 9]

Remains. Due to untopping many interesting remains including the 1925 'Beau Geste Fort" powder house have vanished.

Near the lake are several structures including traces of the (latterly steam powered) Lake mill. The newer, slate built, end of the much photographed 'Cwmorthin Terrace' survives but the older country-rock end is ruinous and the 'Tiberias' chapel decays almost before one's eyes.

The modern mill is approximately on the site of the Cross mill. The site of the Lower 'London House' mill was cleared as a 'slate garden', the Pelton being housed with a small generator. It has a nice feed-leat and holding pond. In this area the river was channelled in connection with the original Dolwen power station

On the hill above the site leats can be traced and one can see where the ground has sunk as a result of the underground collapse. Also the cast iron markers defining the surface boundary with OAKLEY.
The two-incline (Tan y Murian & Village) exit tramway with its cutting and embankment is a delightful feature. [6]

CWT Y BUGAIL SH734468 BUGAIL, NEW WELSH SLATE

A remote, partly underground quarry, dating from the early 19th century, developed following its connection to the Rhiwbach tramway in the 1860s,at its peak producing over 3000 tons pa with well over 100 men, many living in barracks. Early work was at a high level with inclines down to the mill, which was extended and re-extended to eventually accommodate 20 saws and 20 dressers. Subsequently as the pit and chambering off it went deeper material came out by tunnel with a short incline down, then by a tunnel at mill level. Then, from an adit from the deepest workings, the mill was reached by a water balance. Finally material was raised by ropeway. Steam (latterly an oil engine) powered the mill. Worked on a reduced scale until the 1960s.

Remains. The principal feature is the surprisingly large mill, constructed in three sections with a separate engine room. This building survived almost intact into the 1980s but is now much collapsed. There are wooden bases of dressing machines and various fragments, including dust-extraction ducting that became obligatory post WW2. There are several other buildings on site including a workshop and office. Near the mill are vestiges of the head of a water balanced incline with the table and the balance tank running on slightly different levels. The foot of this incline, at the site of the lowest has traces of a possible mill.

The incline behind the main mill (with a nice powder house alongside), leads down from extensive early workings. There is a second powder house and an eating caban with fireplace, half buried against the bitter winds. The Welsh for a slate making shelter (g) wal means 'wall', here one can see the origin of the term, there being the remains of a long wall behind which the slate makers crouched. There are signs that part had projecting walls added to make the usual three-sided shelters. Slate sleepers suggest that at this early level the tramway gauge was 2' 3"

Access to the big main pit is by a cutting and a curved tunnel passing a blast shelter. At pit bottom, are tractor remnants, an Austin car engine and other components of the jury-rig haulages and so on, from the post WW2 reworking. Tunnels lead off north to part flooded chambers containing relics that include a carbide generator for lighting. The chambers to the south are normally dry, the mill-level adit has been tipped over but there is possible access from both the pit floor and where they break out to bank. There is rail on the pit floor and in tunnels Regrettably the gem of the site, the traction engine, double winch and weighbridge at the peak of the working has been removed. One drum up-hauled rubbish from the big pit to the weighbridge, the other raised block (and possibly rubbish), via two pulleys (still in situ), from chambers directly below, to the present access level.

The connection to the Rhiwbach Tramway had a slight adverse gradient, so trucks were pulled by a winder driven from the mill shafting. The mounting for the sheave survives near the junction. Also near the junction is a barracks that included a rent-free dwelling for a worker whose wife cleaned and cooked for the barrackers.

The tramway branch was at one time intended to continue (via a water balanced incline) to CWM MACHNO [Section 4]. [25]

DIFFWYS (CASSON) SH712463 Incorporating PENFFRIDD

Opened in the 1760s by Methusalem Jones of Nantlle who is said to have dug here as a result of a dream. The first organised quarry in the district, it was a pioneer user of saws, inclines and internal tramways. (Originally 3'4^1/2" gauge plate ways, unique to the industry, later 2'2" gauge edge rail was also used). This gauge difference may have accounted for their reluctance to use the Ffestiniog Railway, a reluctance demonstrated in 1845 by building the Afon Bowydd powered PANT YR YNN mill alongside their road. This was not their first mill, a small water-powered sawmill (later enlarged and converted to steam as No 4 mill) slightly predated it. Their No 6 steam mill of 1861 was the first integrated mill in the area. They used a unique type of dresser a big guillotine operated by an overhead crank from the line shafting.

They eventually connected with the F.R. in 1860 via the BOWYDD incline (later to become No 1 Incline of the Rhiwbach Tramway), having their own direct incline in 1863.

The earliest, open, workings (Hen Gwaith) were at the top of the site with work more of less progressing downhill with some tentative underground working. Serious underground extraction started much lower down and this was followed by work, (Drum Boeth) higher up, close to the original diggings. In 1882 an entirely new underground venture, known as New Quarry started, to the east of the site, was not successful.

By the early 1820s its tonnage of over 6000 pa dominated the scene but it was swamped by the spectacular growth of its neighbours, it being the 1870s before its former glory was regained. Semi-derelict in the 1890s, it was re-opened, electrified, in the 1920s with 23 saws and dressers (about half its peak total). It continued on a diminishing scale until the mid 1950s. In the 1980s untopping work was commenced by LLECHWEDD.

Remains. The site is now somewhat confused by modern untopping and access roads. Also, near the lowest part of the site, there is some intermingling with the BOWYDD site, since they had a tip to the southeast of this site using a tramway that bridged the main DIFFWYS incline.

At the top of the site are some of the earliest buildings, weigh houses etc constructed of massive blocks of country rock. There are also ponds and an interesting stone embanked leat and some tramway formations with the old "wide" gauge slate sleepers. The original Hen Gwaith workings have been obliterated by the progression of the later Drum Boeth operations.

Nearby are the separate New Quarry workings with adits and some buildings and a tramway that led, via two inclines and a narrow terrace through a tunnel (collapsed) to the Upper mill. Near the lower of the two inclines, is a fine flight of steps.

There are about, various balanced incline drum houses ingeniously converted to other uses such as electric winding houses for up-haulage. Great ingenuity is show clearly adapting scrap or disused components and adding driver's accommodation and so on

The No 6 mill walls are in fair condition. The rubbish track alongside still has rail on the ground and a rubbish wagon in position. There are parts of guillotine type dressers.

Lower down there are several other interesting drum houses, one immediately below the upper mill is singularly massive. Another, which has a fine flight of steps nearby, has been converted into an office type building. Much at the lower levels including the original mill and other buildings have been covered by debris from late untopping work. On the other hand, untopping has revealed chambers and underground inclines (some with rail in situ).

Landscaping in the mid 1980s obliterated much of the main incline but the drum house is extant incorporating a weighbridge. Most unusually, the drum is in two halves with a central brake between. It used automotive type linings. This incline also served BOWYDD by means of mid run hitching, after its use by Diffwys was abandoned. Many of the nearby houses were quarry properties. [19]

FRIDD Y BWLCH SH693483,
A tiny working overlaid by railway tunnel ventilation shaft debris.
Remains. One adit open another may have been buried, vestiges of walling. Also adit (collapsed) at 692482. [10]

GLAN Y DON SH697467 PEN Y BONT
Tip (& mill) for OAKELEY reached by viaduct over the river, the Ffestiniog Railway and the (Ex-London & North Western) main line. An incline and narrow-gauge line from here to exchange sidings at the L&NWR Blaenau station superseded the use of the PANTYRAFON exchange.
Remains. Tip has been levelled but the viaduct pillars are extant. Line to station traceable. [11]

GRAIG DDU SH724454 With (OLD) MANOD 723452
Working quarry do not enter.
There was substantial investment at MANOD in 1801, including a magnificent road. It was run partly in common with MOELWYN, but was of little account until absorbed by GRAIG DDU in the 1840s. Being unable to reach the Ffestiniog Railway, it had to continue using the road and boating down the Dwyryd (the last major quarry to do so).

This all changed with the opening of the 2' gauge Ffestiniog & Blaenau Railway, an incline system to it laid in 1865 enabled their loaded trucks to travel from the quarry to Porthmadog. After 1883 when the F&BR was subsumed by the GWR the quarry tucks were pic-a-backed to Blaenau on standard gauge carriers.

In the 1880s the problems of water shortage on site, were solved by establishing a mills area (Lefel Dŵr Oer SH717455) at the foot of the upper incline. Water was brought in to holding ponds, from the north by streams and from the south from Llyn y Manod via a water wheel driven pump. One mill at this level was driven by a totally buried wheel fed via a tunnel and a further two mills by a part-buried wheel driving shafting under the mills. In the 1900s this wheel was replaced by a producer gas engine. .

There was a total of over 30 saw tables (including 3 Hunter saws) and a similar number of dressers, in the various mills. A quarry mill made redundant by Dwr Oer, was converted into a barracks

Output in 1882 was 3140 tons with 110 men. Underground working started in the 1920s, closed in the 1940s but small scale working continued. In the 1980s untopped in conjunction with BWLCH Y SLATERS

Remains. Massive untopping has followed the dip northwards obliterating its inclines, two tunnels, mills and other buildings. The now vast pit exposes some of the chambering.

The 1800 workings to the south have been filled with tipped material obliterating almost everything apart from a powder house and a very fine "keyhole" underground powder store. Vestiges of several of the latter are extant in the area, and there is a tiny one at CAE'R GORS [Section 7], but no other full-sized example is known.

The obvious feature is the cascade of inclines. The topmost drum house has an interesting wall screening the top of the incline from the winds that howl at this height. A road now cuts the incline, near the 1930s adit bored to drain the chambers and with possible future access in mind,

Regrettably little survives of the mill complex at Lefl Dŵr Oer, other than the base of the gas engine and the ponds. The pumping-wheel pit and leat trenches are to the south. Part way down the shorter second incline are vestiges of a very small hydro generator house.

The magnificent third incline down to road level, has some wrecked wagons alongside it, including some GWR examples. It is incredible to think of the workers descending these inclines on the unique "Wild Cars" right up to the 1940s. Anecdotally, children rode on their father's laps for a 'treat' and two or even three men would pile onto one car.

The final incline, to the west of the road, down to the railway is less clear but its line can be visualised to the site of Manod station.

The old road is traceable to where it joined the Cwm Teigl road at 716431, or less easily to its alternative route to cross the present road at 707437. Nearby at Cae Ddu are the ruins of a powder store. [22]

LEFEL DŴR OER SH715455
Mills area for GRAIG DDU.
Remains. Site almost cleared, see GRAIG DDU. [21]

LLECHWEDD SH700470 GREAVES Including ELLECHWEDD Y CYD & TAL Y WEINYDD **Working quarry do not enter.**
This mainly underground quarry opened in 1846, rapidly becoming one of the largest in the district, one of the most efficient in the industry and a leader in methodology. Both the Greaves Dresser and the Greaves Saw becoming the standard machines almost worldwide.

In 1882 553 men raised 24723 tons, producing even more in the 1890s. Their near-50 tons per man-year and 9-1 waste-to-make ratio were benchmark figures.

There were mills on several levels from 1852, extensive use was made of waterpower to drive them (with steam back-up) and to pump and haul, the latter both by water balance and direct cranking. Chambering went down almost to sea level with 20 miles of tunnels with many inclines.

Steam locomotives were used from the early 1878. Electricity generated by a dynamo, was pumping and ventilating in 1892, followed by a full-scale hydro station in 1904. In the 1930s, under Col. Martyn Williams-Ellis' leadership there were 400 men in work and much innovation, including electric traction and the unique adaptation of a Blondin for tipping and to assist pioneering untopping methods of extraction. Post WW2 manning was a mere 75, now it is even less but innovation continues.

An early user of the FR, although direct incline connection was not made until 1852. From 1879 this incline, which remained in use until 1964, also reached the main line railway at PANT YR AFON.

Remains. Opencast untopping of chambers to work the pillars and demolition of buildings has left the site much devoid of remains. Reduction is concentrated in the rebuilt and re-equipped No. 7 mill. The successively water, steam and electrically wound 'Inclein Bôn' has vanished but the main exit incline passing under the main road survives.

Quarry Tours Visitor Centre based around the original No 1 mill has happily preserved a number of buildings and rare artefacts and provides a fine exhibition and demonstration display. Tours by rail and by incline to interpretive areas underground are provided.

At the entrance to the site, Plas Weunydd once the owner's house is now the main office. Behind there is a barracks and houses, some of which are in use, and above the site there are extensive leats fed from Llyn Newydd and Llyn Bowydd. [14]

MAENOFFEREN   SH714465   FFRIDD   Y   GELLI
incorporating DAVID JONES & HYSFA

A substantial, entirely underground quarry operating on a compact site at over 1300' amsl. Originally opened in the early 1800s and was unsuccessful until developed by Greaves in the 1850s flourishing during the latter half of the 19th cent, and the earlier years of the 20th. Achieving in the 1890s, over 14,000 tons pa with more than 400 men employed. Two mills, originally water-driven contained almost 50 saws and as many trimmers. Locomotive power extensively used. An underground trunc incline was water balanced (later electrified).

Electricity was introduced in the 1890s; a hydroelectric station built in 1918 remained in use until the 1980s. The Greaves company re-acquired the site in the 1970s and using a re-built mill, continued to work it as the last totally underground quarry in the district, pioneering the use of wire saws.

Use was made of the DIFFWYS incline prior to the construction of the Rhiwbach Tramway that ran through the site. Thereafter the Nos 1 & 2 inclines of this tramway were used until 1920 when a new incline was made through VOTTY & BOWYDD to avoid allegedly excessive charges. When RHIWBACH quarry and tramway were acquired in 1928, that incline was abandoned and the Rhiwbach line again used. Immediately post WW2 some use was made of No 1 incline to reach the main line railways but up to 1976 most was dispatched by lorry from the foot of No2 incline, From July that year a new road made No2 redundant, thus the last self-acting incline in the industry was abandoned. The quarry closed in 2001

Remains. Sadly little is extant, the underground workings on two levels served by the last underground inclines in the industry, controlled to the last by the original brine-bath regulators, is closed. The mills area is cleared save for the empty shell of the magnificent mill that still shows how the roof was made good when, after electrification, the water-wheel, that projected through it, was removed. The curious 'kinked flue' to one old engine house can be seen and, adjacent, on the long abandoned DAVID JONES part of the site there is a machine bored adit, relics of an unsuccessful, 1870s, use of a Hunter twin-head boring machine. Of interest is the "cut and cover" tunnel for a line to where tipping was done on the old Votty site. The No 2 Incline and its remote drum house are in sad condition, but below it a nice rail formation and bridge show a route from a VOTTY underground working. The tramway route through BOWYDD property to the No 1 incline is clear and the incline formation itself is intact, with a compact remote-type drum house set into the rock. The No 3 incline up from the site, leads onto the level main section of the Rhiwbach tramway and has a fine drum house. Alongside the first section of this line is a notable, slate lined and slate covered leat with a piped feed to the power station. There are winders and other artefacts on site, The old HYSFA open workings are to the north. [20]

MOELWYN SH661442 Incl BWLCH STWLAN SH656442 & 658442 CLODDFA SION LLWYD. 661439

A grandly situated but largely unsuccessful undertaking. Originally opened in the 1800s as small levels on the bleak eastern flank of Moelwyn Bach some 1700' amsl. There was some very unsuccessful work in the 1820s, but in the 1860s it was developed underground on the south-eastern slopes of Moelwyn Mawr, with a mill some distance away at 668444 with 6 saw benches and 7 dressing machines driven by a 40' x 4' wheel fed from Llyn Stwlan. There were barracks and family dwellings on site, (with children going to school at Tanygrisau!) .

Active in the 1870s and again in the 1890s, closed about 1900, with workings merged with PANT-MAWR. [Section 7] Material originally removed by packhorse down Cwm Maesgwm by a track built in 1826, but from about 1860 used the Ffestiniog Railway via the spectacular inclines.

Remains. At the original workings to the south, there are barracks and other building remains and a possible incline. There are adits, (gridded) and some vestiges of buildings from the 1860s development,. The upper two pitches of the incline system were partly lost when Llyn Stwlan was enlarged in 1960 for the pumped storage scheme. This scheme largely destroyed the mills area but some slight vestiges are extant. The four pitches down past the generating station to the old line of the FR re still a magnificent landscape feature. [1]

NYTH Y GIGFRAN SH689462 GLAN Y PWLL

A small and most improbably sited undertaking. Dating from about 1860, adits were driven from a natural ledge in the cliff face. A later adit was driven some 30' below, reached by a rock-cut platform.

Material was lowered by part timber, part stone, incline to a siding on the Ffestiniog Railway at Glan y Pwll. Allegedly used the Nant Ystradau mill (At 677433) vacated by MATHEWS.

Following a lease dispute, it was absorbed by OAKELEY, and a tunnel connection made.

Remains. There are two adits open, the upper stoped out to bank, and the lower giving onto a precipitous stone platform. Near the upper adit are some small buildings and some nice rock cut steps, also a possible smithy. The stone part of the incline formation is a prominent feature, and cutting and boltholes suggest where the wooden upper part ran.

Sawn ends suggest sawing on site and there is are verbal accounts of a boiler being lowered from the site in the early 20th C.

At Glan y Pwll, alongside the site of the railway siding are some buildings in re-use, possibly connected with the quarry. The tunnel connection with Oakeley is open. [7]

OAKELEY SH691470 Comprising from 1878 CESAIL, (UPPER QUARRY or HOLLANDS) and MATHEWS, (MIDDLE QUARRY, GLODDFA GANOL or RHIWBRIFDIR); from 1883 WELSH SLATE, PALMERSTON'S or LOWER QUARRY (Originally RHIW) **Working quarry do not enter.**

The amalgamation, although never equalling the total output of its three constituents had, when, subsequently joined by CWM ORTHIN and NYTH Y GIGFRAN an output nearing 60,000 tons pa, and a 1700 payroll. It was, PENRHYN and DINORWIG apart, the largest in the industry, representing half and more of the Blaenau total.

The original quarry was RHIW developed by Samuel Holland in 1818, on ancient works that his father had taken in hand. Having sold out to the WELSH SLATE COMPANY in 1825, he re-started two yeas later at CESAIL higher up the hillside, going underground in 1840. A pioneer user of steam for mill power, his annual output eventually neared 14,000 with well over 500 men. A sponsor and early user of the Ffestiniog Railway, his extensive 2'g tramway system was connected to the railway at Dinas by a gravity incline with its head inside the 'Horse Tunnel'.

By 1830, land between the two quarries, had been taken by Nathaniel Mathew, trading as the RHIWBRYFDIR Company. Also underground by 1840 he pioneered the use of dressing machines, (the Mathew's Dresser of 1852), and was early user of steam for both mill power and for haulage. Curiously, as an interim measure, some sawing was done at a mill at 677433 on the Nant Ystradau on the site of the winding wheel for the 1836-42 incline of the FR.

By the mid 1870s output was over 10,000 tons p.a. with well over 300 men. Product also reached the FR. at Dinas by an incline.

In 1878 the leases on both quarries expired, landowner W.E.Oakeley not content with the royalties and wayleave he enjoyed sought to augment his revenues by taking them into his own hands.

Not a wise move since the slate market promptly collapsed.

In the meantime at the WELSH SLATE COMPANY, there had been after a shaky start, fifty years of spectacular progress. There were extensive underground workings serviced by a variety of inclines and lifts, with a network of surface tramways that had been connected by incline to the FR. in 1836. By the mid 1870s the payroll exceed four figures and annual tonnage neared 50,000. This success was only achieved by reckless underground working resulting in collapses culminating in the great falls of 1882/3 that almost wrecked the quarry and damaged the two Oakeley owned quarries above it. Following legal action W.E. Oakeley took over and amalgamated it with his own workings, although twenty years later steam shovels were still clearing the collapse.

The combined workings extended from sea level to 1500' on 30 floors lettered down to R and numbered up to

16 (some letters and numbers were omitted or merged). There were said to be 50 miles of track underground besides the loco-worked surface tramways. There were 9 mills plus 3 at CWMORTHIN) with almost 200 saw-tables.

In addition to water-wheels and a vertical water balance, there were almost twenty steam engines for the mills, pumping and the underground up haulages, including one of 6 tracks, plus a dozen or more locomotives from the early 1870s. Electricity started to displace steam after the opening of the Cwm Dyli hydro-station in 1906.

Rubbish disposal was a constant problem, some was backfilled, some was dumped in the old Holland workings, eventually a new tip was made to the east of the railway, reached by a viaduct, later forming the site for the PENYBONT mill. There were some 30 cottages and a hospital on site.

Even in the difficult times up to WW2, combined with BOWYDD and DIFFWYS, the payroll topped 1000 (over half of the Blaenau total) and they fared comparatively well immediately post-WW2, but men and markets were lost in the 1960s. Closed in 1970 but reopened by local entrepreneurs as two separate but associated undertakings, sold in 1997 when regrettably a cornucopia of artefacts was lost. .

Remains. Owing to vigorous untopping work the site is constantly changing and relics are vanishing almost on a weekly basis.

What was WELSH SLATE has become a deep pit with roads and tipping obscuring remains. To the south are some old buildings in reuse and modern sheds. To the north are the old Bonc Shafft mill and other buildings, vestiges of a steam powered tipping incline and traces of the vertical water balance. Nearby is the modern pulverising plant producing powder that is taken to south Wales for the manufacture of moulded slates.

The large area higher up, the old No.5 level has a number of buildings from GLODDFA GANOL the old Mathew workings, including some cottages, as well as the modern mill. Ruins of some other buildings are extant.

At the southern end of this level, is the prominent drum house of the 1906 incline, with zigzag steps leading up from the town. Behind this are vestiges of Samuel Holland's first steam mill and traces of other structures. The 'Horse Tunnel' runs through the workings from here, but Holland's early inclines, which fed it from the far end, have been mostly quarried away. The earliest workings at the top of the quarry are, for the time being, undisturbed with several open workings, accessed by short tunnels, each with its own tramway formation and weigh house leading to tipping areas. A tunnel leads to a sort of balcony where rubbish was tipped down the cliff face. There is also a powder house and some buildings possibly dating from Holland's original work. There is a tunnel through to the NYTH Y GIGFRAN workings, with some chambering off it.

A proposal to exploit the tips on a major scale will undoubtedly further degrade this site. [9]

OWAIN GOCH SH704473
Not a quarry but the site of a large waterwheel which, via rods in a 200' deep shaft, pumped water from levels B & C of LLECHWEDD to level 2 and also hauled from Floorl B to Floor 2. **Remains.** Vestiges only. [15]

PANT YR AFON SH697469
Exchange sidings for both LLECHWEDD and OAKELEY.

Remains. The LLECHWEDD area has storage sheds and a crane as well as the hydro-electric station, which is still in use. On the other side of the railway, there is little trace of the much smaller OAKELEY sidings.[12]

PANT YR YNN SH709454
The 1845 mill for DIFFWYS CASSON, driven by the Du Bach stream, subsequently a woollen factory. During WW1 was a factory sponsored by Welsh-Americans to provide an income for wives (and widows) of the many men serving in the forces.

Remains. Building still in use with disused waterwheel alongside. [18].

RHIWBACH SH740462
An 18th century digging seriously developed from the 1840s. The initial working immediately south of what became the main complex, being underground. Pits were also worked some distance further south again. In the 1860s, having built the Rhiwbach tramway, pit working to the east was considerably extended underground, ultimately going down 8 floors.

A mill was built, the mill engine, besides powering the exit incline up to the tramway, wound up from underground. It may have also, for a short time wound a vertical shaft and certainly powered a short incline up from the small 'New' mill. Just beyond the main mill a "village" of houses, barracks and a schoolroom/chapel was established. One of the housewives kept a "Parlour Shop", but main shopping was done in Blaenau on Saturdays, purchases coming the Tramway with the first rake of empty wagons on a Monday. Also brought up the inclines, daily was the schoolmistress, who returned to home by a GRAIG DDU 'Wild car'

Output reached a peak of over 8000 tons by 1869,

although within a few years it fell back to less than half this. Well before the end of the century its fortunes became mixed (81 men 2260 tons 1890), and the costs of maintaining a big layout complete with steam locos, were undoubtedly subsidised by revenues from other quarries use of the tramway.

From the 1890s all but the two lowest levels of the eastern chambers were dewatered by a 600-yard long GLYN ABER tunnel. [Section 4].

By 1935 with tonnage down to 1000, electricity displaced steam. Beset by manning problems, closure came in 1952, with two men still barracking in a temporary building.

Material was originally carried via Cwm Machno for shipment at Trefriw, stock being held at Betws y Coed owing to high charges at Trefriw wharf, but from the 1830s until the opening of the Rhiwbach Tramway in 1863, product was carted down Cwm Teigl to Maentwrog for shipment on the Dwyryd. In the 1920s the Council were rather cheekily asked surface the track down to Cwm Machno to enable all-lorry dispatch, but in the event the tramway continued in use until closure.

Remains. The massive sheave mounting incorporating a brakeman's cabin at the head of the incline provides a fine viewpoint of the quarry.

The incline has wooden sleepers attached to slate slabs still in place and also support wheels for the return rope, some in their wooden mountings. At its foot is the big stack and alongside it is the house for the 20-hp engine and its fuel store with the later electricity building between. Behind are the ruins of the main mill that had 18 saws and 18 dressing machines. A shallow tunnel runs under the floor of the mill, with apertures clearly intended for the disposal of sawing waste. The choked state of the tunnel suggests that the presumed water scour used to clear it was not too effective. Alongside this mill are some stanchions for the rope that hauled the main incline.

There are vestiges of a number of other buildings but prominent is a big group that were part dwellings, part barracks. Alongside is a building clearly identifiable as the schoolroom/chapel. Facing these, are traces of the manager's house, unusual in being so close to the workers dwellings and to the operating site. There are carefully decorated lintels etc. incorporated into these buildings and the sweep of road to this domestic site is lined on one side by a most interesting slate "post & rail" fence. Nearby, there are two rows of lavatories.

Immediately south of the exit incline, are the "old" workings. There are several adits off these leading to some underground chambering. At a lower level are traces of the "New" mill, which had 6 saws and 7 dressing machines driven by a 7-hp engine. The incline up from this mill, hauled by a rope that passed through the rafters of the main mill, is now buried

The so-called "new" workings are a little way off to the south. These comprised two pits, one being later partly dammed as a reservoir. There are ruins of the house for the 12-hp engine that up hauled from these workings and off to the east is the pit of the wheel that pumped them, the flat rod trench being obvious. There are some traces of several other buildings.

The main underground workings to the east begin in a large pit, which was worked in the open down to floor D, the incline continuing underground. The opening is now gated so it is no longer possible to descend to floor H to reach the drainage tunnel, which has rail track in place. There is evidence of "pillar robbing" and "cupboarding" and test bores can be seen emerging from the roofs. There are also a number of bore-cores on the surface.

Floor I is flooded. There was a proposal during the early 1920s boom to cut a second tunnel and develop below floor J, but ground levels would have prevented it being lower that I. [27]

RHYD Y SARN SH690421
Not a quarry but notable as it is believed that before 1802, slate was sawn here in a water powered sawmill. Site of early circular sawing experiments using a horse whim.
Remains. Wheel pit & leat. (Buildings are later) [8]

SOUTH POLE SH726452.
Very old, associated with neighbouring BWLCH Y SLATERS.
Remains. A delightful little open working, with several buildings including a barracks and houses. Waste tipped directly down the hillside. [23]

VOTTY SH706465 FOTTY, HAFOTTY, CWM BOWYDD
Pit working, operated from the 1830s to 1870s when it was amalgamated with. BOWYDD. Possibly originally raised material by horse-whim.
Remains. The main pit is flooded as a water source, the site being mostly tipped over, little if any original work can be identified. [16]

WRYSGAN SH676458
Underground on a small, elevated and inaccessible site. Opened in the 1830s having their first mill in 1854 and a second in 1865, having in all 18 saws, (including at least one Hunter), 20 dressers and 2 planers.

In 1850 a balanced incline down to Cwmorthin obviated a precipitous zigzag descent by pack animals.

This was replaced in 1872 by a spectacular incline that gave direct connection to the FR. some 600' below; its head was approached by a deep cutting and its upper part was in a tunnel. The gradient on the lower section proved too slight to properly self-act so a steam engine had to be installed to raise the empties.

The tiny Llyn y Wrysgan proving too small, a steam engine was installed c1890 in the lower mill, another drove the underground incline serving the levels then being opened below lower mill level.

Output built up by fits and starts to 3000 tons in 1904 with over 100 men, working on 8 levels, but declined markedly afterwards. In 1890 with steam proving costly and negotiations to rent the disused water-powered Cwmorthin Cross Mill having failed, a 50-hp producer gas engine was installed for mill drive. The underground steam incline was abandoned in favour of an external water balance alongside the original exit incline. Later this incline was powered by an old car engine. (From the manger's Lea Francis!) Steam proved continually troublesome on the exit incline, mainly due to an inadequate boiler. Following electrification in the early 1920s, this incline was powered by "borrowing" the electric motor from the workshop, and coupling it to the haulage drum each time a journey of empty wagons needed to be raised. The eventual attempts to use a lorry engine were unsuccessful. Sensibly, having a steam engine underground, there was fan ventilation.

Manning was down to thirty in late 1930s tapering to a dozen before the 1950s closure.

Remains. The obvious feature is the big incline. The access cutting, tunnel and upper parts of the formation are in good condition but it was severed in the 1950s by the Stwlan dam road, and the lower end is obliterated.

The old drum house has collapsed but much of the drum gear is on site as well as parts of the steam haulage engine and the remains of the lorry chassis intended to be used as the final power source.

On the Cwmorthin side there are only traces of the gravity incline but the packhorse track at its foot; the landing platform (Cei Mulod) and some runs of steps are in good condition. The later haulage incline is visible with some parts of its motorcar engine.

The upper incline from the highest adit is in fair condition and at the higher level (Floor 3) are the ruins of some of the early dressing sheds, the upper mill and barracks. The main mill on Floor 6 is much degraded, but there is an interesting under-floor tailrace

The stone-embanked reservoir, with its double dam, trapping water in a saddle above the site is a nice feature.

Most of the adits, from 2 down to 8 are open and at the top of the site workings break out. There are relics of the underground ropeway, that was used in the final small-scale working. The roof is unstable and falls are continuing, so entering is most unwise. There are several outlying trials to the southwest and another alongside the main incline. [4]

Section 9
NORTH MEIRIONNYDD

General
This area has a large number of small, ephemeral, and often ancient quarries working isolated outcrops. Some, although within the old county boundary, are economically allied to Denbighshire, so are included in North East Wales [Section 13]. The Llan Ffestiniog quarries and LLANFAIR were underground, the others are almost all open workings, few were mechanised. The long-established village of Llan Ffestiniog was augmented but no significant communities were created.

LLANFAIR is open to the public with informative displays. There are few artefacts to be seen at the others, but many offer an interesting insight into working methods, often in remote but scenically rewarding locations.

Transport
Most were far too small to call for any organised system of transport, some carted, and there are several well constructed access roads to be seen. Some used packhorses and some, doubtless, man-carried.

Those in the Llan Ffestiniog area carted to the Dwyryd, later they used the 1868 2'g. Ffestiniog & Blaenau Railway and after 1882 the GWR Bala-Blaenau branch that substantially occupied its roadbed. The GWR which south of Trawsfynydd was lifted in 1961, may be readily traced much of the way along the spectacular stretch of hillside ledge until, after the fine Cwm Prysor viaduct, it was incorporated into the main road. From there it may be followed until its tracked is drowned in the Trewyryn reservoir. South of Treweryn it can be discontinuously traced to its junction with the Llangollen-Dolgellau line south of Bala.

On the coast Llanfair had its own nearby shipping point before the arrival of the Cambrian Railway in 1868.

1]	SH577305	Bryn Bugeiliaid
2]	578307	Nodddfa
3]	580288	Llanfair ** Visitor Centre
4]	590266	Coed y Llechau *
5]	593252	Pantgwyn *
6]	597243	Brydir
7]	649268	Graig Uchaf
8]	681320	Moel Y Gwartheg
9]	681408	Cae'n y Coed *
10]	684336	Cefn Clawdd
11]	684344	Ffridd Llwyd
12]	694342	Muriau Bychan
13]	713421	Y Cefn
14]	718384	Braich Ddu **
15]	719412	Bron y Rhiw
16]	728328	Gelli Gain
17]	728413	Cwm Cynfal
18]	728414	Bron Goronwy *
19]	729402	Hafod Fawr
20]	729433	Carters
21]	730445	Chwarel Llew Twrog *
22]	731436	Sarn Helen
23]	732316	Bedd Porus
24]	732423	Brynglas **
25]	732448	Clogwyn Garw
26]	735431	Drum **
27]	736446	Cwm Teigl *
28]	742444	Y Garnedd
29]	744428	Foelgron *

30]	750384	Moel y Croesau
31]	751438	Nantpistyll Gwyn *
32]	754416	Moel Llechwedd Gwyn
33]	754424	Croes y Ddwy Afon
34]	757304	Tai Cynhauf
35]	763388	Conglog
36]	776414	Serw *
37]	786396	Chwarel Llechwedd Deiliog
38]	806376	Cefn Glas
39]	811398	Tai Hirion
40]	848362	Fridd y Gloddfa
41]	862291	Tŷ Mawr
42]	875258	Aran *
43]	897330	Coed Cerrig Hwdion
44]	915407	Wernfawr
45]	921371	Tyn y coed
46]	937326	Moelfryn
47]	944338	Bued y' Fridd
48]	946341	Gelli Grino
49]	959208	Afon Hirddu
50]	959343	Dolfeirig.
51]	965250	Afon Nadroedd
52]	969243	Nant Alltforgan *
53]	973353	Rhiwaedog
54]	974361	Llandderfel
55]	975315	Nant y Sarn
56]	985348	Cletwr *
57]	987328	Afon Clwtwr
58]	995341	Queens *
59]	997314	Foel Cwm Sion Lwyd
60]	SJ051346	Carnedd y Ci
61]	052336	Cwm Tywyll

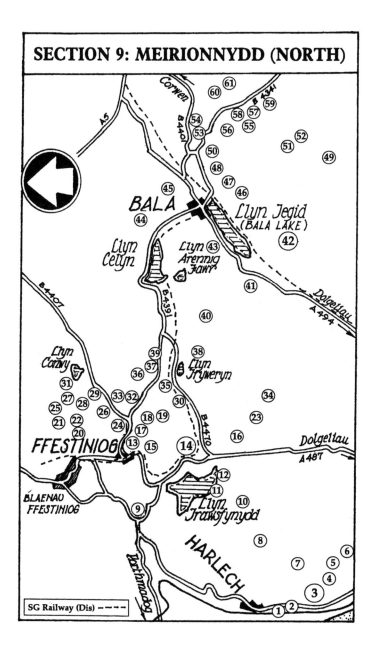

SECTION 9: MEIRIONNYDD (NORTH)

SG Railway (Dis) — — — —

AFON CLWTWR SH987328 HAFODLAS
Small. **Remains.** Flooded pit, traces of buildings, access track. [57]

AFON HIRDDU SH959208
Tiny open working. **Remains.** Excavation and access track. [49]

AFON NADROEDD SH965250
Trial? **Remains.** Collapsed adit in forestry. [51]

ARAN SH875258
Very small, 18th century open working, later some underground.
Remains. Open workings into a steeply dipping exposure. Vestiges of shelters, lower down there are two adits, the larger one open but flooded. The access track is readily traceable to near the quarry. [42]

BEDD PORUS SH732316
Named for the nearby Roman grave, some slate won here
Remains. Working face. [23]

BEUDY FFRIDD SH944338
Tiny early working. **Remains.** Excavation only. [47]

BRAICH DDU SH718384 HENDRE DDU **Working quarry do not enter.**
A shallow, dispersed working that, exploiting the Cambrian series, had a name for producing a good coloured slate. Water powered mill (with Hunter saw). Finished product carted to the Dwyryd up to 1868 almost certainly the last quarry to use the river. When the Great Western Railway opened in 1883 a tramway was planned to the railway, but was built only to the site boundary,
  Some small-scale extraction into the 1980s, revived in

the early 2000s.

Slabs extensively used in neighbouring Gellilydan.

Remains. The site is disturbed by later operations, besides the contemporary building; there are the ruins of a mill with wheel pit, a barracks and some other buildings, including a possible earlier mill. A notable feature is the rough slab causeway, with an interesting bridge that carried the tramway to a loading point on the road. [14]

BRON GORONWY SH728414 CHWAREL OWEN SIONM CHWAREL BRYN LLECH

Underground working producing slab and roofing slate on a small scale.

Remains. Ruins of a tiny mill possibly for a hand powered circular saw. Vestiges of a forge. Tip and access track encroached on by road widening.

Underground, a tunnel, partly worked out to bank, leads to chambering. Later downward working in this tunnel left inner workings isolated. [18]

BRON Y RHIW SH719412 BRON ERW

Small underground working with 2 tandem adits, possibly never had any buildings. **Remains.** Collapsed adits. [15]

BRYN BUGEILIAID SH577305

Trial? **Remains.** Much overgrown face. [1].

BRYNGLAS SH732423

Underground working with small interconnecting chambers, reducing in an adjacent steam mill. Later, working was at a higher level from the other side of the hill, but this work seems to have been confined to some extraction from a short, unfinished tunnel. Closed 1920's, reworked 1960s when a new entrance was made adjacent to the mill.

Remains. Ruins of the mill, some other buildings and the tramway and incline from the upper adit. The Upper tunnel which appears to have been driven from one of the several tiny earlier surface workings, comes to blind end with attempts at chambering only close to the entrance, near which are the remains of an 'A' frame. There is some chambering in the more extensive lower working and evidence of an abandoned attempt to roof up to the upper level. There are remains of the 1950s ropeway and cradle used to bring block out from underground.

There is a small reservoir and leat to supply the boiler. The access track defines a short-lived tramway to the Ffestiniog-Bala road. [24]

BYRDIR SH597243 & 595242
Nothing known. **Remains.** Excavation. [6]

CAE'N Y COED SH681408 LLECHRWD
Small working in a river gorge, the probable source of the Owen/Humphrey memorial of 1746 at Llandanwg church SH569283. An early example of a sawn slab and just possibly the very earliest example of power sawing. Later site of woollen mill.
Remains. Earliest digging in gorge abreast of the mill. (Extant, rebuilt and in re-use), higher up the gorge is the "main" quarry and above is a little- used working connected by a fine revetted tramway and incline (with pit for under floor sheave). Launder pillars and leat traces, and ceramic pipes probably for woollen mill era. Possible lower incline ends at a loading platform without obvious connection to the mill. [9]

CARNEDD Y CI SJ051346
Tiny hillside scratching. **Remains.** Slight traces of excavation. [60]

CARTERS SH729433
Very small. **Remains.** Excavation. [20]

CEFN CLAWDD SH684336
Tiny unmechanised pit working accessed by an adit that also drained it.
Remains. Pit & Adit, rubbish run and possible working area to South of the road. No buildings. [10]

CEFN GLAS SH806376
Putative site. **Remains.** Some digging in forestry. [38]

CHWAREL LLECHWEDD DEILIOG SH786396
Tiny roadside working. **Remains.** Virtually none. [37]

CHWAREL LLEW TWROG SH730445 MANOD MAWR
Despite the original name was a tiny underground working, active 1890s-1914 with 2-3 men. Llew "Twrog" worked it single handed in the 1920s.
Remains. Tiny dressing shelter, using a rock outcrop as a third wall. The 150-yards tunnel has produced surprisingly little rubbish and ends in 2 branches with some limited roofing shafts cut. There is some bar rail in situ, tenoned directly into sleepers. [21]

CLETWR SH985348
Open quarry developed into a deep pit working (possibly with underground workings off it?) with a tunnel connecting to a mill lower down the hillside. Finished product taken by cart to the main line railway. 1882 output 50 tons 6 men. Stated to have had a 12-hp steam engine and 10 saws. By 1886 output was down to 9 tons, and by 1890 was idle.
Remains. Site now largely in forestry. At the edge of the pit is a ruin of a small building and nearby another in re-use as a shooting lodge, both presumably dating from the

early open workings. The mills have been levelled but vestiges of a wheel pit and under floor water channels are to be seen. The access tunnel is blocked (dammed as a water source for Pale House hydro-electric plant). The cart way is partly traceable, a stopped up arch shows where it passed under the main road near the railway. [56]

CLOGWYN GARW SH732448
Trial. **Remains.** Excavation. [25]

COED CERRIG HWDION SH897330
Putative site. **Remains.** Possible excavation. [43]

COED Y LLECHAU SH590266
Hillside quarry on two levels with incline down to mill. **Remains.** Site much disturbed by later stone quarrying. There is a fine mill building with a nice graduated slate roof and other buildings in re-use. The incline has been quarried away. [4]

CONGLOG SH763388
Putative site of slate working
Remains. Was certainly a source of material for the construction of Cwm Prysor viaduct. The temporary tramway for this purpose is traceable. [35]

CROES Y DDWY AFON SH754424
Underground, worked sporadically on a small scale from around 1870 to the 1920s, material hauled out by incline to a water-powered mill. Finished product removed by cart. Re-opened in 1987 by local men. Later sold and briefly but vigorously untopped.
Remains flooded pit and structures from the 1990s re opening. [33]

CWM CYNFAL SH728413
Small underground trial, possibly metal, not slate.
Remains Adit & small building. Tunnel goes in about 30 yards and turns left and right to blind ends. [17]

CWM TEIGL SH736446 ALAW MANOD
Underground. In spite of its trifling scale it had a water-powered mill. Material carted to Ffestiniog.
Remains. Small mill that probably contained one saw table. Wheel pit, launder pillars and a neat slate lined leat leading down from a small reservoir on hill above. At a nearby trial is an interesting vaulted half-underground shelter. Adit collapsed, access track obvious. [27]

CWM TYWYLL SJ052336
Pit, very early, 1706? Possibly some underground, quite large for an entirely unmechanised site.
Remains. Water-filled pit, dressing shed, wall with curious cwtch, rubbish runs, stock of slates. (10x16 & 8x14). [61]

DOLFEIRIG SH959343
Putative site, may not have been slate. **Remains.** Excavation. [50]

DRUM SH735431
Pit/underground, sporadically worked from 1860's, originally a hillside working with hand dressing, but deepened into pits and developed underground following the opening of the Ffestiniog & Blaenau Railway. Peak output 1872 when 30 men produced 532 tons.
Remains. At the upper level, dressing sheds etc Ruined drum house at the head of the well-engineered incline and a nice mill building.

From one pit an incline descends underground into

water, but chambers are accessible from the southern pit. Some distance away are 3 collapsed adits with tramway formations, tips and weigh houses and on one level a curious building. The original access track to the site is traceable and the track to the mill is well defined, it appears to have been levelled as a tramway but there is no evidence that rails were ever laid. [26]

FFRIDD LLWYD SH684344
Putative site. **Remains.** In forestry. [11]

FFRIDD Y GLODDFA SH848362
Tiny open working. **Remains.** Excavation and ground disturbance. [40]

FOEL CWM SION LLWYD SH997314
Trial. **Remains.** Excavation. [59]

FOELGRON SH744428 PEN Y LLYN
Open quarry, from around 1850, later underground. No water was available at the quarry, so when a water-powered mill was erected it was sited at SH747423, alongside the main road and connected to the working by a tramway. Had some 30 men in the 1870s but by 1882 was down to 4. Closed 1890's revived in the early 1900s with 8 men.
Remains. Owing to subsequent granite working little to be seen directly connected to the slate operation. There is a fine 5-bay building which may have originally been for the slate operation. The tramway is defined by the present approach road. The mill, originally breast wheel driven, later oil-engined, was destroyed in the 1980s during landscaping work.

Alongside the tramway there is a curious structure with a wheel pit. [29]

GELLI GAIN SH728328
Putative site. **Remains.** Possible excavation. [16]

GELLI GRIN SH946341
Tiny open working. **Remains.** Excavation only. [48]

GRAIG UCHAF SH649268
Tiny open pit working. **Remains.** Excavation. [7]

HAFOD FAWR SH729402
Early 19th century trial. **Remains.** Lost in forestry. [19]

LLANDDERFEL SH974361
Very small. **Remains.** Ground disturbance. [54]

LLANFAIR SH580288 Visitor Centre
An almost totally underground working an excellent band of Cambrian series rock, from the mid-19th century, going down five floors. Closed in the 1870s slumpm re-opening at the turn of the century, Closed again during WW1. Between the wars machinery was installed for the crushing of stone and for the production of tiles, about 20 men being employed. Used as an explosive store in WW2.

Product was loaded onto the Cambrian Railways but earlier was shipped at Pensarn on the Afon Artro.
Remains. Several chambers are open to the public and some of the buildings have been reused in this connection. The buildings at the nearby Pensarn wharf may be re-builds of quarry-associated structures. [3]

MOELFRYN SH937326
Small pit working. **Remains.** Lost in forestry. [46]

MOEL LLECHWEDD GWYN SH754416 NANT Y PISTLL GWYN
Possible trial. **Remains.** Almost nothing. [32]

MOEL Y CROESAU SH750384
Tiny open pit. **Remains.** Only the pit. [30]

MOEL Y GWARTHEG SH681320
Small underground working, entirely unmechanised.
Remains. Two collapsed adits and a dressing area. There
is a tiny dug out stone lined shelter with storage niches,
which was possibly the sole shelter on this bleak, remote
site. No trace of a track, so. It is likely that slate was taken
away on the backs of the men who produced it. [8]

MURIAU BYCHAN SH694342
Trial? **Remains.** Possible excavation. [12]

NANT ALLTFORGAN SH969243
Hillside quarry on a steep site. **Remains.** Dressing sheds
and tips. [52]

NANT PISTYLL GWYN SH751438
Tiny **Remains.** Small flooded pit, holding down bolts (of
manual haulage and/or pump?) Vestiges of a dressing
shed. Narrow, shallow waste run, clearly intended as a
rail track to the road. [31]

NANT Y SARN SH975315
Putative site. **Remains.** Lost in forestry. [55]

NODDFA SH578307
Small hillside working. **Remains.** Overgrown. [2]

PANTGWYN SH593252 LLYN EINION
Small underground working.
Remains. Flooded tunnel, and collapsed adits, rubbish
runs and possible building traces. Adjacent other
tunnelling, probably metal trials. [5]

QUEENS SH995341
Small open working, with possibly some underground.

Remains. Flooded pit. Building ruins, wheel pit, Site in forestry. [58]

RHIWAEDOG SH973353
Small open working
Remains. Face and rubbish runs. Drain under road may indicate an underground trial. [53].

SARN HELEN SH731436
Underground, trial only? **Remains.** Adit to a small flooded chamber. [22]

SERW SH776414 MIGNEINT, NANT DERBYNIAD
A small probably very early unmechanised pit, carted to the Ffestiniog - Bala road by a track way.
Remains. Two small dressing sheds, one of which has a neat little storage alcove. Another structure appears to be a dwelling, but has no trace of a fireplace, also some abutments for a possible haulage. The access road though well engineered in places, has partly sunk into boggy ground. [36]

TAI CYNHAUAF SH757304
Small pit, probably for vernacular use only. **Remains.** Pit. [34]

TAI HIRION SH811398
Trial. **Remains.** Small excavation. [39]

TŶ MAWR SH862291 BALA LAKE, TYDDYN LLYWARXH, GLANLLWYN
Pit working. **Remains.** Used as rubbish dump and landscaped. [41]

TY'N Y COED SH921371
Tiny pit. **Remains.** Almost nothing. [45]

WERNFAWR SH915407
Tiny pit working. **Remains.** Almost nil. [44]

Y CEFN SH713421 CEFN BODLOSGAD
Series of ancient shallow pits. **Remains.** Site now a golf course. [13]

Y GARNEDD SH742444
Tiny, underground. **Remains.** Collapsed adit and trimming waste. [28]

Section 10
MAWDDACH

General

This area comprises a number of quarries dispersed around the lower Mawddach and the Wnion valley, seeking to exploit occurrences, mainly of the Cambrian series. Most were small, some very small, but some of the less remote ones were of respectable size.

Some were handily sited but others, such as GLODDFA GWANAS were most improbably located. ARTHOG, HENDDOL, PENRHYNGWYN and a few others have substantial remains, the latter two include underground workings of some extent. Most of the rest were open quarries, with few remains, but all offer some insight into working methods.

Transport

Most of the quarries relied carting to the river to load onto barges for trans-shipment at Barmouth. In the case of CEFN GAM this involved the building of a considerable length of road, most of which survives. GLODDFA GWANAS reachedthe public road by an ambitious, still traceable zigzag cart track,. ARTHOG, small though it was, had its own tramway to a shipping point, later to the railway. TYDDYN SHIEFFRE had similar arrangements. HENDDÔL/GOLWERN had an incline system, which after 1868 enabled them to benefit from a short, level, cartage to the Railway.

1]	SH603191	Ffridd Olchfa
2]	605205	Egryn *
3]	605206	Hendre Eirian *
4]	619122	Henddôl ***

5]	620122	Panteinion *
6]	621122	Golwern ***
7]	621127	Friog
8]	625129	Bryn Neuadd
9]	631125	Cyfannedd *
10]	625131	Bryn Gwyn *
11]	628173	Llwyn Onn
12]	630135	Tyddyn Shieffre **
13]	639141	Tap Tŵr
14]	645245	Tanydarren
15]	650151	Arthog ***
16]	652152	Tyn y Coed *
17]	677176	Abergwynant
18]	678245	Cwm Mynach
19]	680256	Cefn Gam ***
20]	702184	Fridd Isaf
21]	704149	Penrhyngwyn **
22]	709198	Ty Nant
23]	717171	Rhiw Rhedyn Cochion
24]	718161	Tan y Gader
25]	720160	Bryn Rhug
26]	728160	Bryn Mawr
27]	732152	Pant yr Onnen
28]	738151	Idris
29]	741175	Fron Serth
30]	745151	Gau Graig
31]	749181	Groes Llwyd
32]	755175	Coed Fridd Arw
33]	756174	Pant Cra
34]	777195	Garth
35]	784233	Cae'r Defaid *
36]	798160	Gloddfa Gwanas *

SECTION 10: MAWDDACH

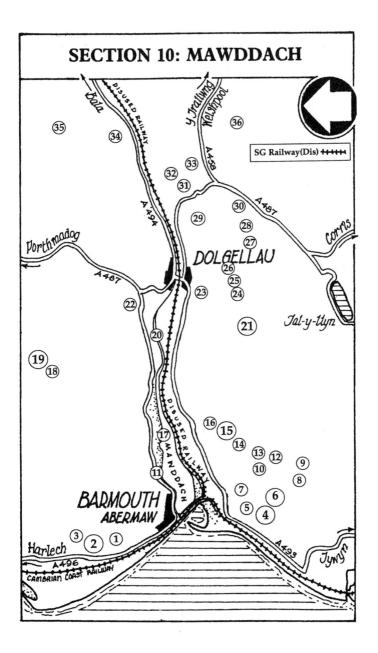

SG Railway(Dis) ┿┿┿┿┿

ABERGWYNANT SH677176

Putative site. **Remains.** Possible excavation. [17]

ARTHOG SH650151

Opened in the mid 18th century, it worked terraces connected by inclines.

A tramway took material across the main road, and through a short tunnel to a track,-way down to a jetty. This was replaced by an incline that was diverted to Garth siding on the Cambrian Railways in 1865. In 1868, a mill was built. Closed the following year, re-opened 1879-88.

Remains. On the terraces there are some much decayed vestiges of dressing sheds, drum houses, weigh houses etc. The tramway that was built to utilise TYN Y COED quarry for rubbish is a prominent feature.

At ground level recent bulk working has destroyed much but the dry stone tramway embankment to the mill is extant. A smithy and a possible a dwelling, stands. A caravan park adjoins the attractive, re-used mill. The short tunnel is open. The stone incline formation down to the railway is in good condition. [15]

BRYN GWYN SH625131

Small hillside working, several trial levels.
Remains. Excavations, some traces of buildings. [10]

BRYN MAWR SH728160

Putative site. On the farm whose name Quaker Rowland Elis took to Pennsylvania in 1657, which later became that of the ladies college.
Remains. Possible ground disturbance. [26]

BRYN NEUADD SH625129

A tiny pit, operated around 1860. **Remains.** Excavation. [8]

BRYN RHUG SH720160
Putative site. **Remains.** Possible ground disturbance. [25]

CAE'R DEFAID SH784233 ROBELL, TY UCHA
An underground working from which vast amounts of country rock but little slate, seems to have emerged although in 1897 it was offered for sale as having 'great potential'. Latterly owned by INIGO JONES [Section 3]
Remains. Two adits, the upper one chambered out to bank, shows little sign of profitable activity, the lower one that leads to limited chambering, does seem to have produced some slate. There are ruins of a small building, some tramway formations and a short access track. [35]

CEFN GAM SH680256
A series of shallow pits worked successively over a long period. The slate was of a good colour, but although it did not readily split, where it did, it made a tough flexible product.

Initially everything was hand dressed, at some time a water-powered mill was installed and later, water powered haulage. An attempt was made to avoid up-haulage by accessing the workings via a tunnel, but this project was not completed. Latterly there was some small scale re-working.
Remains. A number of buildings are on site including dressing sheds, a workshop/office and a mill with launder pillars adjacent. The alignment of a slot in the mill structure suggests that the mill power was used, or proposed to be used, for haulage out of the pit. To the south is the exit of the tunnel from the pit, remains suggesting that some slate was taken out this way and that the intention may have been to re-site the mill here.

In the pit are the shelters used in the final small-scale operations.

There is a further building, possibly a barracks and a fine manager's house, with a nice underground food store and a garden that still shows evidence of cultivation.

Except near the quarry the access road is in good condition, the lower section subsequently served the Diffwys metal mine. [19]

COED FRIDDARW SH755175 TYDDYN GARRET
Rough slatey block. **Remains.** Excavation only. [32]

CWM MYNACH SH678245
Small pit alongside track to CEFN GAM. **Remains.** Small quarry face. [18]

CYFANNEDD SH631125
Underground. Was, from around the 1840s, a metal mine, slate was found and worked 1870/80.
Remains. A possible cobbing floor, re-used for slate dressing, has a stock of small slates. Nearby are the crusher house and other metal-mining remains. The adit is open, and inside is a slate block awaiting haulage. [9]

EGRYN SH605205
Open quarry, underground working for a short time from 1896. Make carted to road at Egryn Abbey.
Remains. Two small buildings and possible powder house, run-in adit. [2]

FFRIDD ISAF SH702184
Trial. **Remains.** Ground disturbance. [20]

FFRIDD OLCHFA SH603191 PLAS CANOL
Very small hillside quarry. **Remains.** Excavation. [1]

FRIOG SH621127
Small. Underground. **Remains.** Run in adit and tip runs. [7]

FRON SERTH SH741175
Trial. **Remains.** Excavation only. [29]

GARTH SH777195
Possible trial. **Remains.** Ground disturbance. [34]

GAU GRAIG SH745151
Very early, remotely sited. **Remains.** Tiny working face. [30]

GLODDFA GWANAS SH798160 PENNANTTIGI
Small workings, producing a poorish slate, remotely situated on either side of a 2000 ft peak, sporadically worked from before 1840. Initial development was to the west of the summit, with subsequent working from the east. Besides roofing slate, slab was produced sawn with a hand-cranked circular saw. Material was sent out by pack-animal, later by a short incline to a most elaborately engineered cart road that was later extended right to the quarry.
Remains. To the west a tiny saw mill, an office/forge and a dwelling, the incline formation, partly tipped over, and a collapsed tunnel to the pit. To the north is a small barracks. To the east, at a lower level some dressing shelters and a collapsed tunnel to the pit. This tunnel has itself been worked for product. The two tunnels are the only places where there is any sign of (hand) drilling, so one assumes that explosives were not used for quarrying. Other than on the short incline there is no evidence of any rail ever having been laid. The road is a spectacular feature. [36]

GOLWERN SH621122 GOLEUWERN
A hillside quarry that following the opening of the railway in 1865 was developed into a substantial pit working, with a mill and several inclines, including one

to the road which replaced a steep track. Loadings were made at Fairbourne, taking over a siding laid down by McDougalls for housing development. A tramway link was planned but never built.

The pit was accessed by tunnels, the lowest being later blocked to flood it to provide a water source for a hydro-electric plant for Fairbourne village.

Success was short lived and by 1882 it was down to 4 men producing only 50 tons. United with HENDDÔL extraction continued to 1915, thereafter until 1928, its incline and plant were used by that quarry.

Remains. On the highest, earliest level are dressing sheds and a weigh house with the wagon platform still in situ. There is a nice flight of steps down to the next level built on a disused incline. At this level are further buildings and an under floor horizontal sheave, with three little tunnels which carried, respectively, the two ropes and the brake rod, thus enabling a rubbish run to pass between the sheave and the crimp of the incline. Nearby there is a stone slab covered culvert of unknown purpose.

On the next level down is a further rake of dressing sheds and a tunnel that divides to enter the pit at two points, the flooded pit forming the 'Blue Lagoon'. On this level are some unusual light gauge track and the remains of four Amos & Francis patent trimming machines made by De Winton & Co and of a saw table, but there is no trace of any building nearby to house them. From this level, the main exit incline goes down to the road. The drum house has collapsed but the fragments of the drum are lying in a wheel pit that may possibly never has been used. There is a further working level below this at the head of the original access track is a rake of dressing sheds and the lowest, now blocked, adit.

There are at least three fine stone archways on this site.

At road level, are some remnants of the hydro-generator building. [6]

GROES LLWYDD SH749181
Probably only a trial. **Remains.** Excavation. [31]

HENDDÔL SH619122
Underground, with some hillside working, commenced in 1865, it was rather more successful (410 tons 40 men 1883), than the neighbouring GOLWERN with which it was run in conjunction. After the latter closed in 1915 the GOLWERN incline and mill continued to be used until final closure in 1928. Although annual tonnages cannot have exceeded a few hundred, the combined working employed up to 80 men.

Remains. At the higher levels are 2 nice weigh houses, with fireplaces, for which the steeply sloping ground provides deep mechanism pits. On the next level down is a crude drum for a primitive incline to the level below, possibly from late, small-scale work. There are a number of dressing sheds and some well constructed buildings. From the lowest level a tunnel provides access and drainage for the workings, some chambering may be entered, various rails are situ, including Hughes bar rail. An intermediate level (2 floors up), gated, leads to some chambering. The highest level appears to have been a trial only. There is an airshaft.

The lowest incline seems to have originally gone right down to road level but later appears to have joined the GOLWERN incline presumably with some interchange arrangement. [4]

HENDRE EIRIAN SH605206
Small, entirely unmechanised pit working producing a green slate. Material removed by a cart track.

Remains. Tunnel to pit, some traces of small buildings. [3]

IDRIS SH738151
Underground offered for sale in 1848 as having 'water available' (Afon Aran). **Remains.** Run in adit, waste heap. [28]

LLWYNON SH628173
Putative trial. **Remains.** Possible ground disturbance. [11]

PANT CRA SH756174
Possible trial. **Remains.** Some excavation. [33]

PANTEINION SH620122
Small open quarry straddling the boundary between GOLWERN and HENDDÔL, probably predating both; **Remains.** Working face into which HENDDÔL underground workings break out. Dressing shed unusually combined with a weighbridge. [5]

PANT YR ONNEN SH732152
Small open working
Remains. Excavation and access track. The circular structure is a silage hopper built from scrap materials by Italian POWs during WW2. [27]

PENRHYNGWYN SH704149 CROWN
Originally a small, unmechanised open quarry, developed mid 18th century on several levels underground with a water powered mill.

Despite the large volumes of waste, production was only a few hundred tons p.a., which by 1883 had dropped to 54 tons, their planing machines having been sold off in 1875. Output was carted down to the nearby road.
Remains. Topmost level, old open working. Next level down, old working deepened into a pit with an incline,

possibly water powered, to bring material up from chambers below. There are some rubbish runs, two buildings with fireplaces and track way downhill.

The third level down has a collapsed adit, a forge and other buildings including a barracks, a drum house and, a little way off, a powder house.

Fourth level down has a rake of dressing sheds, a weigh house and alongside the river a well-engineered but partly collapsed tramway to a run-in adit.

On the lowest working level there are, another weigh house, a further rake of dressing sheds and a tramway to an adit with a recently installed door, that leads to some chambering.

At foot of incline is a large mill building formed by twice extending a pre-existing structure. (The second extension apparently never completed). The sparse mill-waste includes circular-sawn ends. At a lower level and not immediately adjacent, is a wheel pit (40' x 2'?), which apparently drove the mill by a belt. The leat for this wheel is clearly visible. Nearby are an office building and a dwelling. [21]

RHIW RHEDYN COCHION SH717171
Not slate? **Remains.** Excavation only. [23]

TANYDARREN SH645245
Trial c1900. **Remains.** Flooded tunnel 200' long, leads to a small chamber. Forms a garden feature. [14]

TAN Y GADER SH718161
Trial. **Remains.** Possible excavation. [24]

TAP TŴR SH639141
Trial. **Remains.** Excavation. [13]

TYDDYN SHIEFFRE SH630135

Open workings that reached a possible mill by a tunnel and a short incline. A further incline led down to a tramway to a shipping point at 633148, with a later branch to the railway near what is now Morfa Mawddach station. Closed by 1901.

Remains. The putative mill area is largely cleared but near the entrance to the now blocked tunnel are some buildings in agricultural re-use and the house of the quarry name is still in occupation and some of the houses on the main road clearly had quarry associations.

The tramway crossed the road near the war memorial, and its formations to the neat river-quay and to the railway is readily traceable, part of the former re-used as a road. [12]

TŶ NANT SH709198

Tiny open quarry. **Remains.** Excavation only. [22]

TY'N Y COED SH652152

A small, early working, later used as a dump for Arthog waste.

Remains. Very little, as so much material has been dumped in the old pits. Notable however is a dry stone tunnel some 50 yards long, built to prevent the ARTHOG material blocking an occupation road. Removal of tip material is constantly degrading this site. [16]

Section 11
DYFI

General

This area includes the Dyfi Valley (Other than Corris [Section 12]. Mostly a widespread scatter of tiny and optimistic diggings from the 1860s/70s boom, serious activity being confined to two areas. One exploiting the easterly continuation of the Corris veins in the upper Dyfi valley, around Dinas Mawddwy and Aberangell. The other was BRYNEGLWYS that created Abergynolwyn village, where the original quarry houses were individually served by a tramway system that delivered goods, and took away night-soil for sale to farmers – an extreme example of exploitation of a workforce!

On either side of the Dyfi estuary dispersed workings flourished during the late 1890s mini-boom, mainly producing slab for the Aberystwyth enamellers. Little activity post WW1.

Although apart from BRYNEGLWYS most quarries were small, a number such as MINLLYN have important relics. Work was generally underground.

Transport

The main port was Derwenlas, until the Cambrian Railways (Neé Aberystwyth & Welch Coast) line, enabled Aberdyfi to develop. Two quarries had their own tramway links to wharves on the river, the short Fron Goch line and the Cwm Ebol tramway, the last quarry-to-water line ever built. In fact the area represents the interfaces between horse v steam and sea v railway distribution. The Corris, Machynlleth and River Dovey Tramway (Later Corris Railway) was laid down in 1859 with no thought of using steam. When BRYNEGLWYS

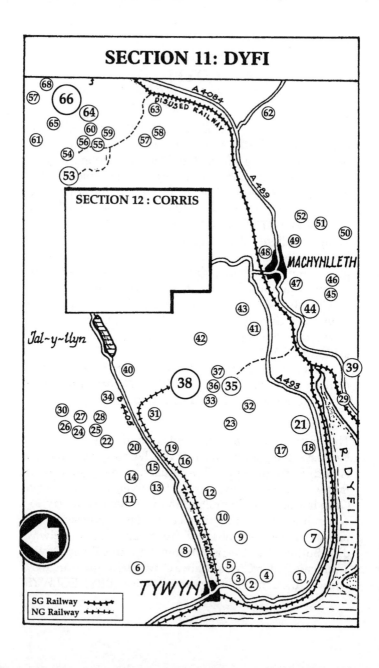

SECTION 11: DYFI

SECTION 12 : CORRIS

MACHYNLLETH

Tal-y-llyn

TYWYN

R. DYFI

SG Railway
NG Railway

opened the Talyllyn Railway in 1866 there was no question of it not using steam In addition until the mid 1860s every quarry rail line terminated at a shipping point, the Talyllyn served notice that great partnership between slate and the sea was ending by terminating at a main line railway interchange.

MINLLYN was served by the 1867 Mawddwy Railway, the sole standard gauge railway in north Wales to be primarily built as a slate route. The track bed is readily traceable. It had a most curious feeder, the little Hendre Ddu 2'g line, serving several quarries and farms in the Angell valley. Originally horse-drawn, it had a variety of lash-up locos before its late 1930s closure. Much of it now forms the valley road and most of the branches are readily traceable.

The little, readily traceable, Cwm Ebol tramway terminates at Llyn Bwtri (702996), a shipping point used by BRYNEGLWYS in pre-Talyllyn Railway times and an important shipping point at least since Roman times

ABERDYFI Grew as a slate port after the railway effectively closed Derwenlas in the 1860s. Like Barmouth, Pwllheli and other places it built and manned vessels to augment Porthmadog's insatiable demand for ships.

1]	SN600962	Yr Horon
2]	600998	Fronheulog
3]	SH603005	Ty Mawr
4]	SN604994	Caethle
5]	SH614010	Cwm Cynfal
6]	614073	Cwm Ych
7]	SN620964	Alltgoch **
8]	SH621040	Ffridd Cocyn
9]	623013	Braich y Rhiw

10]	625017	Rhyd yr Onnen *
11]	626092	Peniarth
12]	630029	Pandy
13]	630055	Perfeddnant *
14]	634070	Garth Fach
15]	643048	Nant y Mynach
16]	645030	Fridd Llwyn Hynydd
17]	SN650998	Drysnant *
18]	652972	Pant Eidal
19]	SH653043	Dôl Goch *
20]	664062	Tai Newyddion
21]	SN664972	Fron Goch *
22]	SH666084	Castell y Bere.
23]	SN666921	Cletwr
24]	SH669094	Gernos
25]	670087	Llechwedd
26]	671097	Pennant *
27]	675095	Tyn y Fach
28]	676091 etc	Cerrig y Felin.
29]	SN677885	Cwm Leri
30]	SH678098	Gwastad Fryn
31]	679055 etc	Foel Fawr
32]	682012	Rhaeadr *
33]	684045	Tarran Hendre
34]	685088	Nant yr Eira
35]	689017	Cwm Ebol **
36]	SN692947	Ty'n y Garth *
37]	SH693024	Afon Alice *
38]	695054	Bryneglwys *** F
39]	SN698961	Glandyfi **
40]	SH700089	Maes y Pandy
41]	706014	Pen y Bryn
42]	708043	Cwm Brechiau *
43]	709019	Gellellog *

44]	SN715991	Morben **
45]	717977	Llyfnant *
46]	724976	Coed Cefn Maes Mawr
47]	SH738002	Graig yr Ogof .
48]	746014	Machynlleth
49]	755005	Parc.
50]	SN755963	Cwm Rhaeadr
51]	763992	Coed Pant Bach
52]	SH763000	Pont Faen *
53]	799125	Hendre Ddu **
54]	818127	Maes Y Gamfa **
55]	822117	Gartheiniog **
56]	825119	Talmeuryn *
57]	828107	Esgair Angell.
58]	830095	Coed y Chwarel
59]	832125	Cwm Du *
60]	837143	Bwlch Siglen
61]	842185	Cwm Cowarch
62]	844031	Wynnstay Castle
63]	845102	Clipiau
64]	846136	Cae Baty **
65]	849144	Nant Minllyn
66]	852139	Minllyn **** H
67]	853157	Nant Dôl Hir
68]	855148	Targwrmoel
69]	872134	Pen y Graig

AFON ALICE SH693024 ALT RHOS FACH
Tiny underground working mid 19th century, early 20th century revival.
Remains. Run in adit, ruins of a mill (just one saw?), rubbish runs, tramway to a cart loading point with rail on ground [37]

ALLTGOCH SN620964

A small Underground working taking advantage of Aberdyfi's 1860s rise as a slate port, but did not long survive the late 1870s slump.

Remains. Much of site is wooded or disturbed, a C.G.I. building occupies the presumed mill site. The main adit leads to some chambering. Another adit some 70' lower leads to a shaft down from main adit, there is an upper adit but this seems to be lost in forestry. [7]

BRAICH Y RHIW SH623013

A small hillside quarry on two levels, material may have been carted to Talyllyn Railway.

Remains. Excavation only. [9]

BRYNEGLWYS SH695054

The largest quarry south of Blaenau Ffestiniog. Early 19th century surface workings on the Bryneglwys and Cantrebedd farms were developed underground in the 1860's by Lancashire men said to be diversifying due to a shortage of cotton during the American Civil War. They built the Talyllyn Railway, superseding pack horsing to Pennal or sledging down to the valley for carting to Aberdyfi. Much use was made of water for hauling, pumping and for mill drives and later also for air compression.

It had an extensive network of tramways and inclines.

Barrackers who, owing to the steep climb, included older Abergynolwyn men, lodged on the upper floors of two buildings, one the carpenter's shop the other a family dwelling and mess room. Most unusually, some men lodged with the manager.

Output reached 8000 tons pa in 1880 with manning nearing 300, which had halved by 1890, recovering somewhat up to the early 1900s, closing in 1910. An immediate post-WW1 reopening briefly touched 4000 tons but thereafter declined to final closure in 1952. It is doubtful if even at its peak, it ever showed a profit.

Remains. Regrettably, virtually all buildings have been demolished on this heavily afforested site, but much is traceable on the surface. The underground workings are most unsafe.

The first relics seen on approaching by the quarry road are the old Broad Vein workings and the tramway formation to the top of the Beudynewydd incline that led down to the Lower Mill area. Just beyond where the access road crosses the Llaeron stream are on the left the remnants of the 1920s compressor/generator house Nearby is a very fine slate-lined leat and launder pillars. Behind is a two-pitch incline formation down from the upper, Narrow Vein adits. To the right, are traces of the manager's house and other buildings Further on, near the collapsed opening of the 'Daylight Tunnel', so called because it ran to an open pit, were the Old & New mills and the two barracks at the foot of the Boundary incline.

Behind are the remains of the unique twin water-wheel haulage that powered the double chain incline (later a normal ramp incline) up from the main Narrow vein workings. Besides the wheel pits and drum housings there are rope tunnels and several maintenance and access passages.

On the Lower mill area at the foot of the Beudynewydd incline is the adit of the Long tunnel. Here were storage yards and the site of the exceptionally long 1880s turbine powered (with a steam back up) mill, which incorporating workshops and a smithy. The three mills had a total of more than 30 saws and dressers and several planers.

There are numerous adits and inclines, but many of

the buildings are lost in tree planting. Behind this is the now dry small Boundary reservoir and much higher is the breached dam of the big Llaeron reservoir. There are a number of trials and detached workings around the main site.

The tramway formation is readily traceable past the Cantrybedd cottages to the head of Cantrybedd incline. The drum house being set well back from the crimp, the brake was controlled by a long rod. A spectacular but much overgrown formation leads to the Alltwyllt incline with its drum house high on a rock shelf, to make end on connection with the Talyllyn Railway and is now incorporated into a designated walk.

The drum house of the Village incline straddled the Talyllyn Railway mid-way between the present Nant Gwernol and Abergynolwyn stations. Unfortunately only the drum of this unique structure, through which the crimp of the Village incline passed at right angles to the railway, is now extant. The incline is traceable down to Abergynolwyn village, where near its foot was a water powered writing slate factory. [38]

BWLCH SIGLEN SH837143
Trial. **Remains.** Run-in adit. [60]

CAE BATY SH846136
A small pit working, material being taken by a short self-acting incline to a dressing area.
Originally material was carted down Nant Blaen y Cwm but was later hauled up a shoulder of Foel Dinas by a tramway connecting to an incline down to MINLLYN. Closed 1911. .
Remains. There are several buildings on site but no evidence of waterpower. There are some artefacts including remains of a derrick for lifting out of the pit,

and the incline drum. The tramway to MINLLYN seems to have been light track laid directly on the ground, leaving little trace. At the summit (848137) there are vestiges of a building and some machine parts, but no hint of power source. It has been suggested that it was hand-winched with ropes connecting the two inclines so a down going load on one incline partly counterbalanced the up going load on the other. [64].

CAETHLE SN604994
Small, material carted to Tywyn.
Remains. Almost none, now a caravan park. [4]

CASTELL Y BERE SH666084
Possibly an ancient working. **Remains.** Excavation? [22]

CERRIG Y FELIN SH676091 & 678094
Possible trials. **Remains.** Some surface disturbance. [28]

CLETWR SN666921
Very small, possibly only a trial. **Remains.** Run in adit. [23]

CLIPIAU SH845102
Trial. **Remains.** Ground disturbance. [63]

COED CEFN MAES MAWR SN724976
Putative site. **Remains.** Excavation. [46]

COED PANT BACH SN763992
Possible trials. **Remains.** Run in adit. [51]

COED Y CHWAREL SH830095
A small slab open quarry, probably closed by then end of the 19th century. Used Hendre Ddu tramway. **Remains.** Site in forestry. [58]

CWM BRECHIAU SH708043
Underground, worked during 1870s boom
Remains. Dressing sheds. Circular sawn ends but no sign of a mill. [42]

CWM COWARCH SH842185
Crazily sited trial. **Remains.** Tramway formation, part built incline. [61]

CWM CYNFAL SH614010
Tiny open quarry little useful make produced. **Remains.** Pit. [5]

CWM DU SH832125
Unsuccessful opening during the 1870s boom.
Remains. Two pits, the lower has been roofed-up from an adit (collapsed) near which is a slab roofed hut and a dressing shed. [59]

CWM EBOL SH689017 RHOS FACH
Originally several pit workings connected by an incline to a dressing area. Later a water powered mill and a new, substantial stone incline were built. This latter incline was replaced by a tramway and a third, shorter incline. Originally product was removed by cart, later a tramway took material to a shipping point on the Dyfi. Output in 1883 260 tons 9 men.

Remains. There are ruins of an upper mill which had an unusual double roof and a low level water wheel, later replaced by a Pelton wheel, fragments of which are on site with traces of its underground feed pipe. To the east are vestiges of a steep incline that brought block to this mill from early workings. A later route along the top of the dam reaches the mill by a shallow incline. The final route being on the level via a cutting.

The present path that was the original exit route was

clearly railed as far as a remote-type drum house and a steep incline with slate sleepers that leads to the abutments of a bridge at the start of the exit tramway.

Up valley from the foot of this incline are the ruins of another mill that had an unusually high roof and a walled wheel pit alongside it. The layout and purpose of this second mill is unclear. A rough path joins the two mills, which may have been an intended incline. Although the exit tramway was 3' gauge, a gauge of 2'3" appears to have been used on site.

There are a number of trial adits further up the valley.

The tramway is easily traceable to the river at Llyn Bwtri (702996). There is the formation of an incline at 695009, near which is a small quartz mine and spillage shows that the tramway was also used to carry this product to the erstwhile level crossing near Pennal. [35]

CWM LERI SN677885 FELINFACH
Tiny working operated in conjunction with GLANDYFI in the late 19th century. Some reworking for aggregate in the 1930s
Remains. Excavation. Machine (crusher?) remnants and bases. [29]

CWM RHAEADR SN755963
Very small operated around 1880s/1890s, possibly for local use only.
Remains. Almost nothing, site disturbed by forestry road. [50]

CWM YCH SH614073
Possible trial. **Remains.** Traces of ground disturbance. [6]

DÔL GOCH SH653043
Worked by men laid off from Bryneglwys in 1910.
Remains. Small face and run in trial adit. [19]

DRYSNANT SN650998

Extremely small underground operation worked in the 1850s, material carted to the road at 668998. **Remains.** Spoil, collapsed adits. [17]

ESGAIR ANGELL SH828107

Very small. **Remains.** Excavation. [57]

FFRIDD COCYN SH621040

Possibly slate. **Remains.** Excavation only. [8]

FFRIDD LLWYN HYNYDD SH645030

Very small, possibly never produced.
Remains. Excavation only. [16]

FOEL FAWR SH679055 & 681057

Putative trials. **Remains.** Lost in forestry. [31]

FRON GOCH SN664972

Underground. Although a small operation it had a steam powered mill and its own shipping jetty. Originally an open working with a track to the beach, but since this route was cut by the 1866/67 railway construction, one assumes that it was underground by this time. Much money was spent during the early 1870s, including the building of the steam mill, but it closed following a disastrous winter frost of 1883/84. Later some trials for copper were made here.

Remains. The tiny mill with brick chimney is in re-use as a small factory. The cottages and a delightful chapel-like structure with cast iron window frames have made way for a modern rebuild. The slate-waste jetty is still useable, but the adit, which leads to a pit, is blocked by a fall. [21]

FRONHEULOG SN600998

Very small open working. **Remains.** Excavation only. [2]

GARTHEINIOG SH822117 HENDRE COED Y FFRIDD, MEREDYDD

Some work c1850, full development from 1870. As the pit deepened material was brought out through a 30-yard tunnel that itself became the basis for underground working. Later a second lower tunnel was used that also overcame their chronic flooding problems. A water wheel (later turbine) powered mill (6 saws, 3 planers) was supplied by a long leat from the Angell without any reservoir, causing problems that were eventually eliminated by a diesel engine.

Being on the Corris Narrow vein the slate did not readily split, but lacked the renowned Narrow vein quality, and outdoors tended to delaminate, so output was concentrated on billiards tables and mantelpieces, the "added value" of this latter market being enhanced in 1920 by installing an enamelling oven.

Like most slab producers a great deal of sawn-ends and other waste was sold as building block. Connected to the Hendre Ddu Tramway.

Remains. Large pit worked into overhangs. Both upper and lower adits are blocked. There are traces of a tramway formation and incline that served the upper adit. A tramway formation can be traced from the lower adit past some machine bases (WW2 forestry machinery), to the mill building (In re-use). This building, originally open-sided, has line- shaft brackets. Behind it is pipe work for the turbine. There is a massive buttress at one end that is modern. The adjacent forestry house is on the site of the quarry manager's house. Opposite is the site of the enamelling building. The tramway link is unclear owing to forestry road construction. [55]

GARTH FACH SH634070

Possibly not slate, at most a trial.
Remains. Excavation only. [14]

GERNOS SH669094

Trial? **Remains.** Slight excavation. [24]

GLANDYFI SN698961 CARDIGAN SLATE WORKS,
CWMERAU, CWMERE

A small working, opened in the 1870s, closed 1910,
mainly producing slab mainly for the Aberystwyth
enamelling industry, that at its turn of the century peak
used over 1500 tons per annum. The mill that had saws, a
planer and a lathe was originally water powered, later
converted to steam. Output 1889 319 tons. Material was
trammed across the river Melindwr to a cart loading
point.
Remains. Quarry area with trial adit, mill in reuse,
abutments of bridge and rubbish runs. [39]

GRAIG YR OGOF SH738002

Small open working. **Remains.** Almost nothing no sign of
the reputed tramway. [47]

GWASTAD FRYN SH678098

Possible trial. **Remains.** In forestry. [30]

GYLLELLOG SH709019

Pit latter 19th century, largely unproductive
Remains. Pit with tunnel access. Dressing sheds, bridge
abutments. [43]

HENDRE DDU SH799125

Developed in the 1850s out of pre-existing trials that had
sought the Corris Narrow vein coming through from
RATGOED [Section 12] to this then inaccessible site.

Ultimately worked on 4 levels, with a 50-hp. water

turbine, mill said to have had 18 saws, 10 planers & a Jenny Lind polisher, although if all were actually installed is unclear. Steam engine backup was planned, but as outputs were disappointing, (878 tons, 31 men, 1883). A barracks (for 22 men), 6 cottages and a manager's house were built. A 10-ton steam crane was used presumably to lift block at the initial open workings. Product that was almost exclusively slab, some in very large sizes and some destined for enamelling; went out via the Hendre Ddu Tramway. (Opened by 1874). Uusually the barracks had a woman cleaner/supervisor

Worked up the late 1930s, not long before closure a steam crane was bought from DOLBADAU quarry in Pembrokeshire [Section 14] and after a long and arduous journey it was wrecked when it was first used!

Remains. Site mainly covered by forestry, workings on 4 levels, including an early open pit. The mill area is cleared but there is a fine 2-storey office building in re-use and the foundations of a number of other structures. There are three adits, the lowest; at mill level has some chambering. Above there is a second adit, flooded. Above is a third adit that leads to some chambering and to open workings. Above is the early pit. At each adit level there are massive spoil heaps, notable for the size of many of the blocks. There are two reservoirs at the top of the site (one dry).

Tramway formations, traceable in forestry lead from each level to an incline down to the mill. There is an isolated trial adjacent to the head of incline. The exit incline down to join the Hendre Ddu tramway is now a road with, part way up vestiges of the barracks, Hendreddu Terrace. [53]

LLECHWEDD SH670087

Possible trial. **Remains.** Ground disturbance. [25]

LLYFNANT SN717977

Small unmechanised underground working, material carted down valley.

Remains. Little apart from the adit itself and traces of one small building. Some rail on the ground. There is a small underground trial at 718975 and an open working at 723975, both possibly associated with this site. [45]

MACHYNLLETH SH746014

Local source on an outcrop.

No remains. Obliterated when the station yard was extended. [48]

MAES Y GAMFA SH818127

Modest pit working but with a quite elaborate mill. Originally material was brought down by incline to the mill, but as the working deepened blocks were run out on the level via a short tunnel. Opened in 1889 and unusually made good slab products such as mantelpieces, billiards tables, urinals etc, out of the less favoured Broad vein, employing 20 men. .

Considerable ingenuity was required to obtain water for the mill wheel that lack of head had to be in a very deep pit. Turbine(s) were used, but whether for mill drive or air compression is not known. Closed 1914 (then down to 3 men). An incline led to a branch of the Hendre Ddu Tramway.

Remains. The only site in the valley to have substantial surface remains. Ruins of a mill (stone robbed to re-build Maes y Gamfa farm?). There is clear evidence of leats and rock-channelling to feed a turbine. There are several other ruinous buildings and a drum house of substantial block construction that had a horizontal sheave, possibly it was a single acting table incline, this incline being redundant when the pit was accessed by tunnel. There is a weighbridge with no masonry, (it may have been in a timber-framed structure). Evidence of the use of a channelling machine. (The rock was particularly hard here). There are parts for ornamental fireplaces in the mills area. At the head of the exit incline is a dwelling now in agricultural re-use. There are some traces of slate sleepers on the tramway formation between the mill area and head of incline. There are rails and incline rollers in the river. [54]

MAES Y PANDY SH700089
Possible trial. **Remains.** In forestry, possible ground disturbance. [40]

MINLLYN SH852139 DINAS MAWDDWY, CARLYLE.
Ancient workings commercially worked from the early 19th century, open quarry developed underground from the 1840s employing 160 men but production never reflected the employment levels. Material was reduced in a mill (initially water-wheel, then Pelton, with steam back-up) and taken by a tramway to an incline down to the valley floor. This mill had 3 dressing machines as well as 3 saws, and possibly also planers. thus pre-dating any such Integrated Mill arrangement at Blaenau Ffestiniog.

Later a large mill was built at valley floor level which reduced material from both the main workings and the several other dispersed workings. It was described as having "40 Machines", (Saws and planers but no dressers?) A further short tramway took finished slate to the nearby terminus of the Mawddwy Railway. All the tramways in site were of 2'4^{1}/4" ("half standard") gauge, an unusual dimension also used in the Glyn Valley.

249

[Section 13]. On the far side of the main road, houses were built in a street that was to have run through to Dinas Mawddwy creating a unified village. Suspended temporally several times, finally closed in 1925, when manning was down to almost 'care and maintenance' levels

Remains. On the upper mills area is the very ruinous mill itself with a contiguous compressor house, workshops, weigh houses etc and traces of an extensive tramway network. The chimney is standing and in the adjacent boiler-house wall is the flue damper. The feed pipe for the Peltonr wheel is in situ. There is a run of pillars for compressed air piping. There are the formations of the long incline which brought material from Cae Abaty and the two shorter ones from the early open workings. A fine stone lined tramway tunnel leads through a pit to the main adit. Above this pit, near an incline head is a crane base. Underground there is extensive, but seemingly almost random chambering. There are several winches and much chain etc as well as rail track. Near a flooded working are remnants of a steam crane. There is much evidence of pillar robbing and also of the use of channelling machines.

From the mills area, a tramway leads past some other buildings, small workings and an airshaft, to the head of the main incline down to the lower mill. Off this incline there are, partially lost in forestry, tramways to other adits. One adit is open leading to a large chamber. This has some chains etc and the fallen timbers of a bridge high above.

The lower mill is in re-use; Most of the station structures are intact. [66]

MORBEN SN715991

Flourished towards the end of the 19th century as a supplier, via the Cambrian Railways to the enamelling works at Aberystwyth.

Remains. Working face, investigative tunnel, drum house ruins of incline to the road. Although dealing with slab neither sawing facilities nor sawn ends have been identified. The office and the two-roomed powder house (in exceptional condition) post date quarry activity, being used as a store by Corris and other quarries. [44]

NANT DÔL HIR SH853157

Trial. **Remains.** Blocked adit. [67]

NANT MINLLYN SH849144

Trial. **Remains.** Collapsed adit. [65]

NANT YR EIRA SH685088

Possibly only a trial. **Remains.** Excavation only. [34]

NANT Y MYNACH SH643048

Trial? **Remains.** Traces of excavation. [15]

PANDY SH630029

Very small hillside quarry, possibly only producing block. **Remains.** Quarry area. The adjacent building was a fulling mill. [12]

PANT EIDAL SN652972

Small open working. **Remains.** Site a chalet development. [18]

PARC SH755005

Trial? **Remains.** Excavation only. [49]

PENIARTH SH626092 AFON DYFFRYN

Possibly could have been slate trial. Also at 625089 & 624084, tiny scratchings with the possibility of carting down the Dysynni valley by existing roads.

Remains. Excavations and rubbish run with a trace of one small building near the main site. [11]

PENNANT SH671097

Small. possibly only a trial. **Remains.** Excavation only. [26]

PEN Y BRYN SH706014 COED RHONWEDD, CYLLELLOG, CAE GRAIG

A small working, material being taken down a short incline to the road, where there may have been a mill. Later material was removed on the level by a tunnel. Active around 1880, but may have been much earlier. Material carted to Pennal.

Remains. Vestiges of incline and drum house, the tunnel is collapsed to surface for most of its length. Any buildings there may have been are obliterated by a forestry road. [41]

PEN Y GRAIG SH872134

Trial? **Remains.** Traces of digging. [69]

PERFEDDNANT SH630055

A small unmechanised hillside working deepened into a pit accessed by a short tunnel. Output conveyed to the main road by a cart track.

Remains. Pit and tunnel. [13]

PONT FAEN SH763000

Pit working, mill with five saws and two planers.

Remains. Flooded pit. The mill area has been entirely cleared and a modern house built. Material was clearly originally moved across the road on the level. Not clear if there was any later, lower level access to avoid up hauling and pumping. Tip runs are surprisingly long [52]

RHAEADR SH682012 TALGARTH

A tiny underground working lodged in a small gorge, operating 1865 – 1905 about 6 men...

Remains. Just upstream of a collapsed adit is a small building possibly a mill for one water powered saw. Slight vestige of a second building and a rubbish run with some rail in place. There is also a massive square stone structure of unknown purpose.

Above the site are two breached dams in tandem. [32]

RHYD YR ONNEN SH625017 BRYNHYFWYN

Small underground working probably operating in the late 1860s, may have been worked in 1910 during the temporary closure of BRYNEGLWYS. May have used the Talyllyn Railway. One time associated with LLWYNGWERN [Section 12]

Remains. Nothing on the surface. The lower adit has collapsed, the upper adit is open but blocked inside by falls. There is a 'Jwmpah' jammed in a shot hole. [10]

TÂI NEWYDDION SH664062

Trial only? **Remains.** In forestry. [20]

TALMEURYN SH825119

A small underground working, active up to the early 1900s, later produced slab for INIGO JONES [Section 3]. Was worked on a part-time basis.

Remains. Early open quarry, below is an adit leading to two chambers containing split slab. Dressing shed and some bridge rail and vestiges of bridge abutments of the incline to the MAES Y GAMFA branch of the Hendre Ddu Tramway. [56]

TARGWRMOEL SH855148

Small open quarry, (associated with MINLLYN?)

Remains. Site now occupied by Water Company's installation. [68]

TARREN HENDRE SH684045
Tiny on a very steep slope
Remains. Excavation with collapsed adit roofing up to it. Some rail used, some trimming waste. Trials at 681048 (site of forestry hut), 684047 (in forestry) and 686049 (source of hardcore) may have been associated. [33]

TŶ MAWR SH603005
Small open working, Local use only? **Remains.** Shallow excavation. [3]

TY'N Y FACH SH675095
Tiny hillside quarry, possibly very early, for local use only. **Remains.** Excavation only. [27]

TY'N Y GARTH SN692947
Pit working producing coarse slab active 1860s-80s
Remains. Pits on either side of the road, northern one accessed by a tunnel. Access to southern pits seems to be lost. Nearby house is much later. [36]

WYNNSTAY CASTLE SH844031
Small underground working.
Remains. Two run-in adits in forestry. [62]

YR HORON SN600962
Two small hillside workings, mainly working shales for building, may have produced roofing slate at an early date.
Remains. Pits. [1]

Section 12
CORRIS

General

This area includes those quarries on the route of the Corris Railway and its feeder lines. Corris was renowned for the quality of its Narrow Vein slab, but transport came too late for it to achieve its true potential.

Besides Corris itself " The Mini Blaenau", there were several single industry slate settlements such Aberllefenni, Upper Corris and Ceinws, whilst Machynlleth provided a technical and commercial focus.

As in most areas, the archaeology has suffered from landscaping, but although many surface remains have gone, much of great interest survives.

Transport

The old road along the eastern side of the Dulas valley and up the Llefenni valley to Cross Foxes seemed, as if with deliberate intent, to avoid all sites of major slate potential other than ABERLLEFENNI. The present main road, built in the 1830s, enabled development of BRAICH GOGH/GAEWERN but it was not until 1859 that the 2' 3" gauge. horse/gravity Corris, Machynlleth and River Dovey Tramway brought the economies of rail, but both road and rail each came a generation later than those at Blaenau. Steam in the form of the Corris Railway, came in 1879, just as slate began its decline.

The Cambrian Railways arrived at Machynlleth in 1867. When the Corris Railway replaced the CM&RD it terminated at Machynlleth station, effectively closing the port of Derwenlas, the "Rotterdam" of Montgomeryshire, a long-established shipping point for slate and lead.

The Corris Railway closed in 1948, but most of its

SECTION 12: CORRIS

(DISUSED)
- - - - HORSE TRAMWAY
++++++ NARROW GUAGE
STEAM RAILWAY

|_____|
0   1 MILES

route is obvious from Aberllefenni station, denoted by its fine cantilevered-step access, all the way to the sidings site at Machynlleth. There are several stations adapted as bus shelters and one fine house, still in occupation. Vestiges of the branches to ERA and LLWYNGWERN can be seen

At Corris itself the station stables house a small museum. The line operates from Corris to the engine shed at Maespoeth about $1/2$ mile distant. It is planned to reach Pantperthog.

Beyond Machynlleth station, the bricked up arch where the main road passes under the railway marks the path of the original tramway, which can be intermittently traced to the terminus at Cei Ward [995710], where several port buildings are in re-use.

Of the three Corris Railway feeder lines, the most important was the Upper Corris Tramway whose track bed partly forms a footpath along the western bank of the river from Upper Corris to Corris. At Corris it passed close alongside the main road in a gully between the road and houses. Through what is now the Braich Goch hotel car park, it runs alongside the road the to Maespoeth junction.

The extension to Tir Stint ironstone mine (763164, was never started, but the formations for the planned extension to GLYN IAGO are extant.

The most interesting branch is from RATGOED. Most of it remains, partly as a track, partly as a forestry road. The remaining branch was the short line from the ABERLLEFENNI quarry to the mill. It ran alongside the road and was in use, (latterly tractor powered) until the 1970s.

1]	719072	Glyn Iago *	
2]	721058	Darren ***	
3]	725064	Hafoty	
4]	729104	Dolffanog	
5]	730082	Mynydd Tyn y Ceunant *	
6]	732088	Cwm Dylluan *	
7]	733070	Tarran Cadlan	
8]	735092	Tap Ddu	
9]	735099	Pen y Garreg *	
10]	738087	Ty'n y Berth **	
11]	744088	Tyn y Ceunant **	
12]	745066	Goedwig West	
13]	745086	Gaewern **	
14]	746093	Abercwmeiddaw ***	H
15]	747030	Coed y Ffridd *	
16]	748073	Bryn Llwyd Uchaf	
17]	748078	Braich Goch *	H
18]	749029	Afon Dulas	
19]	750029	Dolydderwen	
20]	750085	Afon Deri	
21]	751038	Glandulas	
22]	752063	Goedwig	
23]	752082	Abercorris (Trial)	
24]	753071	Bryn Llwyd	
25]	754089	Abercorrts ***	
26]	757045	Llwyngwern **	I
27]	757121 etc	Fron Fraith	
28]	759059	Esgairgeiliog Mill **	
29]	759115	Hengae *	
30]	760054	Rhiw'r Gwreiddyn *	
31]	760064	Era *	
32]	760081	Pandy	
33]	761103	Cwm yr Hengae	
34]	761128	Foty y Waun	

35]	763132	Mynydd y Waun	
36]	765108	Wenallt ***	
37]	766062	Cwm Gloddfa	
38]	768091	Matthews Mill	
39]	768103	Aberllefenni ****	H
40]	775114	Ffynnon Badarn	
41]	777107 etc	Cymerau *	
42]	781126 etc	Dolgoed	
43]	787119	Ratgoed ****	

ABERCORRIS SH754089 CWMODYN

Opened in the 1860s, output at the turn of the century was around 1000 tons pa with about 40 workers, operated on a reduced scale up to 1950s. Consisted of two hillside workings developed into pits accessed by tunnels, with some later underground working. An incline took output to a water-powered mill some 400' below. A later mill was oil engine driven.

Remains. At incline head, one adit to a pit has been tipped over; another leading to underground workings is lost in forestry. One adit at a level above the head of is incline open, leads to some chambering, with a shaft for lowering material to the level below. A remote type drum house is at the top of the main incline with a brakeman's shelter on the crimp. There is a small reservoir, partway down and some rail and rope are on the ground.

Only traces remain of the original mill. The later, galvanised roofed, mill has collapsed. It contained 4 saws a planer but only one dresser, reflecting its mainly slab product (being on the Narrow vein.). Nearby, are a small ruined building and a messing hut. At a lower level, there are an office and dwellings in fair condition. The incline connection to the Upper Corris tramway is traceable, the abutments of its bridge over Afon Deri, adjoins the present footbridge. [25]

ABERCORRIS SH752082
Trial. **Remains.** Collapsed adit [23]

ABERCWMEIDDAW SH746093
A Broad vein working, from 1849? In 1882, 188 men produced 4173 tons. Material at first lowered by incline to a mill. As work developed material was brought out on the level by a locomotive worked tramway.

When workings deepened into a pit, rubbish up-haulage and pumping were avoided by driving a tunnel from pit bottom to emerge below the mill. An incline raised good block to the mill, while rubbish continued along a shelved tramway that crossed the public road to a new tipping area. Finished product went down a short incline and over a bridge to the Upper Corris Tramway. Some underground development was made from within the tunnel. Closed in 1905, but some small scale working continued into the mid 1930s.

Remains. Instability of the massive retaining walls of the tip on which the mill was sited, forced radical landscaping in the 1990s, losing much of interest.

At the quarry itself the prominent feature is the "Corris Binocular" twin tunnels, during experiments with a boring machine. Rail hangs where these bores have been subsequently partly quarried away. The right-hand bore is only about 10 yards long the left-hand about 80 yards. There is a trace of another machine boring higher up. Two trepanned discs are to be seen at the turn off the main road at Upper Corris.

At the south-western corner of the pit is the 250-metre drainage/access tunnel. Some slate sleepers are on the ground, from this tunnel a strike tunnel runs for some 120 metres to a fall.

The original tram road formation at mills level passes some buildings (including a chimnied boiler house), now in re-use, that were a new, but apparently unused mill complex. Opposite is a lavatory served by the nearby leat.

Landscaping has left no trace of the 29-saw, 15-dresser & 1-planer mill. Below this mill area, adjacent to the tunnel mouth, is the pit for the 50' wheel with part of the gearing and line shaft, which was some 15 feet below mill floor level. The up haulage incline, serving the access tunnel is alongside and it is clear how the wheel pit was enlarged to provide extra power for it. . On the far side of the mills-level tramway is the base for the return sheave. Oddly this was listed in 1893 as a water balance and other evidence suggests that besides the 30-hp Robey steam engine back up for the mill there was another for the incline built by Ellis of Salford, who also supplied the vertical-boiler locomotive.

The fine exit incline dropping down between high retaining walls, the revetted platform for the rubbish tramway from the tunnel and the famous cantilevered steps, have all been lost.

Above the mills area there are some small, early workings with possibly an incline down. [14]

ABERLLEFENNI Comprising CEUNANT DDU SH766099, HEN GLODDFA SH765101 & FOEL GROCHAN SH768103.
Slate has been worked here from at least the late 15th century, concentrating latterly on the production of world-class slab.

From the mid 19th century the near vertical Narrow vein was worked underground by a unique method is fully described in an 1882 paper by Sir Charles Forster, summarized by Richards in Slate Quarrying at Corris.

Tunnels were bored at about 60' vertical intervals and starting at the topmost tunnel working downwards, dropped extracted material into the next tunnel below.

Material was reduced in a mill on the hillside at CEUNANT DDU, then when work went underground there was a mill at FOEL GROCHAN, replaced in the late 19th century by a large mill at Aberllefenni village.

Rubbish disposal was a problem, when the capacity of the hillsides was reached, waste banks on the valley floor had to be created, reached by two water balanced inclines.

In 1883 158 men were employed turning out over 4800 tons.

The Aberllefenni tramway that connected the quarry with the mill remained in use until the 1970s, (although tractor powered since about 1950). It was thus the last survivor of the quarry tramways.

Remains. CEUNANT DDU is much degraded. At the top levels (1 & 2) there are exposed chambers and traces of possible inclines. On Level 3 there is the eroded trace of a connection with HEN GLODDFA. On level 4 there is scant trace of the original mill and on Level 5 remains of dressing sheds and the drum house (with all-wood drum)) at the head of the degraded incline down to 6 where there, is a nicely portalled adit, with some concrete bases adjacent, and buildings vestiges. The original route for carting out along the western side of the valley, is obvious. .

At the highest level of HEN GLODDFA is a dressing floor still with a stock of slate, also some rail & trucks and a complete set of cast iron parts for in incline drum (and the winch that raised them!) Alongside is the partly-built drum house and a dry stone anchorage for the pro-tem ropeway. At this level tere is a modern shaft and a fine access road for a 1970s abortive development. .

Immediately below, on Level 1, there are open workings and a reservoir. Level 2 has traces of a vertical shaft, and very fine slate water-troughing. Below at level 3, the lower limit of open quarrying a tramway runs to a remote-type drum house, set well back with extended brake control, and has an embanked tramway towards the south, to the head of a table incline that was possibly never completed. There are some vestiges of buildings. On Level 4 at the bottom of the table incline, an embanked track runs south to a curious drum house built into and truncating a steep incline down from Level 2. At this level there is an adit, open, with rails in situ and some building remains, undoubtedly the old main mill with. to the south a short exit incline.

Level 5, has the ruins of some dressing sheds, and the tramway formations,. Level 6 is built up on waste originating from its adit and also waste up-hauled on the adjacent water balance. Adit 7 is at valley floor level almost overwhelmed by waste. .

At FOEL GROCHAN. The two highest adits are hidden, the "Alma Cavern" spans 3 & 4, but 5,6,7 & 8 (at valley floor) are obvious. Little is to be seen of the incline progressively shortened as activity moved downwards, until finally it was single-acting, rubbish-balanced, just serving Level 7.

Underground, the working down from the highest level has produced a number of spectacular chambers, most breaking out to bank, theoretically there are 13, but bad rock and some haphazard working breaks the strict continuity. Below 8, there was a slant, now abandoned and flooded going down 50' to Drift Level, with work from the final downward working eventually extending over 100' below this. Thus the total vertical headroom approaches 800'.

Ships' steam donkey engines, run on compressed air were the standard haulage device underground

On the valley floor there is much disturbance from modern bulk working of the tip. The old office building and the modern compressor house stand, beyond them are the foundations of the mill and the water-powered compressor house. Little is left of the water balance and the cross-valley tramway. Nearby is the terrace - "Blue Cottages", now truncated and converted into a single residence.

The WENALLT reservoir up-valley was rebuilt to feed the hydro-compressor. There are two penstock towers, accessed by bridges partly made of bridge rail, to respectively control the drain and the feed-pipe.

At SH773106 the workings were accessed from the east, there is a Rushton crane that in the 1950s raised material from the back chambers. At a higher level is part of an old hand-winch that served the same purpose. A tractor hauled blocks to the mill on a trailer.

The reservoir to power the village mill is a nice feature with its slate leats and sluices. The dam carried the Ratgoed tramway. The mill that once had 20 saw-tables, has been re-equipped with modern machines, including several large diamond saws. There are also polishing and edging machines, some of which were brought from Caernarfon, when the Fletcher-Dixon works at Victoria dock closed in 1988. Outside in its own building is a large horizontal, multiple frame saw, (unique to the industry). The lower half of the central water wheel that protruded through the roof of the mill is still in place below the floor.

The mill remains in use and is one of the best equipped in the industry.

Aberllefenni Terrace was built and owned by the

quarry forming a very much "one industry" community. The present company office was the Post Office. The original chapel-like office survives (just).

An electricity plant, from 1920s, on the Nant Llwydiarth, once supplied the quarry and village. Some traces remain. [39]

AFON DERI SH750085
Trial, possibly 20th century.
Remains. Run in adit, vestiges of a hut. [20]

AFON DULAS SH749029
Underground trial **Remains.** Trace of possible adit. [18]

BRAICH GOCH SH748078 In Re-use Do not enter
This was the largest quarry in Corris itself. Due to a doubling back of the Narrow vein (the Appendix) it effectively worked two seams of exceptional slate. Very early users (1830s?) of sawing machines (Owen Owen hand cranked). The first mill was on the hillside. Later, material was brought, by a bridge over and also by a tunnel under, the old main road to an extensive mills area through which the Upper Corris tramway ran. Output in 1882 5858 tons pa, 187 men. Mainly produced slab, being able to make very large sizes. Latterly GAEWERN and TYN Y CEUNANT material was reduced in the mill. Abruptly closed in 1906, it survived into the 1970s under various owners.

Remains. The southern part of the site has been landscaped, obliterating the mills area and all traces of the workings and incline system of the southern workings (the main road now runs over the site of the mills). The present "King Arthur's Caverns" is at Level 6, the old mills level, above was the Level 5 adit and its attendant short incline and bridge. A little way up valley was the Vane's Level adit from where output was dropped by incline to mills level. The 1950s Vane's to 6 incline that superseded that was the last underground incline ever constructed in Wales The 2 levels below 6 have been flooded for many years.

On the surface the track bed of the rail connection to GAEWERN is traceable with some building vestiges.

Quarry housing on the line of the old main road is still in occupation. [17]

BRYN LLWYD SH753071
Very small, being worked in the early 1900s.
Remains. Ground disturbance, some levelling of site. [24]

BRYN LLWYD UCHAF SH748073
Trial on Braich Goch property.
Remains. An adit, open. [16]

COED Y FFRIDD SH747030
A small and early unmechanised working.
Remains. Pit with tunnel access (collapsed) Trimming waste but no buildings. [15]

CWM DYLLUAN SH732088
A small working in 2 pits, active in the 1850s and in the 1890s possibly with several periods of extended idleness in between, It suffered from lack of transport facilities which would have been solved had the projected extension of the upper Corris Tramway to GLYN IAGO been built.
Remains. Site mostly in forestry. There are the pits with possible underground investigation, traces of a tramway layout and rubbish runs and the extraordinarily massive stone-built incline with unusually sturdy remote drum house, as well as traces of few small structures. [6]

CYMERAU SH777107 etc. TROED YR ESCAIR

Opened on the 1860s, for most of its life ran in conjunction with RATGOED, whose tranway passed through the site. From 1921 owned by INIGO JONES [Section 3] Underground chambers were pumped and hauled by water wheel, mill had 4 saws and 2 planers driven by a 75-hp Pelton wheel, electricity 1936. To the north was a series of diggings with an incline down to tramway level and to the south of them a similar but less successful series of diggings. In 1883 762 tons with 29 men.

Remains. There are some ruins of the mill & wheel pit, and the adjacent adit (flooded) with pump remnants. Cottages associated with the quarry are still in use.

Up valley there are various collapsed adits and the track ways associated with them are traceable. At 779116 there is a series of 4 adits. The topmost leads to a shaft down, the 2nd to a pit. The 3rd & 4th are run in. Near the upper adits are further trials. There are traces of a drum house and an incline. At valley floor are many sawn ends probably from a portable saw,.

At 777111 there are several run-in adits. There are traces of a magazine, alongside the tramway, which may have been latterly shared with Ratgoed.

Here there are also sawn ends fro re-working.

At 777107 is an old adit into which a chamber below breaks through. There is a surprisingly great amount of development and mill waste.

Upstream is a reservoir, with a nice valve chamber and spillway. The feed pipe is buried with a surge-pit partway along. [41]

CWM GLODDFA SH766062

A small open, unmechanised, digging in a constricted

little valley.

Remains. Some rubbish runs and several collapsed adits that seem to have been unsuccessful trials. There is a curious drum house with an outcrop of rock forming one wall with the brakeman's platform cut into a ledge. This name is used locally for Abercorris quarry. [37]

CWM YR HENGAE 761103

Trial **Remains.** Two collapsed adits, tips. [33]

DARREN SH721058

Pit/underground working that was a vain attempt to develop an ancient site., that being on a packhorse route, had provided slate for local use.

In the 1850s a first attempt was made to roof up to the old pit and a mill and other buildings were erected. The iron content made the slate difficult to sell and work was abandoned. A further attempt was made at lower level in the hope that a better product would result but this was unsuccessful. Subsequently there was some small scale working on the opposite side of the hill, but quality apart, the lack of water for power and the difficulties of transport made this site a very doubtful proposition.

Remains. Near the collapsed adit which passed under the ancient quarry, are compact suite of buildings including a, a blacksmith's shop, a shelter for dampening slab, office and a tiny mill that contains fragments of a hand operated saw table. There is a big stockyard area and this, and a large area of the adjacent ground is covered with many thousands of finished slates, most are broken or decayed but thousands remain intact. At the lower adit is another small mill with remnants of a hand-cranked saw. Lack of waste suggests that little work was done here.

Around the southern shoulder of the hill are several collapsed adits and a small dressing shed. There is some finished product on the ground. Unusually, for such a remote site, there are no barracks or dwellings. [2]

DOLFANOG SH729104
Little more than an unsuccessful trial.
Remains. An adit (blocked) tucked in a little valley, waste, and site of a possible building. [4]

DOLGOED SH781126 etc.
Some mid to late 19th century optimistic diggings.
Remains. On the northernmost site, reclamation has eliminated almost all traces. On the other two sites there clearly was some limited slate working, one or possibly both went underground. There are no buildings other than possible vestiges of a dressing shed. [42]

DOLYDDERWEN SH750029
Very small vernacular working. **Remains.** Quarry face. [19]

ERA SH760064 CAMBRIA WYNN
Open working, started in 1870s, in a not entirely successful attempt to better exploit the CWM GLODDFA vein. About 50 men produced around 600 tons pa. Material trammed to ESGAIRGEILIOG mill.
Remains. Face, incline formation and a tramway to the mill. [31]

ESGAIRGEILIOG MILL SH759059
Built in the 1870s on the site of an old grist mill and connected to the Corris Railway, to process material from ERA. The elaborate layout quite out of scale with the disappointing output of the quarry included an enamelling oven. Subject to much speculation,. Some work done here in the 1920s
Remains. Much is complete, the main mill building, an excellent example of a small integrated mill, is in

industrial reuse, but there is little trace of the water wheel and launder. The ruins of the bridge of the Corris Railway branch hang precariously over the river. [28]

FFYNNON BADARN SH775114

Unsuccessful late 19th century trial. A tramway was planned to join the Ratgoed line near CYMERAU. **Remains.** Excavation. [40]

FOTY Y WAUN SH761128 Y WAUN, WAUNLEFENNI WAUNLEFENNI

Tiny Scratching from the 1870s, briefly revived 1934.
Remains. Pit, possible adit, vestiges of dressing shed. [34]

FRON FRAITH SH759125 & 757121

Opened at 759125 in the late 1860s with limited success. Fresh and short-lived revival at 757121 in the 1920.s
Remains. At earlier site. Two adits with cgi-roofed shed. Later site much overgrown, two collapsed adits, curious square building with central pillar, sawn-ends indicate sawing here (possibly with oil-engine power). [27]

GAEWERN SH745086 TALYLLYN Including GLANDERI. RHOGNANT, SGWD

Diggings from the 18th century or before being merged into one in the 1830s, but suffered many speculations and tribulations until taken over by the Birleys of BRAICH GOCH.

Sand-sawing by hand by 1832, later hand-cranked circular saws were used, eventually there were two water-driven mills one on site, one to the east of the main road, the latter working off the tail-race of the former. Exit to the second mill and to the Upper Corris Tramway was by tunnel under the road. Following amalgamation material was taken by surface tramway to BRAICH GOCH.

Underground the mismatch of levels at RHOGNANT, SGWD and later BRAICH GOCH. presented challenges.

Remains. Near the main road are traces of the ancient GLANDERI open workings with the quarries and adits of ROGNANT and SGWD to the east and west respectively. At the top of the site is the dried-out bed of the upper reservoir, with a slate covered leat leading down to the site of the upper mill. Above is a shaft (Sgwd 1).

Beyond are the open workings of 2 & 3 Sgwd levels with a rubbish run line curving round from Sgwd 2, with traces of a building. The Sgwd tramway parallels below it at Sgwd 3 level. A table incline with drum house goes down to the Rhognat tramway below. There are also vestiges of another Sgwd 2-3 incline and of a Sgwd 3-4 incline.

The line passes prominent traces of the old Rhognant No. 1 adit and as it leaves the site towards BRAICH GOCH, it passes the ruins of a powder house and farm buildings behind which was the Sgwd No.7 adit. Below is the lower reservoir, still holding water and beyond it Gaewern farm. There are slate sleepers in situ. Further on, landscaping has obliterated the line and its incline that ran to near BRAICH GOCH Vanes level.

At a lower level is the formation of the Rhognat tramway starting at Sgwd No.4 adit, near which is a weigh-house and from where water emerges from the collapsed open workings. The line passes the foot of the table incline and finishes near the top of the present access track to the site. At the end of the line there is a cleared area that was the site of the upper mill. There is an obvious opening and traces of the drum house masonry where the incline went down underground, to connect with Rhognat No. 4 adit under the main road. The tunnel has, like the lower mill to which it led, been completely lost.

Underground, there is much chambering on several levels, extending to above the northernmost Braich Goch workings.[13]

GLANDULAS SH751038
A tiny roadside digging. **Remains.** Quarry face. [21]

GLYNIAGO SH719072 Y GLYN Very small underground working, from early 20th century. Ownership by the Maglona (Late Towyn) Company suggests that they hoped to extract enamelling stock from the Narrow vein. Allegedly up to 12 men employed, with the tramway uncompleted output was negligible
Remains. In forestry, original digging is open to chambers, but the second adit, and all buildings including the (possibly temporary) barracks have been lost. The tramway bed forms a forestry road and the incline down to Upper Corris is obvious. [1]

GOEDWIG SH752063
Trial. **Remains.** Adit in forestry. [22]

GOEDWIG WEST SH745066
Trial. **Remains.** Vestiges of an adit. [12]

HAFOTY SH725064 TAP LLWYD
Trial in conjunction with DARREN. **Remains.** Traces of adit. [3]

HENGAE SH759115
From the 1860s, high hopes but little substance, even as late as the 1920s much interest but no activity.
Remains. One flooded adit, tree planting may have concealed a second adit. The forestry road follows the access track and may have destroyed any dressing sheds etc. Near Hengae farm there are buildings that may have been used for slate reduction and also a stock of slabs. [29]

LLYNGWERN SH757045 GLANDULAS

Worked from at least 1835, opening and closing several times. Output almost certainly never exceeding 1000 tons pa. (1883 915 tons 35 men), even after connection to the Corris, Machynlleth and River Dovey Tramway in the early 1860s. Material was taken to the mill by incline, that was replaced by a tunnel as the working deepened into a pit. In 1900 steam replaced the 30' mill waterwheel, it being in turn replaced by an oil engine . An incline from the mill went down to a branch of the Corris Railway.

As overburden and the position of the reservoir limited the advance of the working face, the pit was deepened into chambering. A tunnel was bored from near the foot of the exit incline, under the mill area to a point below the quarry (As at ABERCWMEIDDAW), to act as a drain. Rails were laid in it but only to facilitate the boring, it never served as an exit route.

Due to site constraints a tip was established high up on the hillside, reached by a ropeway powered by a producer-gas engine.

The 1890 tie up with the Towyn Company who had an enamelling works at Bod Talog (SH498991), the demand from the Aberystwyth enamellers and a good market in mantelpieces; brought relative prosperity. Output declined during the 20th century, finally closing in 1953.

Remains. The mills area is now in re-use by the National Centre for Alternative Technology. The quarry has several loading platforms, a derrick and the base for a late haulage winch. There is some chambering on either side. Adjacent is the lower mounting for the ropeway and high above, the tip site with traces of buildings and the upper mounting of the ropeway.

The reservoir is still in use as a water source for the passenger water balance. The present car park is in the loading area for the Corris Railway branch, the abutments of the railway bridge across the Dulas can be seen and the high-embanked approach causeway to it is a notable feature. [26]

MATTHEWS MILL SH768091

This is the enamelling works was established by T.E.Magnus in the 1850s

Remains. Nothing remains of the ovens and water-powered sawing mill. A private house now occupies part of the site. [38]

MYNYDD TY'N Y CEUNANT SH729084 & 730082

Tiny diggings, trimming waste shows that 730082 may have yielded some product **Remains.** In forestry much degraded traces of diggings with adits roofing up to them. [5]

MYNYDD Y WAUN SH763132

Trial? **Remains.** Excavation and tip. [35]

PANDY SH760081 CLODDFA FRONFELEN

This was the start of a bold attempt to seek slate by tunnelling south towards the ERA vein. Abandoned at an early stage.

Remains. Excavation & spoil. Wheel pit and some stonework of never completed surface structures. [32]

PEN Y GARREG SH735099

A re-working of the DOLFFANOG occurrence

Remains. Collapsed adit in a cleft, waste made into a platform with a building vestige. Trimming waste but exit route is unclear. [9]

RATGOED SH787119. ALLTGOED, RALLTGOED.

Mainly underground, opened in the mid 19th cent. Three mills operating at various times. The early, mostly open, workings near valley floor level were actually on the Broad Vein, The main, Narrow Vein workings were on 8 levels, in a compact area, high on the hillside Annual Output probably peaked at around 800 tons but the 434 tons (with 35 men) of 1882 was more typical. Produced mainly slab, some in finished products such as mantelpieces. By the 1850s were enamelling at Machynlleth.

The Ratgoed tramway was the only link, apart from field paths, to the village that grew up around the quarry. The chapel ceased services in 1925 but Sunday school continued until WW2. An attempted post-war restart was abandoned in 1946

Remains. Clear felling has eased interpretation, but disturbed geology and lack of planning led to complicated working and movement of material. The topmost level, Level 1 above the forestry road, is a tiny open working with Level 2 breaking into it. Below it is a large pit divided into three parts. The adit at Level 3 is reached by a shelved tramway. Level 4 has largely been quarried away. At Level 5 is the cutting access to the pit, there is some underground chambering off and workings break out from below.

On Level 6 there are several dressing sheds and other buildings including the Upper mill, a double structure, of country rock augmented by sawn-ends, it has mountings for overhead shafting. There is a weigh-house and other buildings and vestiges of what must have been a barracks. Where men living beyond say Corris, would lodge here from Monday to Saturday.

At Level 7 is an adit (collapsed) leading to chambering that breaks out into the pit workings. An isolated rubbish run emerges from this adit, it is possible that after subsequent tipping isolated this adit, a wire rope was used to bring blocks up Level 6. On level 8 are vestiges of Middle mill, the last to be built and the last to work. There are traces of the base of an i.c. engine that replaced the Pelton wheel. Nearby are some building foundations and a stocking area. There are several rubbish runs at this level emanating from an adit with rail in situ, some 200 yards long, cut through country rock, with no workings but with 2 vertical shafts dropping from the chambering above.

The incline system is unusually complex. The short 5-6 incline has evidence of a horizontal sheave. The 6-7 incline, with a nice flight of steps alongside, has traces of an under floor sheave.

Of the other 4 inclines, all of the table type, the oldest seems to be the 7-Down, which is near the northern boundary of the site. It has a semi-circular structure at its head, probably for a horizontal sheave. Part way down is a most delightful powder house with "air bricks" formed out of drilled slate and traces of the wooden flooring. This probably went out of use either when adit 7 became isolated or when Middle mill was built.

Middle mill was fed by 2 inclines 5-8 and 6-8, both with conventional drums.

From Level 8, a further incline, (now cut by a forestry road), runs down to the valley floor. The drum gear is similar to the 5-8 and 6-8 inclines, and like them both drum, brakes and housings show signs of repair and modification with considerable, presumably local, ingenuity. There is a further powder house on this incline.

Near the foot of both lower inclines, are buildings, some apparently adaptations of pre-existing structures.

There are several ruined buildings at valley floor level, including the original mill (like the others, Pelton wheel powered), with some evidence of under-floor shafting and embedded in the ground is the table of a saw-bench, and remnants of an "A" frame slab wagon.

Close above this are some small, open pit workings and also a flooded adit, with a possible short incline; these may well be the original workings.

Along the tramway from the lower mills area, are the ruins of a row of 4 cottages, (the end one was a shop), the chapel and between them the site of a manse, all 5 dwellings served by a double lavatory over the stream nearby. In front are ruins of the manager's house, complete with lavatory, served by the same brook as, the communal convenience. Ratgoed Hall, the owner's residence, has a most elaborately ornate stable block. [43]

RHIW'R GWREIDDYN SH760054

Opened about 1818, developed in the 1870s. Material was originally brought down by inclines to a water powered mill, fed by a launder from Ceinws along the line of the present road (the road then being at a lower level). but as the workings deepened it was hauled out on the level. Almost 70 men were employed in the late 1890s when the northerly working was developed and on-site enamelling prospered.

The tip was reached by a bridge over the old road opposite the northern workings. A tramway along the present road connected the two workings. Closed 1934. A connection to the Corris Railway at Ceinws was proposed but never made. The site is in industrial reuse.

Remains. On the southern site there is much tipping from early work and a flooded pit. There is a weigh-house and a redundant drum house converted into a lean-to shelter, (possibly a powder house). A fine range of buildings remains, some in reuse, consisting of a double mill and a rake of ancillary structures, later altered and extended in brick. There is a small reservoir, with piping to a turbine housing (which may have replaced a water wheel). A covered channel carries the tailrace under the stocking area. There is the remnant of a large preheating room and vestiges of a furnace. On the northern site there is little but the excavations themselves. The abutments of the tramway bridge to the tipping area near the river still stand. The old road, which passed beneath it, is discernable. [30]

TAP DU SH735092 RUGOG
Briefly worked mid 1870s. **Remains.** Excavation and waste. [8]

TARRAN CADLAN SH733070
Trial. **Remains.** Adit, blocked by a fall. [7].

TY'N Y BERTH SH738087 HILLSBOROUGH
Developed underground in the early 1850s in anticipation of rail transport being available. Material was brought down by incline to a water-powered mill. It was closed by the time the Upper Corris tramway opened.
Remains. In forestry, but at least six adits in tandem, some small buildings, traces of a reservoir and the incline formation are discernable.

Near the road is a fine range of buildings, now in reuse as houses, the garage of the endmost house being the site of the mill wheel. There are (quarry owned?) houses "Hillsborough", on the main road. [10]

TY'N Y CEUNANT SH744088 RHOGNANT
Two small workings 1830s –1860s? Material brought down by incline to road level.
Remains. Little apart from traces of buildings, the incline formation and run-in adits. The ruin across the road was variously a mill and a chapel. [11]

WENALLT SH765108 CWMBERGI

Hillside terraces spectacularly developed on 9 levels with an incline down to the valley floor where there was a water-powered mill. Generally working on the south side (allegedly trespassing onto Aberllefenni land!), with tipping on north side. Some tentative attempts to go underground. Open for only a few years around the 1880s, a proposed extension to the Aberllefenni tramway was never built road.

Remains. The multi-pitch incline, now much degraded, is a main feature, with several ruined drum houses, Dressing sheds at the various levels. Some working above top of incline level.

The valley floor the mill reputed to have 9 saws and a planer (Belt slots, suggest only 8 machines), is of great interest. The machines were driven by a shaft in a "basement", powered by a wheel behind and below the mill. There is a leat from a reservoir some distance up valley and a tunnel takes the tailrace to the river. Dearth of waste suggests a minimal output. [36]

Section 13
NORTH-EAST WALES

General

This region comprised broadly four separate areas each having a group of fairly substantial quarries, surrounded by outliers.

These groups were Corwen, the Horseshoe pass, the Glynceiriog valley and the upper Tanat valley. There were other isolated occurrences, notably south of Denbigh town.

Silurian Series rock was worked, predominantly for roofing slates. Several of the quarries were 18th century or earlier. A number were underground.

Glynceiriog and Llangynog were settlements much augmented by slate working as were to a lesser extent, Glyndyfrdwy and Llydiart-y-Parc.

Substantial remains are to be found at CAMBRIAN, CRAIG RHIWARTH, MOELFFERNA and PENARTH, and much of interest at several others.

Transport

The ancient sites in the east of the area had a long history of cartage direct to markets in the English Midlands. A few were able to use canals and from 1856 the stiff cartage down to the Llangollen canal from the Horseshoe pass quarries was obviated by the opening of the 3'g Oernant tramway. This is readily traceable from MOEL Y FAEN, through OERNANT and BERWYN to the head of a big incline, that has the vestiges of a unique "2-storey" drum house that gave the brakeman an elevated view of the run. There are slate sleepers on the ground. From the foot of the incline, the line is then obvious partially as a lane, partly alongside the main road. There is a prominent

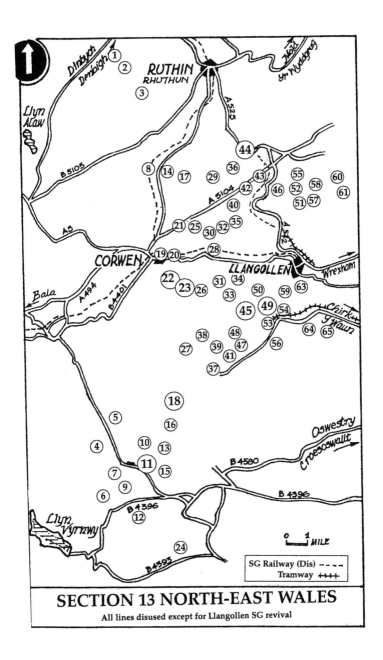

SECTION 13 NORTH-EAST WALES

All lines disused except for Llangollen SG revival

SG Railway (Dis) – – – –
Tramway ++++

0   1 MILE

embankment near the canal, which was crossed by a bridge to the PENTRE FELIN works. From 1865 the Llangollen-Corwen GWR line could be used.

The Glynceiriog units used the Montgomeryshire Canal and from 1873, the CAMBRIAN, and other quarries could reach it by the 2'4^1/4"g horse drawn Glyn Valley tramway that ran to a wharf at Gledrid basin, making use of part of the track bed of an old colliery tramway. In 1888, the line was steamed and diverted to an interchange at Chirk GWR station. The line closed in 1935; most of both courses are readily traceable.

After 1805 the Tanat valley quarries could cart to the canal at Llanymynech, and from 1861 to the railway at the same place. When the Tanat Valley Railway was eventually opened in 1904, CRAIG RHIWARTH was able to make direct connection, and the neighbouring quarries had only a short cartage. If this delightful railway had been opened 30 or 40 years earlier, it might have had a dramatic effect on the fortunes of slate in the valley. Closed 1967, it is easily traceable over its entire length.

In the Dee valley PENARTH and DEESIDE/MOELFFERNA, had access to a main line railway, the 1865 GWR line to Corwen (later Dolgellau), enabling their rapid development. The former reached an interchange siding by incline, but the latter used the fascinating 2'6" gauge Deeside Tramway. Opened around 1870, one of the last wooden railed tramways in Europe, it was gravity powered, empty wagons being recovered by horses each morning. Originally running from DEESIDE to Glyndyfrdwy via DEESIIDE SLAB WORKS mill, it was later extended (with steel track), to MOELFFERNA, remaining in use until the 1940s. Most of the route is readily traceable. The intermediate incline, immediately above DEESIDE quarry, still has its horizontal sheave gear, remotely mounted in a block housing. In the vicinity of DEESIDE SLAB WORKS there is some wooden rail on the ground (minus the iron sheathing), complete with iron tie-rods. Near the main road, the drum house of the final incline still stands, but the horizontal sheave gear has been removed. The manager's house is nearby.

1]	SH977594	Aber *	
2]	978598	Nantglyn *	
3]	SJ031546	Nilig	
4]	041271	Glanyrafon *	
5]	042291	Bwlch Gwyn	
6]	043230	Clochnant	
7]	047262	Craig y Cribin **	
8]	048478	Clegir	
9]	049259	West Llangynog	
10]	051289	Llwyn Onn	
11]	053263	Craig Rhiweirth	
12]	057243	Chwarel Ddu	
13]	060279	Moel Crynddyn	
14]	065481	Wernddu	
15]	066274	Craig Glanhafon	
16]	074294	Powis *	
17]	074464	Ty'n y Rhos	
18]	075326	Cwmmaengwynedd **	
19]	081434	Corwen	
20]	085434	Colomendy	
21]	089444	Caer Drewyn	
22]	107424	Penarth ***	I
23]	125399	Moelfferna ***	H
24]	126223	Brithdir	
25]	130442	Coed Tir Llanerch	
261	138404	Deeside *	

27]	141327	Sarphle *	
28]	148417	Deeside Slab Works	
29]	157453	Cwm Tydi	
30]	160448	Foel Forfydd *	
31]	161398	Ty'n y Graig *	
32]	162448	Cymmo *	
33]	163342	Ty Nant	
34]	165382	Nantyr	
35]	169453	Rhiw Goch **	
36]	171478	Westminster *	
37]	176303	Ty Gwyn	
38]	176342	Ty'n y Rhyd	
39]	177325	Bwlch Adwy Wynt	
40]	177446	Rhewl Mill	
41]	182311	Nant Fach Gynan	
42]	185463	Berwyn **	I
43]	185469	Oernant	
44]	185477	Moel Faen **	H
45]	189378	Cambrian ***	I
46]	193462	Craig Las	
47]	195326	Fron Ucha	
48]	199351	Spring Hill	
49]	199379	Wynne *	
50]	199385	Tan y Foel	
51]	201468	Pentre Dŵr	
52]	202473	Craig Wynnstay *	
53]	207375	Tŷ Draw	
54]	208378	Hafodgwynfawr	
55]	208476	Ffynnon y Gôg	
56]	209344	Llechwedd Gwyn	
57]	210469	Foel *	
58]	210471	Abergwern	
59]	215382	Pen y Bryn	
60]	215478	Pant Glas *	

61]	216472	Eglwyseg
62]	218436	Pentrefelin Mill *
63]	229399	Craig y Dduallt
64]	234362	Craig yr Orin *
65]	239364	Cilnant

ABER SH977594

A small, primitive and shallow open slab working, allegedly sawing by hand right up to the 1920s closure, although site examination shows that mechanical sawing was used at some time. Unlikely that rails were ever used, all movement being by barrow.

Remains. Shallow pit, partly backfilled with rubbish, with vestiges of a number of little buildings and tiny alcoves. To the south west, in forestry, is a trace of a low dam, downstream of which is a curious little building that could have housed a Pelton wheel, (although the water head seems inadequate), with possible pipe saddles behind it. In front of this is a floor about 15' x 4' consisting of 3 massive slabs 4' 8" x 4' divided and edged by slate kerbs. In front of this is what could have been an open-fronted working shed. Whilst sawn ends in the quarry itself were hand-sawn, those around this latter area were cut by a mechanical sand-saw, (many are oddly bevelled). It therefore seems that there was a power sand-saw(s) on this base. This area was connected to the quarry site by a cart track. [1]

ABERGWERN SJ210471

Small hillside quarry, early 19th century carting to road.

Remains. Access tunnel (blocked) small dressing shed and other buildings, access track. [58]

BERWYN SJ185463 CLOGAU **Working quarry do not enter**

The rock here is unsuitable for roofing slate, but can yield slab in very large sizes, examples up to 20' x 10' having been made.

Shortly after the quarry's 1844 opening, the PENTREFELIN mill was built, block being carted to it by the Horseshoe Pass road that was reached by a short incline. Product was sent out by canal. The Oernant tramway obviated cartage in 1857, and from 1865 dispatch could be made by rail.

Employing up to 100 men in the 1870s, by which time a mill with 4 saws and 2 planers, driven by steam, had been built on site, although some hand sawing was done up to c1960.

Declining into closure during the 1890s, little if any work was done until 1934 when it reopened on a smaller scale with diesel power. By the mid 1990s activity again having tapered off with mill drive being supplied from an old tractor, it was taken over and extensively re-equipped to with modern machinery capable of producing slab in the largest sizes.

Remains. At the top of the site where there are vestiges of the earliest working is the ruin of a dressing shed with forge attached and a walled stocking area.

Below is the main pit, with a cutting leading to an incline formation down to the mill, with another cutting opposite leading to the rubbish tips. Extraction here is now by wire saw, with rubbish being handled by a digger and loader.

A road now leads to the mill, rebuilt using part of the original structure. It houses diamond saws and polishers, the largest in the industry. Adjoining are the back walls of the old big slab dressing sheds. The office/smith/store has been rebuilt as a modern dwelling.

The Oernant tramway formation runs through the site and forms the present access road. In front of the mill is the bed of the original exit incline, which became part of the Oernant tramway, and was reused after the tramway closed.

There is are mid-19th century trial excavations at 193461. [42]

BRITHDIR SJ126223
Slate extraction at least proposed here, an old metal working site, in 1880 and machinery bought, but not installed.
Remains. Pit and possible rubbish run. [24]

BWLCH ADWY WYNT SJ177325
Possibly only building block.
Remains. Roadside scratching. [39]

BWLCH GWYN SJ042291
1880s trial. **Remains.** Excavation. [5]

CAER DREWYN SJ089444
Trial. **Remains.** Excavation. [21]

CAMBRIAN SJ189378 Incorporating CHWAREL ISAF, CHWAREL UCHAF, DENNIS', MARTIN'S, McEWEN'S, TOWNSEND'S.
Serious exploitation commenced in 1854 at MARTIN'S, the old CHWAREL UCHAF (186381) a waterwheel hauled and pumped the pit. In the 1860s there was vigorous development at McEWEN'S, close to the ancient CHWAREL ISAF (192378).

A tunnel was bored for some third of mile emerging from the hillside below McEWEN'S. Rail track though it led to a mill at the adit and on to an incline down to the

Glyn Valley Tramway. By the mid 1870s, benefiting from that tramway, a shaft had been sunk down to the tunnel a little to the east of MARTIN'S and another between it and McEWEN'S, these shafts being developed into TOWNSEND'S and DENNIS' quarries respectively.

All four pits were thus drained, with MARTIN'S, TOWNSEND'S and McEWENS able to send out block and some waste by steam (later petrol) locomotive haulage, along the tunnel. The shallower DENNIS' was accessed by two independent tunnels. These latter emerged to the south, one was abandoned early, and the later lower one being connected by tramway to the mill at the main tunnel adit.

Underground work was commenced off and under the main tunnel near TOWNSEND'S and via an extension of the main tunnel beyond MARTIN'S into new ground to the west. These later workings extended to 4 levels.

Due to lack of space to the east, some rubbish from underground was up-hauled out of MARTIN'S and TOWNSEND'S and also by a fresh up haulage slant from the westerly chambering. DENNIS' was later abandoned and used as a reservoir.

In the late 19th/early 20th century annual tonnage averaged more than 2500, peaking at almost 4000 in 1908, with an 80-100 payroll. Remarkably output continued almost undiminished up to WW2. Final closure only came because most of the 50 men found better-paid work during the lay-off in the hard winter of 1946/47.

Remains. The whole site is afforested and demolition and the highly degradable nature of the material has left few surface buildings and even much of the waste has reverted to soil.

To the NW of the by-road that skirts the top of the site, adjacent to the reservoir, a rubbish haulage incline with an engine house and weighbridge at its head, emerges from underground chambers. These are flooded up as falls prevent drainage into the main tunnel.

The pit of MARTIN'S is immediately within the loop of the road that was diverted in 1878 to allow expansion. Almost no trace survives of the water-powered mill, dressing sheds etc. that were to the NE of this pit, as much ground was quarried away in the 1880s.

In the pit is the much-degraded ramp of the up haulage incline, the frame of a trwnc carriage, ruins of an engine-house and coal bin. There are also an air-receiver, cranks and other compressor parts. The tramway formation runs through the pit, with an adit at either end. The NW adit, leads to a fall-blockage, sealing off the extensive chambering beyond and above. Immediately inside are the frames of two trwnc-incline carriages, a rusting body nearby of similar size suggests a tank for a water-balancing, presumably to lift rubbish internally. There are parts of a hand-pump and a 2-seater lavatory.

The SE adit, which is the start of the main drainage tunnel, also leads to chambering. Inside there are 2 triangular wooden structures apparently further incline trwnc frames, their origin being unclear.

Within the convoluted chambering, with evidence of 'cupboarding' and pillar robbing, is a flooded incline down to the lower chambers abandoned long before closure. At its head is a substantial engine mounting, possibly compressed air driven. Another chamber contains the mounting and earthenware supply pipes for the Pelton wheel of a compressor, with discarded saw-blades acting as "washers" for rods bracing the masonry. A further chamber breaks out up into TOWNSEND'S. Within this open chamber are a well-preserved caban and an iron vessel that may have been a boiler or an air-receiver. Close by is a mounting for the steam engine that powered, an up-haulage chain incline.

On the main tunnel there is some heavy rail and weighted-lever points.

Continuing along the main tunnel, one passes a side tunnel concrete-plugged with a valve, which connects to the flooded DENNIS'. On from here are some signs of a trench in the tunnel floor, possibly for a feed pipe for a Pelton wheel or turbine pumping the chambers below tunnel level.

MCEWEN'S is on a side-loop of the main tunnel and it can be seen how the original tunnel serving this pit was utilised as a final part of the main tunnel. Shortly beyond MCEWEN'S the tunnel has been culverted into a 3'diameter pipe for its final 30 yards.

On the surface the flooded, DENNIS' pit is in two parts connected by a, short tunnel, well above water level, with another at a lower level.

At the outer end of the piped exit tunnel there are few traces of the water wheel (later i.c.) powered mill, office, workshops etc., one more recent structure is possibly built from stone robbed from the old buildings. The head of incline with extensive rubbish runs alongside, is obscure, but traceable to its junction in the village with the Glyn Valley line. [45]

CHWAREL DDU SJ057243
Tiny open quarry pre 1870s?
Remains. Workings with vestiges of a dressing shed. Rubbish tipped down a now afforested hillside. [12]

CILNANT SJ239364
Putative site. **Remains.** Possible ground disturbance. [65]

CLEGIR SJ048478
A small face working yielding a very pale coloured slate, opened in the 1870s. **Remains.** Excavation and access track. [8]

CLOCHNANT SJ043230
Very small underground working.**Remains.** Two adits, one to an open shaft above. Dressing shed. [6]

COED TIR LLANERCH SJ130442
Small open working. **Remains.** Rubbish runs. [25]

COLOMENEDY SJ085434
Early 20th century producing "coarse slate".
Remains. In forestry. [20]

CORWEN (or Corwen Stone) SJ081434
Possibly building stone only. This name also applied to PENARTH. **Remains.** Possible excavations. [19]

CRAIG GLANHAFON SJ066274 (also 066276)
Tiny pit/underground, early 20th century.
Remains. Excavations, tips [15]

CRAIG LAS SJ193462
Briefly worked during c1840, allegedly sawing at RHEWL. **Remains.** Excavation. [46]

CRAIG RHIWARTH SJ053263
Open,,underground later. Working in 1760, possibly even 16th century. Material from early, high-level workings sledged down to the valley floor some 800' below. (Aitken account 1797) This sledging continued up to the mid-19th century when the big exit incline was built.in the course of developing further galleries and an extensive tramway system. Output 1856 1000 tons, falling to 329 tons in 1882. Circa 40 men.

Material was carted to the river, later to the canal at Llanymynech, and after 1861 to the railhead at Porth-y-waen.

Down to 240 tons in 1890, declined further in that decade but there was some temporary revival following the opening of the Tanant Valley Railway in 1904, the incline being extended under the road to exchange sidings at the terminus. There was some very limited activity in 1938 when men moved here after the closure of WEST LLANGYNOG. An oil engine was then used probably for winching, generating and/or driving the hitherto treadle-operated Greaves dressers. Final closure in 1940.

Remains. The salient feature is the main incline at the foot of which are traces of the old cartage wharf. The tunnel under the road is lost but there are vestiges of the exchange siding area and a possible trimming shed or small mill behind the present cafe. At the head of incline with the remains of the drum gear, (unusually, the spiders being in 2 halves), is a drum house with an adjoining workshop. To the west a track leads to a powder house.

To the east the tramway formation is benched out of the steep hillside to reach some dressing sheds and the foot of a short incline. At the head of that incline is a drum house (remote type, as are most on site) with the remains of gear, some buildings and a steel stanchion that held a powerful (Carbide?) lamp for night working. There are a hand winch, head frame, rail track etc in chambers in this, the last section to be worked.

From the top of this incline the tramway continues to the foot of another incline. Part way up is a level with chambering. At the top is a working area with various buildings, including a drum house, with most curious flat bar tie-rods and a dressing shed with a neat aperture to allow trimmings to fall down the mountainside. There are the much degraded remains of another incline above this and some rather confused workings and structures, possibly abandoned at an early date.

There are higher up, workings unconnected with any incline system and also some further east at a slightly lower level. These are possibly the very earliest workings. Below is a path system which may have been the old sledge way. There are also structures that suggest a ropeway from the lowest working level to this path (this could be the original first-built "incline" as there is no trace of any incline down the mountain other than the obvious one). [11]

CRAIG WYNNSTAY SJ202473 TAN Y BWLCH
Small pit working opened briefly 1840, reopened, also briefly in 1886 with 30 men. Abandoned 1909 following several attempts to reactivate.
Remains. Access tunnel (blocked), small building, access track. [52]

CRAIG Y CRIBIN SJ047262 PENGWERN
A small hillside/underground working dating from mid-19th century. Closed in 1880s.
Remains. Dressing sheds, a great deal of stock (including flags) on ground. Chambers accessible at 2 points. Powder house. [7]

CRAIG Y DDUALLT SJ229399
Small, possibly mid 19th century. **Remains.** Excavation. [63]

CRAIG Y ORYN SJ234362 NANT GWRYD
Well established by the 1790s when tonnage was 300-600 of slates plus slab. It, seems to have declined after this and possibly only worked. part-time 1887 55 tons 2/3

men. Underground in the 1890s

Remains. Some small buildings, tunnel under road, possible drum house and incline, very limited underground chambering, access track. [64]

CWMMAENGWYNEDD SJ075326

Operated in 1867-71,1876-86 and 1899-1910, apart from '06/07 when up to 20 men employed, manning averaged about 4. The first phase worked the outcrop, with some attempt to go underground, The second phase started as open working lower down subsequently going underground, both epochs had hand powered sawing on site. Then finally, on a lower level still, more substantial underground working via a long tunnel with a tramway, to a water-powered mill at some distance.

There were at least two proposals for a railway down the valley but apart from post-1904, when a traction engine towed trailers to Llanrhaeadr-ym-Mochnant, product had to be carted to the main line at Porth-y-waen.

Remains. At the top of the site are the original open workings with an abortive tunnel, (open) and vestiges of a building that might have housed a hand-powered circular saw. Lower down at further working are two adits, the un-collapsed one leads to some chambering where there are blocks stacked ready for working, bar rail directly tenoned into sleepers is in situ. All shot holes are hand-drilled. Part-way along the tunnel is a side-cutting (now banked with off cuts & rubbish). the presence of sawn ends outside and in the tunnel up to this point, suggests that hand-powered circular sawing was done underground in this alcove.

A quantity of aluminium tubing presumably comes from a crashed, geodetically constructed aircraft (Wellington?).

Adjacent to these workings is a building, domestic and/or forge with a shaft with gears that might be part of a saw-table drive, although there are no sawn-ends to be seen. From this area a cart track leads out.

Lower down is the 'main' adit (collapsed) and adjacent are traces of a building, either the forge or the office that were both near this adit. There was apparently also a small waterwheel to drive a ventilation fan but no trace remains but a depression with traces of walling above may have been a reservoir to feed it. Near this is a run-in ventilation shaft.

A tramway formation leads to a drum house with an uncommon, 4 spider drum by Turner of Newtown. One pillar carries the initals D.P.LL. (D.P.LLoyd was manager 1906). The incline forms a forestry firebreak. At the foot of incline are the pillars of a tramway bridge leading to a mills area and traces of a Pelton wheel-powered mill building which lacked a fourth wall, other building remains and a loading bank.

Uphill there is a fine granite dam and a powder house. Nearby is a ruin of a rake of four barracks or cottages.

At the edge of the forestry below the dam are two spoil runs, one to a run-in adit, the other to a 30' deep cutting that does not appear to have gone underground, both apparently abortive trials. [18]

CYMMO SJ162448
Two very tiny workings on either side of a hilltop.
Remains. Traces of a dressing shed. [32]

CWM-TYDI SJ157453
Very small, part underground, possibly a trial only.
Remains. Run in adit, spoil heap. [29]

DEESIDE SJ138404

Open hillside working developed in the 1869 notable for its 2'6" gauge wooden-railed Deeside tramway, that ran through the substantial water powered mill complex at 148417. To, via a table incline, Glyndyfrdwy station where there was a massive wooden gantry to facilitate transhipment of slab which was their main product.

600 tons were produced in 1883 by 34 men but tapered off, finally closed 1921. The tramway continued to serve MOELFFERNA until 1947.

Remains. Very little to be seen at the quarry site apart from some slight vestiges of small buildings. The one internal incline has been entirely quarried away. The incline carrying the tramway extension to MOELFERNA has a remote type horizontal sheaves common in this area.

The tramway formation is reasonably intact for much of its length. There are some nice embankments and cuttings. [26]

DEESIDE SLAB WORKS SJ148417

Sited here on the Deeside Tramway, since water was lacking at the actual quarry site. Closed 1921.

Remains. The substantial buildings are extensive and apart from being roofless are in fair condition. The pit shows where the 30' wheel towered over the mill building that housed planers and sand saws. There are several other structures, including am office, stable and stores. Formations and two bridges indicate an extensive tramway network. Leat-work and fine launder pillars connect to a small reservoir. [28]

EGLWYSEG SJ216472

Tiny working

Remains. Face and tip, vestiges of access track. [61]

FFYNNON Y GÔG SJ208476 PEN Y GOG
Late 19th century with, 2 or 3 men, finally abandoned 1909.
Remains. Almost all destroyed by forestry & roadworks. [55]

FOEL SJ210469 CRAIG Y FOEL
Tiny offshoot of ABERGWERN? **Remains.** In forestry, some buildings. [57]

FOEL FORFYDD SJ160448 WERN DDU
A tiny hillside quarry that mainly produced block.
Remains. Ruins of a tiny shed and some trimming waste is evidence of some slate-making. [30]

FRON UCHA SJ195326 Incl NANT GANOL
Trials. **Remains.** Excavations here and at 195329 & 190321. [47]

GLANYRAFON SJ041271
Underground. **Remains.** Traces of dressing sheds, deep shafts, adit near the road is open but flooded. [4]

HAFODGYNFAWR SJ208378
Small 18th century (?) working.
Remains. Quarrying face. [54]

LLECHWEDD GWYN SJ209344
Small, partly underground. **Remains.** Excavations, run in adits., vestiges of 3 dressing sheds, access track. Possibly associated trial at 215340. [56]

LLWYN ONN SJ051289
Tiny digging. **Remains.** Excavation. [10]

MOELCRYNDDYN SJ060279
Tiny underground working c1870. **Remains.** Flooded adit, tip. [13].

MOELFFERNA SJ125399

An almost entirely underground working opened in the early 1870s, a substantial and efficient producer, annual tonnages occasionally exceeded 6000 tons with well under 200 men.

In 1911, in a century's leap in technology, an oil engine-driven mill was equipped with sand saws. In 1923 an oil-engined generator enabled them to be a pioneer user of a diamond saw, a second followed in 1925 and a third in 1933.

Adits were on 7 levels, 6 being connected by a table-incline that doubled as an exit incline to the Deeside Tramway. In a further across-the-centuries mix of technologies, men travelled to work by motor-cycle to tend a wooden railway!

The post-WW2 payroll was under 60, which like most slate workings was half the pre-war number, closed in 1960, due to manning problems at such an inhospitable site.

Remains. On upper level, an adit and a large splitting and dressing shed that later housed the loco used underground. A plummer block hints at some kind of machinery. There is a weighbridge, a remote type drum house that housed horizontal sheave gear and the remains of an incline table.

At intermediate level, an adit, weigh-house, a double rake of dressing sheds also two massive pillars which supported the gantry that may have been for transferring wagons from 2'g to 2'6"g. The narrower gauge was used underground with the wider, tramway, gauge also being used on the surface.

At an intermediate level, are a further adit, a large stockyard, a weigh house, offices etc, a powder house and a mill. The construction of the mill is unusual, fairly crude walling with cgi roof and along one side a sort of lean-to with sloping walls giving a buttressing effect, but with a surprisingly restricted access to the mill itself. At one end of the mill is a massive concrete base for an oil engine. There are a very large number of collapsed dressing sheds, besides many that have been lost under tips.

Underground, there is much chambering on several levels, but since all adits were closed on abandonment, access is difficult. On level 4, there is an intact bridge over workings below. Above this levels 5 and 6 and levels 6 and 7 were connected by underground gravity incline. They both have rollers in situ but no rail. The 5/6 drum is intact but on the ground, the 6/7 incline drum is still in its mounting. For reasons of space it is most unusual to use drums rather than sheaves underground

On level 6 there is a massive wooden, coalmine type "cog" supporting the roof of a chamber, (Men from the Wrexham area, with coal-mining experience may have been employed). There are various artefacts including winch frames and a hand pump. There are several air doors and a ventilation shaft rises to bank from level 7. [23]

MOEL FAEN SJ185477
Early 18th century open workings of considerable extent with some underground working east-west veins dipping steeply to the north. Developed in the 1820s mainly producing roofing slate; expanded following connection to the Llangollen canal in 1857 by the Oernant tramway. Peaked in the 1870s with 160 men producing about 5000 tons per annum, the six or seven separate diggings being concentrated into three pits, accessed by tunnels with some underground chambering. Suffered badly during the 1880s recession and closed in 1936 following some years of very limited working mainly

from the easterly pit.

Remains. Three main pits, with some intermediate hillside working. The largest, (easterly) pit has vestiges of dressing sheds, some of the many on site including large ones intended for the hand-working of slab, at the highest level. Lower down is a cutting access, with an incline down with some slate sleepers on the ground and further dressing sheds etc.

Lower again is a run-in adit, open at the pit end, where there are two entrances. Inside there is rail on the ground and some attempt at chambering. Lower again, roughly at pit-bottom level is a further run-in adit. Inside the pit rock-falls all but obscure the floor, part way down there are several places on the north side where a line of chambering has broken out. These are inaccessible and presumably connect to the run-in lower adit.

The middle pit, partly water filled, has cutting access with traces of what may have been a winding house for a chain incline. The cutting to a run-in adit, at a lower level is a clear feature.

The westernmost pit, also partly water filled, is at a slightly lower level and adjacent are the foundations of what may have been a steam winding house.

The processing area is much disturbed and little remains apart from a freestanding smithy hearth and the foundations of several buildings. To the north are Tai Newyddion, a row of workers cottages.

A tiny trial at 192483 may have been associated with this quarry.

The line of the Oernant tramway, with some slate sleepers in situ, is a clearly traceable. [44]

NANT FACH GYNAN SJ182311
Trial? **Remains.** Excavation. [41]

NANTGLYN SH978598

Extensive, shallow working for slab from horizontal beds, reminiscent of nearby ABER, mainly for local use, all sawing was by hand up to the 1950s closure. At one time a tramway to the main road was proposed.

Remains. Very shallow working face, curious spherical inclusions. Some vestiges of several small buildings. [2]

NANTYR SJ165382

A small pit working an offshoot of CAMBRIAN operating in the mid 19th century. Had the hoped for extension of the Glyn Valley Tramway been made, development might have taken place.

Remains. Now a picnic area, the pit forming an ornamental pond. [34]

NILIG SJ031546

Small open working. **Remains.** Excavation only. [3]

OERNANT SJ185469

Roofing slate was being made here in the 17th century. Paradoxically, better product from elsewhere forced the 1860s closure only shortly after benefiting from the eponymous tramway.

Remains. The original working is in trees below the main road and the processing area has buildings in agricultural use that may have been adapted from quarry structures.

The later and larger working above the main road is much disturbed by bulk fill removal etc. There is a trial at 189471 [43]

PANT GLAS SJ215478

Elongated hillside working from where, material taken away by an incline. Started by ex-Moel Faen men c 1881, by 1883 735 tons were produced by 35 men. WYNNE became involved but transport problems bought closure in 1886.

Remains. Some vestiges of buildings, drum house and incline. Trace of a collapsed trial adit. [60]

PENARTH SJ107424 CHWAREL GRAIG, PEN Y GLOG
A moderate sized quarry, initially worked unmechanised in open terraces. Development and underground extraction closely followed the 1865 opening of the Llangollen & Corwen Railway (Later GWR).

The railway was reached by an incline near the foot of which the Wharf Mill with water powered sand and circular saws. 150 men initially employed but by 1883 numbers were down to 10, but they produced a very creditable near 500 tons.

Closed in 1890 but reopened six years later with a sawing shed at the eastern end of the site with a 12-hp Blackstone engine driving sand saws that may have come from PENTREFELIN. These were augmented in 1906 by a reciprocating shot-saw (A rarity in slate working), and the oil engine was replaced by a Hornsby 40-hp gas engine that also hauled a short incliner

Closure came in 1932 when a useful 1000 tons pa was produced.

Remains. There are a number of buildings on site including many dressing sheds some the large dressing sheds typical of the area. The mill contains remnants of shafting, pulleys etc and at one end there is motor room bearing the date 190? There are remnants of the open-air horizontal gang shot saw with carriage and alongside it, concrete machine bases.

The nearby adit has been blocked and internally dammed to provide a limited water supply (for saws?) and on the ground outside is some curious pipe work presumably for the gas producer. Near the (blocked)

drainage/rubbish adit is a weigh-house containing mechanism.

The main incline is an obvious feature with its unusual drum house that is a shallow structure nestling in the rock above and behind the incline head. It almost totally enclosed the usual "Denbigh Style" horizontal sheave gear against the weather. It was controlled from a brake cabin by a rod. Much of this mechanism is in situ including traces of an interesting remote controlled crimp sprag. There are traces of an incline table.

Where the incline passed under the main road is now denoted by a culvert. Nearby are some vestiges of the 'Wharf' mill.

There are a number of artefacts around the site, including sand-saw blades. No trace of the use of water-power on the site itself.

In the pit, where the underground workings break out to bank, (providing access), there is a stock of small slates. Behind there are the old and quite extensive terrace workings, with ruinous dressing sheds etc and a further considerable stock of, much degraded, product. Little trace remains of a fine multi-pitch incline system here, stated to have horizontal sheaves.

Above the pit are traces of a small block making operation using country rock. It is believed that in the early years of the 20th century this rock may have been sent to LLANFAIR quarry [Section 9] for crushing.

There is quarry housing near road level but no vestige has been found of the row of cottages that was immediately below the site.

Underground there are extensive tunnels on 3 levels, the seemingly haphazard chambering system appears to exploit two veins. There is rail on the ground and at least one incline with rail in situ. There are a number of artefacts including winches and at least one wagon. [22]

PENTRE DŴR SJ201468

Quite extensive working with an eponymous quarrying settlement. Disused by the late 1840s.

Remains. Much degraded tips etc. [51]

PENTREFELIN SJ218436 (WORKS)

Built in the 1840s close to abundant water, with its own canal wharf. and equipped with sand-saws driven by an 18' x 4' water wheel, to saw material from BERWYN (and possibly RHIW GOCH). Its capabilities were successively enhanced by the opening of the Oernant tramway, the provision of its own rake of GWR sidings, and re-equipping with 3 circular saws, 8 planers, a sand-polisher and ultimately an enamelling oven. Despite allegations that their waste blocked the river, it remained active into the 1890s and possibly beyond.

Remain. Buildings in re-use, canal wharf and leat for water supply are extant. The railway sidings area has been cleared. [62]

PEN Y BRYN SJ215382

Slab quarry, active in 1870s, disused by about 1890.

Remains. Excavation. There several other trials round about. [59]

POWIS SJ074294 CRAIG Y PISTYLL RHAEADR

A small hillside quarry, with possibly some underground working, opened 1834, closed 1873, and revived 1909 to 1911 when just 93 tons were produced. Block lowered by incline to a mill.

Remains. Quarry face, traces of incline, and concrete base of 1909 oil engine. Now a caravan park. Leat for a lead mine crosses the site. [16]

RHEWL SJ177446 (WORKS)
Reputed site of an (extremely early) 1830s/40s slate mill for CRAIG LAS.
Remains. Ruins of a woollen mill fed by Afon Cymmo, but no evidence of slate use. [40]

RHIW GOCH SJ169453 BWLCH Y GARNEDD
A mainly slab working, dating from 1847. Poor rock and bad communications scarcely justified the elaborate 1890s buildings. Following a period of closure, 34 men were employed in the early 1900s. Operated up to WW2, latterly employing about 5 men, producing well under 100 tons pa. A 12-hp steam engine drove two saws & two planers.
Remains. The quarrying area is much decayed and the formation of the hand-wound incline is scarcely visible. There are several substantial mill and other buildings of nice architecture, but the layout is confused. Notable are the marine tanks used for water storage. [35]

SARPHLE SJ141327
Very small. **Remains.** Quarry face rubbish runs, building traces. [27]

SPRING HILL SJ199351
Probable site of 1920s trials. **Remains.** Run in adit. [48]

TAN Y FOEL SJ199385
Open pit latterly owned (but not worked?) by CAMBRIAN.
Remains. Excavation, and two pits at 196388? [50]

TŶ DRAW SJ207375
Working in 1751. **Remains.** Traces of excavation. [53]

TŶ GWYN SJ176303
Trial. **Remains.** Excavation. [37]

TŶ NANT SJ163342
Trial. **Remains.** Excavation. [33]

TY'N Y GRAIG SJ161398 GLYNDYFRDEY
Small, old open working, possibly revived during early 1870s boom. Cart road to Glyndyfrdwy. **Remains.** Dressing sheds and rubbish runs. [31]

TY'N Y RHOS SJ074464
A tiny pit. **Remain.** Virtually none. [17]

TY'N Y RHYD SJ176342
Very minor digging. **Remains.** Excavation. [38]

WERNDDU SJ065481
Stone quarry, possibly was slate.
Remains. Nothing slate related [14]

WEST LLANGYNOG SJ049259
Underground , operated on a small scale from mid to end of the 19th century. Revived by the opening of the Tanat Valley branch railway in 1904, reduction being done at a mill to the south of the public road. In later years a 'home made' (diesel?) loco was used. Producer gas engine running off anthracite, powered a generator. Abandoned 1938 when pillar robbing to meet an urgent order caused a collapse.
Remains. Little in the quarry area apart from confused heaping of rubbish. A building is in use, possibly quarry connected, but on the tip area to the south of the road only bases of buildings remain. The adit at road level is collapsed, above chambers break out to bank. [9]

WESTMINSTER SJ171478 CRAIG NEWYDD, CRAIG Y GLEM.
The largest of several tiny pit workings, (171472, 176477 & 180485). Had a table incline, initially water balanced,

later possibly wound by a steam engine Operated 1870s-80s, revived in the 1890s with i.c driven mill. 1930s revival with sawing in a temporary shed. Closed 1935.

Remains. Bulk working has cleared much of the tips. Pit has been filled in. Vestige of top of haulage incline and some concrete machine bases from the 1930s revival. [36]

WYNNE SJ199379 BRONYDD ROCK

Originally a hillside working opened c1770, one of several in the area e.g. 188391 & 203390 developed in present form in the 1870s, underground from around 1890 with a water-powered mill in a compact area with an incline to the Glyn Valley Tramway. A steam haulage raised material, and later a water balance lifted rubbish to the tip. Subsequently an adit and a mill, were opened at a lower level. After amalgamation with CAMBRIAN a Pelton wheel drove a generator and a compressor. Peak output in its early 1900s heyday was around 2000 tons pa with 70 men employed. Closed 1905. Re-opened 1910-191 and again in 1923 with an oil engine to drive the compressor and another to back up the mill drive. Closed 1928, WW2 military storage, public water-source until 1952. Visitor centre 1970s-1990s.

Remains. On the upper site, buildings, including a fine drum house, re-used. Traces of wheel pit, exit incline, water balance, later gravity incline and a cut-an-cover tunnel. Lower site cleared. [49]

Section 14
SOUTH & MID WALES

General

Most of these quarries, almost all in the north of the old county of Pembrokeshire, were very small; the only 100+ employer being BELLSTONE/ROSEBUSH. Many ephemerally catered for very local requirements, using hand tools to produce a trifling output. Although subject to notorious speculation, several nucleated small communities, and in the 18th century Cardigan rivalled Caernarfon as a slate port. There were a few that were mechanised with an established pattern of trade and employment; several others have remains that are of note.

A feature of the area are the cliff-face sites, working (often unauthorised, between tides in isolated coves. A further feature is the absence of sand saws, apart from the few places having powered circular saws (and the mysterious saws at SOMMERTON), almost all sawing was by toothed hand-saws

On the Eastern Cleddau the slate is, uniquely to Wales, of igneous rather than sedimentary origin, its texture and green cast commanding a premium price in a niche market.

Near Carmarthen, there is a (rebuilt) mill at LLWYNPIOD, the nearest approach to a north Wales style integrated mill, in the area. Near Builth, PENCEULAN has the only genuine underground chambering work to be seen in south Wales. At Rheidol, PENTALWR has the only reasonably complete incline formation.

Transport

The majority of quarries were too small and their markets too local, to have developed of significant transport

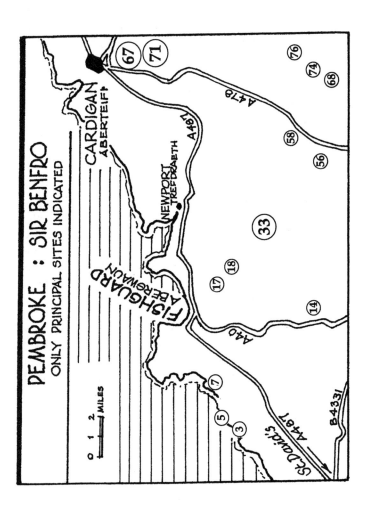

PEMBROKE : SIR BENFRO
ONLY PRINCIPAL SITES INDICATED

0 1 2
MILES

CARDIGAN
ABERTEIFI

NEWPORT
TREFDRAETH

FISHGUARD
ABERGWAUN

ST. DAVID'S

A487

A478

A487

A40

B4331

67 71

76
74
68

58

56

33

18
17

14

7

5
3

routes. A number on the coast such as PORTHGAIN loaded directly into boats and the only tramways were the 2-mile, 3′g PORTHGAIN - ABEREIDDI, horse-drawn line of circa 1860, and the short PENLAN and PENCELLI links. All are traceable.

Most interesting are the Teifi barges (At one time man-hauled) that served the FFOREST & CILGERRAN quarries.

Relatively good roads enabled ports such as Solva, Haverfordwest, Blackpool, St Clears and Carmarthen to be readily reached.

From the early 1850s the South Wales Railway (GWR) was available, remarkably two standard gauge branches from it were built principally to serve slate quarry needs. The North Pembrokeshire (Neé Maenclochog) Railway was laid down in 1876 almost solely to serve ROSEBUSH/BELLSTONE. Similarly the Whitland and Cardigan Railway of 1873 was built initially to serve GLOGUE. Closed in 1949 and 1962 respectively, both are traceable

Outside of Pembrokeshire, with the notable exception of the magnificent cart road of CHWAREL YSTRAD FFIN, no transport routes were developed although from the late 1860s some were able to use the L&NWR Central Wales line

1]	SM776304	Castell Coch
2]	794303	Cae Rhys
3]	795315	Abereiddi **
4]	798263	Treflodan
5]	813325	Porthgain ***
6]	817328	Henllys
7]	832329	Trwynllwyd **
8]	840331	Pwll Long

9]	845337	Longhouse
10]	864327 etc.	Trefelyn
11]	893384	Pwll Deri
12]	948336	Pantyphilip
13]	948374	Windy Hall
14]	960275	Sealyham **
15]	967341	Pant y Wrach
16]	971346	Esgyrn *
17]	985353	Cronllwyn *
18]	992302	Summerton **
19]	997389	Hescwm
20]	SN007292	Dyffryn
21]	010344	Cwmgwaun *
22]	017301	Catleblythe
23]	019399	Chwarel Pwdr
24]	020397	Chwarel Gerry
25]	026394	Fforest Farm
26]	034396	Parrog
27]	042342	Penralltddu
28]	063278	Blacknuck
29]	071402	Llwyngwair
30]	073281	Trebengych
31]	073282	Gotty Isaf
32]	076286	Glaslyn
33]	079300	Rosebush ***
34]	079303	Bellstone *
35]	080313	Pantmaenog
36]	081400	Ietgoch
37]	084404	Trefach
38]	085275	Mill
39]	094387	Coedcadw
40]	095283	Galchen
41]	096284	Vagur
42]	097312	Craig y Cwm

I

43]	098272	Temple Druid *
44]	104272	Llandeilo *
45]	105270	Llandeilo South
46]	106265	Noble Court
47]	108268	Teilo Vale
48]	110262	Lily *
49]	112272	Llyn
50]	113395	Henllys
51]	115265	Llangolman Farm
52]	119264	Pencraig
53]	124260	Clyngwyn *
54]	126269	Dandderwen
55]	126272	Cnwc y Derin
56]	128271	Gilfach *
57]	129262	Llwyn yr Ebol
58]	145294	Tyrch *
59]	158419	Llantood *
60]	163442	Pant y Grundy
61]	163454	Cwm Degwell
62]	167300	Klondyke *
63]	177290	Garwen
64]	178446	Dolau
65]	180452	Ridgeway
66]	186254	Tre Hir
67]	190450	Fforest **
68]	192278	Pencelli
69]	192359	Castellan
70]	192448	Rosehill
71]	195431	Cilgerran **
72]	197334	Troed y Rhiw
73]	202333	Pencware
74]	207284	Penlan
75]	211328	Nant y Geifr
76]	220328	Glogue **

77]	223327	Cwmgigfran
78]	226326	Cwmllwyd
79]	230324	Spite *
80]	296419	Pont Ceri
81]	313545	Lochtyn

Owing to there being so many tiny, ephemeral sites with a dearth of remains, only those with worthwhile relics are mapped.

Subsection 1 CARMARTHEN
1]	SN226227	Corngafr
2]	388311	Nantgerdinen
3]	418328	Nant yr Hebron
4]	420326	Penygraigygigfran
5]	425327	Cwmgraigeaufawr
6]	428339	Blaengyfre
7]	433299	Llwynpiod
8]	465244	Pantyglien
9]	505511	Llechwedderi
10]	535238	Eistedda Egwad
11]	585487	Cwmrhys
12]	603233	Dineswr

Subsection 2 LLANDOVERY.& MID WALES
1]	713256	Coed Sion
2]	727427	Pontarllechau
3]	735417	Cwm Merchon
4]	736421	Cwm Gwenlais
5]	741808	Pentalwr
6]	752428	Craig Rhosan
7]	757799	Ty'n y/ffodd
8]	787461	Chwarel Ystradffin
9]	851500	Cwm Irfon

10]	876565	Chwarel Ddu
11]	892608	Escair Ceiliog
12]	901614	Llanerch
13]	902616	Craig y Mynach
14]	905536	Penceulan
15]	906715	Pontarelan
16]	912617	Moelfryn
17]	958637	Graig Ddu
18]	925567	Alltyddians
19]	SO067479	Henallt

Also LLANIDLOES (Not mapped)
        SN844932   Dyfyngwyn

ABEREIDDI SM795315
A maritime quarry with land access. Worked in 4
galleries. Deepened into a pit, material being raised by a
horse-whim, replaced in 1849 by an 18-hp steam driven
lift Up to 60 men employed. Originally product was
loaded directly into boats, from the early 1860s a 3'g horse
tramway took material to PORTHGAIN. Closed c 1914.
Remains. The quarry pit is now open to the sea as a
passage was blasted in an attempt to make a small
harbour. This severed the line of the tramway and now
isolates the engine house, the lift structure and some
dressing sheds/ Alongside the line are a few survivors of
the 15 dressing sheds, various buildings including an
office, manager's house, powder house and a forge.
Below rail level is Abereiddi Row, a terrace of 7 workers
cottages. The rail formation round to PORTHGAIN is
readily traceable but much overgrown. [3]

BELLSTONE SN079302 PRECELLY
Hillside quarry, contiguous with ROSEBUSH, Operated

intermittently from 1825. Latterly used by Rosebush as a tip and water source.

Remains. Appears as three pits accessed and drained by cuttings. The southernmost pit also has a tunnel; the sole incline leads from this to a tip. Movement seems to have been mostly by cart or barrow. Several dressing sheds including a lean-to, in an access cutting The manager's house is still in use, in front of which are domestic buildings, possibly stabling. Much tipped material. [34]

BLACKNUCK SN063278
Extremely small pit working, 1870s?
Remains. Overgrown face. [28]

CAE RHYS SM794303 PORTH Y MEIBION
Early 19th century? **Remains.** Quarry face. [2]

CASTLEBLYTHE SN017301 GWARN
Small working possibly active through much of the 19th and early 20th centuries. Although the North Pembrokeshire and Fishguard Railway (1898 extension of the Maenclochog Railway) adjoined, it was not used. A quarry of the same name at SN020294 was not slate
Remains. Main working accessed via a cutting through an earlier tip. Some bar rail on site. Two trials nearby. [22]

CASTELL COCH SM776304
Two tiny cliff workings. **Remains.** Some scarring of cliff. [1]

CASTELLAN SN192359
Small, nothing known. **Remains.** Excavation. [69]

CHWAREL GERRY SN020397 CRAIG Y DYFFRYN?
Tiny cliff top working 1870s? **Remains.** Excavation. [24]

CHWAREL PWDR SN019399
Tiny cliff side working. **Remains.** Excavation, evidence of boat-accessed working in the vicinity. [23]

CILGERRAN SN195431 – 209431 Comprising; BBWMDWLL, DOLBADAU, PWDWR, PLAIN, CEFN, and other diggings.
A series of riverside diggings into the southern flank of the Teifi gorge, the ancient system of family-based partnerships having persisted here well into the 19th century. Originally all output was boated to Cardigan.

BWMDWLL (195432) an amalgamation of UPPER CASTLE with CASTLE was a substantial but unmechanised unit that lasted until the 1900s.

DOLBADAU (198431) being adjacent to the town dock had the advantages of wharfage and road access, but was constrained by the proximity of the town so had to excavate down using a steam crane. A steam mill was sited at town level, reached by a chain incline. Slate was enamelled on site, survived until the middle 1930s. By contrast although PWDWR (199431) absorbed some small neighbours it remained modest

PLAIN (204429) was on a larger scale, being an amalgamation of several small diggings. It had a mill building beside the main road, along which a horse walked to haul block up a ramp via a pulley and rope.

To the east of there were half a dozen diggings, that despite having the advantage of a riverside littoral had mixed fortunes and in the 1870s the landlord, Captain Gower amalgamated them as CEFN (207431) equipped with a steam mill having 3 saws, 3 planers a lathe etc. There was a steam crane, a 120-hp gas engine for a compressor, steam worked chain inclines and later a Blondin. Working was in terraces, specializing in slab.

Failing in the early 20th century part was re-constituted as PATS. Failing to restart after WW1, its Blondin and some workings were taken in by PLAIN who worked pits by steam crane until 1924. In 2000 work at CEFN recommenced on a small scale **Remains.** The BWMDWLL (CASTLE) workings are obliterated. The DOLBADAU pit has been filled but working faces remain; the mill foundations and a re-used building are at their upper site. Workings and building vestiges are at PWDWR while at PLAIN, at the riverside there is much disturbance from 1960s river works. At the top of the haulage ramp is the fine mill in reuse, a wall-crane being in situ. At the riverside at CEFN there are a number of building ruins. Above are an office and other structures including the mill now in agricultural use. There are modern sheds connected with the current small-scale working. [71]

CLYNGWYN SN124260
Hillside workings operating intermittently up to 1930s
Remains. The larger of the two lower workings, just a face, the smaller has traces of dressing sheds. The upper area, (traces of incline connection with sheave mounting) has a rake of three tiny alcoves. Three dressing machines (Originally from ROSEBUSH?) were bought in the late 1920s from GILFACH One was broken in transit, the wreck of one is in situ and the third is in the National Slate Museum There is a quaint powder store built into the rock near the river. Much overgrown. [53]

CNWC Y DERIN SN126272 also at 127270 GARN (GREEN), WEST GILFACH, WHITLAND ABBEY GREEN.
Two small workings operating at least from the mid 19th century, 1937 4 men. Now idle but still officially open.

Remains. One long cutting plus another small working, much rubbish, modern temporary building. At 127270 tiny overgrown pit, possibly the earliest working. [55]

COEDCADW SN094387
Pit, 16th century. **Remains.** Shallow pit. [39]

CRAIG Y CWM SN097312
In 1825 an opening was made at this considerable height but after just 4 years it was abandoned and (60!) men transferred to BELLSTONE.
Remains. Two scratchings, possible building and access track. [42]

CRONLLWYN SM985353
Terraced workings opened in the late 18th century extensively developed in the 1840s but geological problems caused it to close in 1860s.
Remains. No buildings on site, the tunnel that passed under the farm road from the larger of the workings has long since collapsed. Possible traces of a corresponding tunnel from the smaller working. [17]

CWM DEGWELL SN163454
Very small 16th century digging.
Remains. Excavations. [61]

CWMGIGFRAN SN223327 SOUTH GLOGUE
Moderate sized, contiguous with but separate from GLOGUE. Worked 1860s – 1880s. Had a planer so presumably also had powered saws.
Remains. A modern house occupies the working area, but there are traces of machine bases and buildings. [77]

CWMGWAUN SN010344
Tiny digging, the only one of a number in this vicinity to have yielded product. **Remains.** Two tunnels, one of

which seems to be an attempt to roof-up to a pit. [21]

CWMLLWYD SN226326 CLARE, LLWYN Y HWRDD, PARK
A small, pre 1820s, pit working the subject of 1860s speculation.
Remains. Excavation, traces of a building. [78]

DANDDERWEN SN126269 & 127268 WHITLAND ABBEY, TAN Y DDERWEN.
Two small quarries, operated up to about 1914. One described as 'slate' the other as 'Slab'. The easterly of lower working dates from the 18th century or before. Both the usual sedimentary and the igneous "Green" slate were worked. Great 1880s plans, including a rail link, never came to fruition.
Remains. Lower quarry is just a face with traces of buildings. The large, shallow and overgrown Upper quarry gently slopes down the vein. It reputedly had sand saws but sawn ends are hand sawn. [54]

DOLAU SN178446
Small hillside quarry.
Remains. Slight traces of excavation. [64]

DYFFRYN SN007292
Very shallow working opened 1860s, revived 1920-23 after a lengthy closure but did not use adjacent North Pembroke & Fishguard Railway.
Remains. Long shallow working, rubbish run and trimming waste. [20]

ESGYRN SM 971346
Two unconnected pits subject to doubtful speculation 1860s/70s.
Remains. Easterly pit just a face; westerly one is a narrow

319

cutting with, below a tunnel with sleepers and fragments of bridge-rail in situ. . [16]

FFOREST SN190450 – 193444 Including CAERNARVON, FFYNNON, TOMMY, BACH, GIGFRAN, FOREVER.

Originally independent diggings, 17th century or earlier, using the river for transport. In about 1860 they were developed as a unified working connected by a riverside tramway to a mill. This tramway continuing on to carry rubbish to a tipping area on marshy ground to the west. A steam crane was used. A proper wharf was built and housing provided on site. Good rock yielded a merchantable product, but the competition of North Wales slate brought in by rail, forced closure in 1885.

The on-site community survived up to the late 1920s.

Remains. The site is now a wildlife park, accessed by the track bed of the old railway, which post-dated the quarry working. The original entry was past Fforest Mansion.

Several buildings and dwellings in the mill area have been re-used but all trace of the turbine- driven mill with saw(s) and a planer, has gone. Most of the workings are overgrown but TOMMY, the easternmost of the three "Big" quarries, has a tramway/drainage tunnel some 40m long. The tramway route along the riverbank is clear and there is possibly a concurrent leat. The slate-built wharf is a nice feature. A limekiln, clearly much antedating the quarry is near the mill area. [67]

FFOREST FARM SN026394

Tiny working 18th century or earlier material dispatched over beach. **Remains.** Working faces, much slate on the beach. [25]

GALCHEN SN095283
Trial 1911? **Remains.** Digging, access track. [40]

GARNWEN SM177290
Ancient working, subsequently a source of stone.
Remain. Nothing slate-connected. [63]

GILFACH SN128271 LLANGOLMAN, including BACH,
CWAR GLAS, & GILFACH DDOFN
The largest and most successful of the Eastern Cleddau
quarries dating from at least the 16th century, developed
in the mid 19th century, but the late 1870s recession ended
plans for a rail link Able marketing of its speciality
'Green' igneous product enabled a workforce of 40 to be
maintained throughout the inter-war years. Closed late
1980s.
Remains. The site is much disturbed by bulk working
and tipping covers the early riverside workings, the later
working slants downward to a substantial quarry face
with traces of terracing. Extant is the base for the car
engine that powered the shallow incline. There is a
modern galvanised shed, an office, ruins of a smithy and
some dressing sheds. There are some tramway
formations but barrows were much used.
   At 128259 little BACH working has been engulfed by
waste. Down river at 128166, is the tiny CWAR GLAS pit.
GILFACH DDOFN at 132270 has been completed filled
in. [56]

GLASLYN SN076286
Putative site. **Remains.** Possible excavation. [32]

GLOGUE SN220328 GLÔG
A substantial hillside quarry formed by the merging of
two (early 17th century?) workings. Material was

321

lowered by incline to a 4 saw/2 planer mill powered by a water wheel, (later by an 18-hp turbine). As the pits deepened this incline was superseded by tunnels. Carting to Blackpool and later Narberth station was eliminated by the opening of the Whitland & Taf Vale, (Later Whitland and Cardigan) Railway in 1873.

When the eastern pit was abandoned, work centred on roofing slates from the western pit, a further tunnel being cut to part way down the exit incline as this pit deepened. At its peak almost 100 men were employed but trade faded towards the end of the 19th century.

There was bold attempt at revival in the mid 1920s with the mill being driven by electricity from a generator powered by an oil engine. The turbine was retained to grind waste for a brick-making plant.

Bad trade and the freight on the heavy bricks brought closure in 1926

Remains. The eastern pit has been filled with waste from later working of the western pit. There are vestiges of the upper incline and of the inner end of the upper west pit tunnel. The mill area is impenetrably overgrown; bulk working has obscured the rest of the site. The railway spur is traceable; several dwellings were undoubtedly quarry houses. [76]

GOTTY ISAF SN073282
Tiny hillside quarry possibly not slate. **Remains,** Excavation only. [31]

HENLLYS SM817328
Cliffside working, 1870s-1880s, later owned by PORTHGAIN.
Remains. Traces of a wall (building?) high up on cliff. [6]

HENLLYS SN113395
Small. 16th century working. **Remains.** Shallow diggings. [50]

HESCWM SM997389
Tiny cliff-face working. Material from this and other workings on the west side of the Dinas peninsular were boated, possibly to Parrog. Company abortively formed 1870s. **Remains.** Vestiges near the top of the cliff. [19]

IETGOCH SN081400 & 081404(?)
Vernacular workings. **Remains.** Pits at roadside. [36]

KLONDYKE SN167300 DOLMAEN, FOEL
Small quarry subject to much speculation in the laterhe 19th century.
Remains. Flooded pit with collapsed tunnel, traces of buildings. [62]

LILY SN110262 LLANGOLMAN
Subject of much mid-19th century speculation.
Remains. Excavation, traces of dressing shed(s). Trial at 108265. [48]

LLANDEILO SN104272 etc including CHWAREL GLAS
The two CHWAREL GLAS workings at 103276 and 103277 had a mill and workshops from around 1870 the larger working at 104272 is later.
Remains. The southernmost, quarry is flooded, the mill is in reuse, there are dressing sheds, abutments of a bridge and a short tunnel [44]

LLANDEILO SOUTH SN105270
Operated in a small way from c1860 to the 1950s.
Remains. Narrow working, site cleared. The sole machine seems to have been a dressing machine probably ex-ROSEBUSH, that was on site for many years. Possibly

used barrows. There is a nice cart-loading platform. Cottage buildings nearby are obviously associated. [45]

LLANGOLMAN FARM SN115265 CHWAREL FAWR
Tiny pit latter 19th century. **Remain.** Much overgrown excavation. [51]

LLANTOOD SN158419 & 157418 etc.
Very small. **Remains.** Possible excavation. [59]

LLWYNGWAIR SN071402
Source for estate use only. **Remains.** Working face, waste heaps. [29]

LLWYN YR EBOL SN129262 & 127260
A working right on the boundary of the "Green" igneous slate that was the subject to an ambitious C1880 scheme to unite this and neighbouring quarries into one vast unit with a rail-served mill on the valley floor.
Remains. On the easterly site a deep pit, tunnel (one of two?) open. The building and embanked rubbish run may pre-date the big scheme. At the near-river site are two adjacent faces with a small two-roomed building (Smithy?) and much waste, some tipped into the river. [57]

LLYN SN112272
Tiny hillside trial one of a number in this valley. 6 men 1937.
Remains. Trifling excavation.. [49]

LOCHTYN SN313545
Cliffside working active (Part time?) to 1930s. **Remains.** Scant. [81]

LONG HOUSE SM845337
Tiny working c1860. **Remains.** Excavation. [9]

MILL SN085275

Small pit possibly closed c1850.

Remains. Overgrown pit some walling, building with fireplace, dressing waste. Posssibly also tipped on the far side of the road. [38]

NANT Y GEIFR SN211328

Small, producing coarse slate for local use. **Remains.** Quarry face. [75].

NOBLE COURT SN106265

Disused by the late 19th century. **Remains.** Heavily overgrown. Other workings or trials at 107264 & 108264 etc. [46]

PANTMAENOG SN080313

Small working in tiny "slots" also traces at 080314. **Remains.** Pits blocked for ROSEBUSH water supply. [35]

PANT Y GRUNDY SN163442

16th century? **Remains.** House and transport depot on the site. [60]

PANTYPHILIP SM948336

A modest operation mainly slab and block, it has in late years been used for bulk stone and perhaps some slab. **Remains.** Quarried area only. [12]

PANT Y WRACH SM967341

Mentioned 1870s-80s by which time any extraction had ceased.

Remains. Excavation, tunnel at 968942 may have been connected. [15]

PARROG SN034396 etc

Cliffside quarry. Material was dropped down to the beach at Traethbroden, which was only accessible by boat.

There were other similar workings to the east of Cat Rock that were accessible by cart at low tide. Material was brought to Parrog harbour from where they were re-shipped.

Remains. Scarring of cliff faces. Much slate waste at harbour. [26]

PENCELLI SN192278
A bold late 1870s development to take advantage of the (then) Whitland & and Taf Valley Railway. Lasted little more than months. A schedule mentions saws and planers and quaintly a "machine for lifting stones".

Remains. Pit with blocked tunnel no sign of buildings. The incline leads down to a tramway that passes under the railway to what may have been the site of a mill and upstream, a reservoir. [68]

PENCRAIG SN119264 PARC?
Local-use digging 1840s? **Remains.** Excavation. [52]

PENCWARE SN202333
Small local source? **Remains.** Filled-in pit. [73]

PENLAN SN207284 ELWYN VALLEY
A hillside working opened at the same time as PENCELLI, equally unsuccessful but did probably last into the early 1880s. . Finished product was taken by tramway to a siding north of Rhydowen station.

Remains. Much overgrown quarrying area with vestige of a small building. The tramway is traceable. Buildings near the railway would seem to have quarry associations. [74]

PENRALLT DDU SN042342
Small. For sale 1842. **Remains.** Possible excavation.[27]

PONT CERI SN296419

Accessibility made this a useful source, possibly over a long period.

Remains. Quarry area closed. [80]

PORTHGAIN SM813325 ST BRIDE'S

A cliff-top pit working, almost exclusively producing slab. Opened in the 1830s and developed into a self-contained community dependant on sea communications. Material taken down by incline to a mill (24' water wheel with 20-hp Hazeldines engine back-up), near the harbour. As the pit deepened, 3 horse-whims were used (Two to raise, one to pump?), later replaced by a 16-hp Robey engine. Employment was very variable but around 50 was typical. Diversified into bricks and granite in the 1890s, slate production ceased by WW1, all work ending in the 1930s.

Remains. The large pit itself and the incline down to the mill. There are traces of the mill with a wheel pit fed by a fine slate leat and having an interesting lavatory above the tailrace. There are several other buildings including a restored warehouse. The harbour office is particularly attractive. The brick built granite hoppers are a most prominent feature; behind them are numerous remains from the granite operation, including a loco shed. The tunnel to the harbour from hoppers under the pit that brought brick-clay is intact but gated.

The village initially of 58 quarry-owned dwellings is now co-operatively owned and to its east are the remains of the brick kilns. [5].

PWLL DERI SM893384

Two tiny cliff-top workings.

Remains. Excavation, access tracks. [11]

PWLL LLONG SM840331

Tiny cliff-face workings. **Remains.** Scarring of cliff face.
[8]

RIDGEWAY SN180452

Working in 1888 as part of Maldgwyn estate.
Remains. Quarrying face. [65]

ROSEBUSH SN079300

A series of ancient hillside workings, were developed on
4 levels in the 1870s into the only undertaking in the
region to operate on anything like a 'North Wales' scale,
with multi-terrace working and certainly the only one to
have its own standard guage line (The Maenclochog
Railway).

A water turbine drove a mill near the railhead, wind
power is said to have been planned, (for slate dressing?).
Its 100-man and near 5000 tons heyday was very brief
and well before the end of the 19th century it was
virtually idle, final closure coming in 1914. Enamelled
slate was advertised, but this would have been from the
Magnus works in London.

Remains. The site is accessed via the rail track bed, past
the manager's house, the shop and the 26 cottages of
Rosebush Terrace, all still in use.

Although the boundary wall still exists it was worked
as one site with BELLSTONE, with disciplined terraces,
sending rubbish to the north and good block to the south.
Little remains of Levels 1 & 2, from where material was
lowered by incline to Level 3, where together with Level
4 (connected by incline). Slate dressing was done in back-
to-back dressing sheds. (The Turner dressing machines,
that were allegedly going to be wind-powered,
eventually found their way to other quarries).

A further incline lowered material down from Level 4.

A tunnel on Level 5, with a nice portal, removed rubbish and one on Level 6 served as a drain and an exit route, (both now blocked). There is evidence of slate making on the quarry floor during its last days.

Small pits (with pipe work) at the old PANTMAENOG quarry have been blocked to form a water supply to the mill augmented by a small reservoir to the north and by leat work on the hillside. Until the mid 20th century village depended on the same supply.

There is a trial boring on Level 4, trial diggings above the site, but no trace has been found of the (mapped) windmill.

The walls of the fine pilastered mill (that had 4 saws and 3 planers) survive with a pit for the Francis turbine in one corner. Opposite is the matching loco shed, but save for a powder house to the west, no other non-domestic buildings have survived.

Other houses in the village were quarry houses and are mostly still in occupation. The Precelli Hotel is still in its temporary galvanised sheet form. The ornamental gardens, laid out to attract visitors after the fortunes of the quarry declined are overgrown but still visible. The station has been revived as an ornamental feature. [33]

ROSEHILL SN192448
Two workings at least from 1820s, across the river from FFOREST.
Remains. Several small diggings, walling and wharf. [70]

SEALYHAM SM960275
A pit working operating from 1825 to 1885 in the 'back garden' of a gentleman's residence. It can scarcely have provided a return on the substantial investment made.

Waterpower originally hauled out of the pit as well as pumping and powering the mill, there being a substantial diversion of the river to keep clear of the workings and to provide supply.

Steam was introduced during an early 1870s development. Finished slate including some slab was carted to Haverfordwest for shipment.

Remains. The carriage drive from Sealyham house turns to follow its diverted route across 'Quarry Bridge' The original route passes overgrown buildings that may be cottages or an old mill, and the site of the wheel of the original pump.

Near the flooded quarry is a shaft and possible adit. A trench suggests flat rods of a pump discharging into the diverted river, the original course of which is obvious. The wheel pit for a subsequent pump and spillway discharging into the river is in a cutting. A fine embankment carried water to this wheel; its pump pipe rising from the floodwater.

To the west are two waste run levels blocking the old line of the river. It is believed that there was an engine on each of these levels. The incline wound by the upper (newer?) engine (12-hp) is just discernable. No location has been identified for the two saws and planer listed as being on site, nor evidence of water having been used at this end of the site, nor have sawn-ends been found. [14]

SUMMERTON SM992302

A substantial working dating from about 1830, deepened into a pit with a cutting access, which also drained. Then, as the workings became deeper still, some kind of ropeway and/or vertical lift may have been used to up haul. It seems to have had a tramway leading to a water powered mill having "sawing machines" in the 1830s. The underground workings are believed to be for metal. Closed 1880s

Remains. A somewhat enigmatic site. In the face of the pit (accessed by a cutting), are three adits, one having evidence of chambering.

Immediately to the west is a structure that could have been a winding house for a slant, and some 300m north is a filled-in square shaft. (All from early metalworking?) . On either side of the pit are pillars perhaps for an aerial ropeway and on the western side are substantial remains of what could have been a vertical lift (Presumably pre-dating the cutting), or it could have been a bucket pump of unknown power source. (Wind?) Nearby on this western side are two further pillars of unknown purpose.

A causeway 250yards long runs to the west, described as a dam it (there was a watercourse leading to it from a pond a mile to the east). It appears to be a tramway leading to ruined buildings. These ruined buildings, much overgrown, include a curious structure resembling a two arched bridge, its purpose is not clear but could be the mounting for the mysterious "sawing engines", sawn ends show diagonal reciprocating saw-marks, like those of the hand-saws universally employed in Pembrokeshire but here possibly water-power driven. Down hill are traces of a building with a wheel pit. Alongside are circular-sawn ends. It is unclear if the two sawing sites were successive or complementary[18]

SPITE SN230324 LILAC, NANT Y WEIRGLODD
Small pit, subject to intense 1860s speculation.
Remains. Shallow working with cutting access, a wall with alcoves suggest an intended rake of 4 dressing sheds; only one being built. [79]

TEILO VALE SN108268
Due to the popularity of the "Green" slate and the success of GILFACH an attempt was made to revive this long-

disused working in 1912/14 in conjunction with KLONDIKE.
Remains. Quarrying faces, possible building. [47]

TEMPLE DRUID SN098272
Some commercial quarrying 1860s. Working of a sort up to 1921.
Remains. Quarry faces, building vestiges and a leat from the pond suggests a water-powered mill. The extant water wheel is from a 1920s electricity plant. Digging at 099467 may be associated. [43]

TREBENGYCH SN073281
Intermittent working 1830-80? **Remains.** Shallow excavation. [30]

TREFACH SN084404 (LOWER) & TREFACH UPPER
Old workings with attempts to expand in mid 19th century.
Remains. Upper is just an overgrown pit but the lower is larger, has an interesting wall and building now in re-use. The nearby mill had no slate connection. [37]

TREFELYN SM864327 & 868326
Small workings latter part of 19th century?
Remains. Two excavations in trees alongside the river. [10]

TREFLODAN SM798263 TREDOLAN?
This is the presumed site of a (possibly fraudulent) 1860s speculation.
Remains. A severely overgrown quarry face, "Slate like" material. [4]

TRE HIR SN186254
Tiny vernacular working, the 1879 report of lead being found was clearly untrue. **Remains.** Filled-in pit. [66]

TROED Y RHIW SN197334

Despite the railway passing nearby, it was not used, possibly because small output did not justify the cost of an access bridge. Worked in the 1920s, with portable sawing machine?

Remains. Quarry face with cutting access. Old saw-ends hand sawn, newer ones circular sawn. Nicely revetted tip, a small curious slab may have been connected with portable machinery. [72]

TRWYNLLWYD SM832329

Cliffside terraced quarry, producing slab, operated in conjunction with PORTHGAIN in the latter part of 19th cent. Steam engine (10 hp) used for both mill and winding.

Remains. Quarry area virtually inaccessible. At cliff top are the ruins of a nice little mill building with engine or boiler house alongside. The run of the chain-incline is clear, the rock being cut out to give a straight haul. At its head is the base for a haulage sheave. The waste runs contain circular sawn ends. [7]

TYRCH SN145294 & 158291 TURKE, TWRCH FOEL DYRCH

A substantial working of the 'Green' volcanic slalte dating from the 18th century. The lower site was substantially developed in 1921 with the upper site acting as a source of block. The water-powered mill was abandoned and a new 2-saw, 8-hp diesel powered mill erected. The 16.5-hp turbine that had replaced the mill wheel in the 1890s was re-used to drive a generator. A 50-hp oil engine drove a compressor. 400 tons p.a. with up to more than 20 men was maintained almost until the late 1930s closure. Enamelled slate offered but this was not made on site,

Remains. On the upper site, a narrow pit, collapsed access tunnel and traces of dressing sheds. At the larger, lower site, behind the road, diverted to allow its expansion, is the flooded pit. A pipe replaces the tunnel under the road to the working area. There, are the ruins of the old mill with water channels plus the part brick modern sawing mill and vestiges of an office and other buildings. The dwelling probably predates the quarry. There are also tiny diggings at 152297 & 145289. [58]

VAGUR SN096284 HAFOD DDU, MAENCLOCHOG
Small working active 1860s/70s and possibly 1912
Remains. Pit to north of road overgrown, pit to the south filled. [41]

WINDY HALL SM948374
Small site producing rough block. **Remains.** Quarry face. [13]

Subsection 1 CARMARTHEN

BLAENGYFRE SN428339
Tiny. **Remains.** Excavation. [6]

CORNGAFR SN266227
Tiny quarry of convenience.
Remains. Excavation. Nearby farm buildings are of great interest. [1]

CWMGRAIGEAUFAWR SN425327
Abortive 1860s attempt to develop. **Remains.** Filled in pit. [5]

CWMRHYS SN585487
Small working used by the Peterwell estate. 2 men in 1906. **Remains.** Pit used as refuse dump. [11]

DINESWR SN603233
Mention of slate quarrying here 1767.
Remains. Possible traces at this location. [12]

EISTEDDA EGWAD SN535238
Hillside quarry, very small, marginal material.
Remains. Possible building. [10]

LLECHWEDDERI SN505511
Small, part time, in use early 1900s.
Remains. Small working area and tip. [9]

LLWYNPIOD SN433299
Pit working from at least 1833. The steam-powered mill, possibly with 2 saws and a planer dates from 1864.

Material trammed in direct from the quarry, then as the pit deepened, by a haulage. When the rubbish area to the south of the mill became full, a bridge was built to permit tipping to the east of the road. The pit was drained by a 120-yard tunnel.

A coarse and heavy roofing slate was produced, but slab product was good. Fines were sent to Carmarthen for brick making at. Closed 1920s. A tramway to Carmarthen was planned but not built.

Remains. The mill has been rebuilt for re-use. The mountings for the gantry over the 3 machine positions can be seen. There is space for trimmers but it is doubtful if these were installed. There is a platform for the engine in one corner and behind the building a boiler house with base of demolished stack. There is an under floor cistern, and some drains, which also seem to have served an adjacent building. The pit having been filled, there is no trace of the incline but there is some evidence of a rope connection to the mill engine to power it.

There is possible trace of the outlet end of the tunnel.

The tip on the far side of the road was largely removed to provide hardcore when Penysarn estate was built. [7]

NANTGERDINEN SN388311

Tiny, worked part time?

Remains. Dressing waste. No buildings. [2]

NANT YR HEBRON SN418328

Small working possibly only for local use.

Remains. Pit, A small house now in re-use was called 'Quarry Cottage', tiny shed and curious stone-lined dugout. [3]

PANTYGLIEN SN465244

Possibly 18th century, mall workings on either side of the road. In the 1860s, in common ownership with LLWYNPIOD, the western site was developed, the eastern being used for tipping.

Remains. Quarry faces, site cleared but housing is still occupied. [8]

PENYGRAIGYGIGFRAN SN420326

Enigmatic working in a narrow valley, possibly 18th century, developed twice in 1860s. [4]

Remains. Pit accessed by a tunnel. A half-buried arch-top, and both observation and map evidence suggest the possibility of at least trials underground. The main feature is the causeway that seems to have been a dam for waterpower for planned machinery, as well as carrying a tramway to the railway, where there is a formation for a never-laid siding. Walling but no buildings. Dressing waste on site, but sawn ends must have been from some kind of portable saw. [4]

Sub Section 2 LLANDOVERY & MID WALES

ALLTYDDINAS SN925567
Small surface workings, some underground?
A number of very shallow workings exploiting outcrops of shales. The reduction process seems to have been mainly by selection and trimming with little or no splitting. Probably a quarry of convenience operating over many years. Work possibly ceased around 1860. Material carted via Cwmdulais farm.
Remains. At least 6 extraction points with associated dressing areas. Tips but no buildings. Lowest working has an adit (open), probably a trial.
   One of the upper dressing floors has a large stock of, much decayed, product, mainly taper top moss-slates. Original cart track traceable. [18]

CHWAREL DDU SN876565
Primitive operation on a scarp exposure.
Remains. Virtually none apart from a zigzag access path. Early slates in the Elan Valley identified with this source. [10]

CHWAREL YSTRAD FFIN SN787461
A 'Classic' tiny hillside quarry, deepened into a pit that was accessed by a tunnel, mostly shale but some material had a good colour and split.
Remains. Extensive rubbish runs, vestiges of several dressing sheds, but the tunnel has vanished under a massive slide. The most spectacular $1^1/2$-mile access track is well engineered with nice retaining walling. [8]

COED SION SN713256
Small pit working, shales? **Remains.** Possible digging. [1]

CRAIG RHOSAN SN752428

A small working of somewhat doubtful material. In grounds of Neuadd Fawr mansion (1784).

Remains. Excavation, waste, working platform and access track. [6]

CRAIG Y MYNACH SN902616

Tiny roadside working.

Remains. Traces of excavation. [13]

CWM GWENLAIS SN736421, 737422, & 742423

The first two are tiny underground workings, the more easterly may have produced saleable product. The third is a slot about 3' wide working a band of shale-like rock, very much like a metal mine.

Remains. The westerly adit has collapsed; the easterly is a cave-like working with dressing waste on the rubbish run. The slot working seems to be deep as there is a considerable volume of waste. There are the abutments of an access track bridge. [4]

CWM MERCHON SN735417

Small hillside working.

Remains. Face and dressing shed ruins. [3]

CWM IRFON SN851500

Underground. In 1890 5 men produced 80 tons.

Remains. Some vestige of an access road, but adit lost in forestry. [9]

ESCAIR CEILIOG SN892608 DALRHIW

Several workings in a tiny rift valley, possibly some underground. Worked late 1880s. In 1886 produced 89 tons

Remains. Dressing sheds, some rail on ground, large quantity of waste. Unidentified building at valley mouth. [11]

GRAIG DDU SN958637

Possible very small-scale extraction.

Remains. Interesting anticline dynamic metamorphosis formation. [17]

HENALLT SO067479

Open quarry, latterly (early 20th C.) producing shale building block identified in nearby housing. May have yielded roofing material.

Remains. Excavation only. [19]

LLANERCH SN901614

Very small working, possibly some underground.

Remains. Dressing sheds on 2 levels. [12]

MOELFRYN SN912617

Small hillside working. **Remains.** Much degraded quarry face. Cleared working area. Access track. [16]

PENCEULAN SN905536

Open quarry/underground. An old quarry of convenience with a notable attempt to chamber work in the Meirionnydd manner. 1889 15 tons.

Remains. Working faces seemingly haphazardly developed in confused rock conditions, with dressing sheds, two sets being in rakes of three.

Adjacent to the upper adit are some buildings including a weighbridge and what may have been a small mill. Possible unfinished incline. This adit penetrates about 50 metres. Part way along a start was made on a cross heading along the strike, opposite this is a strike tunnel from which there are two roofing shafts cut up the dip, one sound, the other collapsed. No extraction appears to have been made.

Lower down site there were possibly two other levels with adits collapsed/tipped over.

At lowest level there is a further adit leading to 2 small chambers one of which opens up to level above, which has been worked out to bank. [14]

PENTALWR SN741808 CADLO
Hillside quarry, very shaley product.
Remains. Intense folding on working face. Drum house, masonry and incline formation that cut the disused Llanwernog lead mine leats. [5]

PONTARLLECHAU SN727427
Hillside quarry of complex geology, possible some slate.
Remains. Interesting quarry face, bases of stone crushers. [2]

PONTARELAN SN906715
Shallow open quarry. **Remains.** Possible vestiges of a building. [15]

TY'N Y FFORDD SN757799
Tiny hillside quarry, nothing known. **Remains.** Excavation only, intense local folding with some cleavable material. [7]

LLANIDLOES

DYFYNGWYN SN844932
Old hillside quarry, possibly slate. **Remains.** Excavation only

Also putative sites 811932, 817931, 847931, 854875, 878858, 89x00x, 90x90x, 929869, 951855, 929868

Selected Bibliography.

Carrington, D.C., *Delving in Donorwig*, GCG, 1994.

Davies, D.C., *Slate & Slate Quarrying*, Crosby, Lockwood, 1878.

Davies, D.L., *The Glyn Valley Tramway*, Oakwood, 1962.

Dodd, A.H., *The Industrial Revolution in North Wales*, U of W Press, 1971.

Edmonson, C., *Chwarel Wynne*, Glyn Quarry, 1995.

Gwyn, D.R., *Industrial Heritage of Slate*, Gwynedd A T, 2000.

Jancock & Lewis, *Conglog Slate Quarry*, Adit,2006.

Holmes, A., *Slates from Abergynolwyn*, Gwynedd A.S, 1986.

Isherwood, G., *Candles to Caplamps*, Gloddfa Ganol, 1980.

Isherwood, G., *Cwmorthin Slate Quarry*, Merioneth F.S., 1982.

Isherwood, G., *Slate*, A.B.Publishing,1988.

Jermy, R.C., *The Railways of Porthgain & Abereiddi*, Oakwood, 1986.

Jones E., *Bargen Dinorwig*, Ty ar y Graig, 1980.

Jones, G.R., *Blaen y Cwm Slate Quarry*, Jones, 1991.

Jones, G.R., *Hafodlas Slate Quarry*, Jones, 1997.

Jones, G.R., *Rhiwbach Slate Quarry*, Jones, 2005.

Jones, I.W., *Victorian Slate Mining*, Landwark, 2003.

Jones I.W. &, *Llechwedd & other Ffestiniog Railways*, Quarry Tours, 1977.

Jones, R.M., *The North Wales Quarrymen* 1874-1922, U of W, 1982.

Kellow, J., *The Slate Trade of N. Wales, Mining Journal*, 1868.

Lewis, M.J.T., *Early Wooden Railways*, R.K.P, 1970.

Lewis, M.J.T., *Llechi, Slates*, Gwynedd A.S., 1976.

Lewis, M.J.T.(Ed), *The Slate Quarries of North Wales in 1873*, S.N.P.S.C., 1987.

Lewis, M.J.T, *Sails on the Dwyrd*, S.N.P.S.C., 1989.

Lewis, M.J.T., *Blaen y Cwm & Cwt Y Bugail Slate Quarries*, Adit Publications, 2003.

Lewis&Denton, *The Rhosydd Slate Quarry*, Cottage Press, 1974.

Lewis & Williams, *Pioneers of Welsh Slate*, S.N.P.S.C., 1987.

Lindsay,J., *The History of the N Wales Slate Industry*, D & Charles, 1974.

Lloyd, L., *The Port of Caernarfon*, Lloud, 1989.

Lloyd. L., *Pwllheli*, Lloyd, 1991.

Lloyd. L, *The De Wintons of Caernarfon*, Lloyd, 1994.

Lloyd, L., *The Port of Caernarfon 1793-1900*, Gwasg Pantycelyn, 1989.

Lloyd, L., *Wherever Freights May Offer*, Lloyd,1993.

Lloys, L., *A Real Little Seaport*, Lloyd, 1996.

Napier, J., *Rhosydd*, GCG, 1999.

North, F.J., *Slates of Wales*, Nat.Mus.of Wales, 1925.

Price, M.R.C, *The Whitland & Cardigan Rly*, Oakwood, 1976.
Rees,D.M., *The Ind. Archaeology of Wales*, David & Charles, 1975.
Richards & Jones, *Cwm Gwfrai*, GCG, 2004.
Turner, S, *The Padarn & Penrhyn Rlys*, David & Charles, 1975.
Williams, G.J., *Hanes Plwyf Ffestiniog*, Hughes & Son, 1882.
Williams, M., *The Slate Industry*, Shire, 1991.
Williams & Lewis, *Gwydir Slate Quarries*, S.N.P.S.C., 1989.
Williams & Lewis, *Pioneers of Ffestinog Slate*, S.N.P.S.C., 1987.
Williams & Lewis, *Chwarelwyr Cyntaf Ffestiniog*, S.N.P.S.C., 1987.

S.N.P.S.C. = Snowdonia National Park Study Centre, Plas Tan y Bwlch

Traditional Roofing Slate Sizes

Empresses	26 x 16
Princesses	24 x 14
Dutchesses	24 x 12
Small Dutchesses	22 x 12
Marchionesses	2 x 11
Countesses	20 x 10
Viscountesses	18 x 9
Wide Ladies	16 x 10
Broad Ladies	16 x 9
Ladies	16 x 8
Small Ladies	14 x 8
Narrow Ladies	14 x 7

Terms Singles, Doubles, Headers etc used for smaller sizes

INDEX

Aber	285
Abercorris	259
Abercorrs	260
Abercweiddaw	260
Aberdeunant	151
Abereiddi	314
Abergwern	285
Aberllefenni	261
Abergwynant	224
Adwy'r dŵr	88
Adwywen	88
Afon Alice	237
Afon Cletwr	210
Afon Deri	265
Afon Dulas	265
Afon Gaseg	26
Afon Hirddu	210
Afon Nadroedd	210
Afon Oernant	88
Afon Wen	26
Alexandra	117
Allt Ddu	43
Alltgoch	238
Allt Llechi	64
Alltwen	43
Alltyddinas	337
Ardda	88
Arddu	43
Aran	210
Arthog	224
Beaver Pool	88
Bedd Porus	210
Bellstone	314
Bera Bach	26
Berthlwyd	151
Beudy Ffridd	210
Berwyn	286
Blacknuch	315
Blaengyfre	334
Blaen Nant	88
Blaen Nant	152
Blaen y Cae	64

Blaen y Cwm	178
Bodegri	34
Bod Silin	26
Bontnewydd	26
Boundary	43
Bowydd	179
Braichmelyn	26
Braich	118
Braich Ddu	210
Braich Goch	265
Braich Rhyd	119
Braich y Rhiw	238
Brechiau	26
Britannia (Works)	34
Brithdir	287
Brondanw Isaf	152
Brondanw Uchaf	152
Brongarnedd	152
Bron Goronwy	211
Bronydd	26
Bronydd Isaf	26
Bron y Fedw	119
Bron y Foel	135
Bron y Rhiw	211
Bryn Bugeiliaid	211
Bryn Castell	64
Bryn Engan	88
Brynygelynnen	152
Bryneglwys	136
Bryneglwys	238
Bryn Fferam	119
Brynglas	211
Bryngwyn	224
Bryn Hafod y Wern	27
Brynhaul	88
Bryn Llwyd	266
Bryn Llwyd Uchaf	266
Bryniau Duon	88
Bryn Manllyn	120
Bryn Mawr	43
Bryn Mawr	224
Bryn Neuadd	224
Bryn Rhug	225
Buarthau	89

Bwlch Adwy Wynt	287	Cefn yr Orsedd	28
Bwlch Cwmllan	120	Cerrig y Felen	241
Bwlch Geuallt	89	Chwarel D Hughes	91
Bwlch Goleu	152	Chwarel Ddu	91
Bwlch Gorddinan	181	Chwarel Ddu	290
Bwlch Gwyn	89	Chwarel Ddu	337
Bwlch Gwyn	287	Chwarel Fawr	45
Bwlch Siglen	240	Chwarel Fedw	91
Bwlch y Ddeufaen	89	Chwarel Gerry	315
Bwlch y Ddwy Elor	121	Chwarel Gethin	92
Bwlch y Groes	44	Chwarel Glyn Lledr	92
Bwlch y Slaters	181	Chwarel Goch	46
Byrdir	212	Chwarel Isaf	46
Cae Baty	240	Chwarel Las	28
Cae Goch	90	Chwarel Llechwedd Deiliog	213
Cae Gwegi	90	Chwarel Llew Twrog	213
Cae'n y Coed	212	Chwarel O Parry	92
Cae'r Defaid	225	Chwarel Pwdr	316
Cae'r Gors	153	Chwarel R Jones	28
Cae Madog	90	Chwarel S Jones	93
Caer Drewyn	287	Chwarel Twm Ffeltwr	182
Cae Rhobin	90	Chwarel y Plas	136
Cae Rhys	315	Chwarel Ystradffin	337
Caermenciau	44	Chwythlyn	93
Caethle	241	Cilnant	290
Cambrian	44	Cilgerran	316
Cambrian	287	Cilgwyn	64
Carnedd y Ci	212	Clegir	291
Carters	213	Cletwr	213
Castell	153	Cletwr	241
Castleblythe	315	Clipiau	241
Castell Coch	315	Clochnant	291
Castellan	315	Clogwun Garw	214
Castell Cidwm	122	Cloddfa Sion Prys	136
Castell y Bere	241	Cloddfa'r Coed	66
Cedryn	90	Clogwyn William	93
Cefn Clawdd	213	Clogwyn y Fuwch	93
Cefn Coch	91	Clogwyn y Gwin	122
Cefn Cyfarwydd	91	Clyngwyn	317
Cefn Du	44	Cnicht	154
Cefn Gam	225	Cnwc y Derin	317
Cefn Glas	213	Coed	28
Cefn y Braich	153	Coedcadw	318

Coed Cefn M's M'r	241	Cwm Bychan	28
Coed Cerrig H'n	214	Cwm Caeth	157
Coed Ffriddarw	226	Cwm Ceunant	29
Coed Madog	66	Cwm Cloch	158
Coed Mawr	94	Cwm Clorod	95
Coed Pant Bach	241	Cwm Cowach	242
Coed Sion	337	Cwm Cŷd	158
Coed Tir Llanerch	291	Cwm Cynfal	215
Coed y Chwarel	136	Cwm Cynfal	242
Coed y Chwarel	241	Cwm Ddu	242
Coed y Ffridd	266	Cwm Degwell	318
Coed y Llechau	214	Cwm Dylluan	266
Coetmor	28	Cwm Dwyfor	136
Colomendy	291	Cwm Ebol	242
Conglog	182	Cwm Eigiau	95
Conglog	214	Cwmerau	267
Cook & Ddôl	46	Cwm Fanog	183
Corngafr	334	Cwm Fynhadog	96
Cornel	94	Cwmgigfran	318
Cornwall	66	Cwmgraigeaufawr	334
Corwen	291	Cwmgwaun	318
Craig Glanhafon	291	Cwmgwnlais	338
Craig Las	291	Cwm Glas	29
Craig Rhiwarth	291	Cwm Gloddfa	267
Craig Rhosan	338	Cwm Irfon	338
Craig Wynnstay	293	Cwm Lefrith	136
Craig y Cribin	293	Cwm Leri	243
Craig y Dduallt	293	Cwmllwyd	319
Craig y Mynach	338	Cwm Machno	96
Craig yr Orin	293	Cwmmaengwyn	294
Craig y Cwm	318	Cwm Merchon	338
Crawia (Works)	47	Cymmo	295
Cregiau Geuallt	95	Cwm Mynach	226
Cribwyd	154	Cwm Orthin	183
Croesor	154	Cwm Penamnen	98
Croesor Bach	157	Cwm Rhaeadr	243
Croes y D'y Af'n	214	Cwm Rhys	334
Cronllwyn	318	Cwm Teigl	215
Crown	123	Cwm Tydi	295
Crymlyn	28	Cwm Tywyll	215
Cwellyn	123	Cwm Ych	243
Cwm Bach	136	Cwm y Foel	158
Cwm Brechiau	242	Cwm yr Hengae	268

Cwt y Bugail	184	Ffridd Ddwy Ffrwd	98
Cyfannedd	226	Ffridd Isaf	123
Cynllyd	98	Ffridd Isaf	226
Dandderwen	319	Ffridd Llwyd	216
Darren	268	Ffridd Llwyn Hynydd	244
Deeside	296	Ffriddllys	98
Deeside Works	296	Ffridd Olchfa	226
Diffwys	186	Ffridd Uchaf	98
Dinas Ddu	158	Ffridd y Bwlch	189
Dineswr	335	Ffridd y Cloddfa	216
Dinorwig	47	Ffynnon Badarn	270
Dolau	319	Ffynnon y Gôg	297
Dolfanog	269	Foel	98
Dolfeirig	215	Foel	297
Dolfriog	158	Foel Clynog	68
Dolgarth	136	Foel Cwm Sion Lwyd	216
Dôl Goch	29	Foel Fawr	244
Dôl Goch	243	Foel Forfydd	297
Dolgoed	269	Foelgron	216
Dôl Pistyll	29	Foel Isaf	68
Dolwgan	137	Foel Isaf	137
Dolydderwen	269	Foel Rudd	100
Donnen Las	53	Foryd (Wharf)	69
Dorothea	67	Foty y Waun	270
Drum	215	Friog	226
Dulyn	98	Fron	124
Dyffryn	319	Fron Boeth	158
Dyfyngwyn	340	Frondiron	53
Drysnant	244	Fron Fraith	270
Eglwyseg	296	Fron Goch	244
Egryn	226	Fronheulog	244
Eistedda	335	Fron Hyfryd	53
Era	269	Fronlog	69
Esgair Angell	244	Fron Oleu	160
Esgairgeiliog	269	Fron Serth	227
Escair Geiliog	338	Fron Ucha	297
Esgyrn	319	Gaewern	270
Fforest	320	Galchen	321
Fforest Farm	320	Gallt y Fedw	69
Ffridd	29	Gallt y Llan	53
Ffridd	98	Gallt y Mawn	29
Ffiidd Bryn Moel	98	Gaenwen	321
Ffridd Cocyn	244	Garreg Fawr	125

Garreg Felen	137	Gwernlasteg	161
Garreg Uchaf	160	Gwernor	70
Garreg Wen	137	Gwydir	100
Garth	137	Gyllellog	246
Garth	227	Gyryn	29
Gartheiniog	245	Hafod Arthen	100
Garth Fach	246	Hafod Dwryd	100
Gau Graig	227	Hafod Fawr	217
Gelli	160	Hafon Gwynfe	297
Gelli Bach	70	Hafod Gwyrdd	100
Gelli Gain	217	Hafodlas	101
Gelli Grin	217	Hafod Uchaf	161
Gernos	246	Hafod y Llan	162
Gerynt	161	Hafod y Wern	127
Gilfach	321	Hafoty	163
Glan Dinorwig (wks)	53	Hafoty	272
Glandulas	272	Henallt	339
Glandyfi	246	Henblas	103
Glanrafon	125	Henddôl	229
Glan y Don	189	Hendre	103
Glanyrafon	297	Hendre Ddu	139
Glaslyn	321	Hendre Ddu	246
Gloddfa Gwanas	227	Hendre Eirian	229
Glogue	321	Hen Ffridd	103
Glyn Aber	100	Henllys	322
Glyniago	272	Henllys	323
Glynrhonwy Lower	54	Hengae	272
Glynrhonwy Upper	55	Hescwm	323
Goat	161	Dr. Hughes	29
Goedwig	272	Hwlfa	104
Goedwig West	272	Idris	230
Gofer	100	Idwal	30
Golwern	227	Ietgoch	323
Goodmans	56	Inigo Jones (Works)	70
Gordeddau	138	Isallt	139
Gotty Isaf	322	Klondyke	323
Graig Ddu	189	Ladas	56
Graig Ddu	339	Lefel Dŵr Oer	191
Graig Uchaf	217	Liberty	104
Groes Llwyd	229	Lily	323
Graig yr Ogof	246	Llan	104
Gwastad Fryn	246	Llandderfel	217
Gwern Bwys	100	Llandeilo	323

Llandeilo South	323	Moel Eilio	129
Llaneilian	35	Moel Faen	299
Llanerch	339	Moelfaban	30
Llanfair	217	Moelfferna	298
Llanfflewin	35	Moelfre	140
Llangolman	324	Moelfryn	217
Llangristos	36	Moelfryn	339
Llantood	324	Moel Lefn	141
Llechan Uchaf	104	Moel Llechwedd	217
Llechwedd	191	Moel Marchyria	105
Llechwedd	248	Moel Tryfan	129
Llechwedderi	335	Moelwyn	194
Llechwedd Gwyn	297	Moel y Croesau	218
Llidiart yr Arian	163	Moel y Gest	141
Lloc	56	Moel y Gwartheg	218
Llwyn Onn	297	Moel y Pen y Bryn	105
Llwyngwair	324	Morben	251
Llwynon	230	Morfa Lodge	141
Llwynpiod	335	Muriau Bychan	218
Llwyn yr Ebol	324	Mynydd Ednyfed	141
Llwyd Coed	70	Mynydd Ty'n y Ceunant	274
Llyfnant	248	Mynydd y Waun	274
Llyn	324	Nant Alltforgan	218
Llyngwern	273	Nant Canolbren	105
Llyn Llagi	164	Nant Dôl Hir	251
Llyn y Gadair	128	Nant Fach	300
Lochtyn	324	Nantgerdinen	336
Long House	324	Nantglyn	301
Lydan	104	Nantgwynant	164
Machynlleth	248	Nant Heilyn	30
Maenofferen	193	Nant Minllyn	251
Maes y Gamfa	248	Nant Pistyll	218
Maes y Pandy	249	Nantlle Vale	70
Manod	104	Nantyr	301
Marchlyn	56	Nant yr Eira	251
Marine Terrace	140	Nant y Fron	71
Matthews Mill	274	Nant y Geifr	325
Mellionen	164	Nant yr Hebron	336
Melynllyn	104	Nant y Mynach	251
Mill	325	Nant y Sarn	218
Minllyn	249	Nant y Wrach	105
Moelcrynddyn	297	Nilig	301
Moel Drongydd	105	Noble Court	325

Noddfa	218	Pennant	106
Nyth y Gigfran	195	Pennant	252
Oakeley	196	Pennant Ucha	106
Ochwr Fwsoglog	30	Penrallt	326
Oernant	301	Penrhiw	106
Ogof Fawr	36	Penrhyn	31
Owain Goch	199	Penrhyngwyn	230
Pandy	251	Penrhyn Llwyd	142
Pandy	274	Pentre Dŵr	304
Pant Cra	230	Pentre Felin	304
Pant Dreiniog	30	Pentalwr	340
Pant Eidal	251	Penybanc	142
Panteinion	230	Pen y Bedw	106
Pant Glas	301	Pen y Bont	106
Pantgwyn	218	Pen y Bryn	72
Pantmaenog	325	Pen y Bryn	252
Pant Mawr	164	Pen y Bryn	304
Pant yr Afon	199	Pen y Ffridd	106
Pant y Darren	31	Pen y Gaer	107
Pantyglien	336	Pen y Garreg	274
Pant y Grundy	325	Pen y Graig	252
Pant yr Onnen	230	Penygraig	336
Pantyphillip	325	Pen y Gwryd	167
Pant y Wrach	325	Pen yr Orsedd	73
Pant yr Ynn	200	Perfeddnant	252
Parc	165	Plas Du	75
Parc	251	Plas y Nant	130
Parc (Slab)	166	Pompren	107
Parc Driscol	57	Pontarllechau	340
Parrog	325	Pontarelan	340
Penarth	302	Pont Ceri	327
Penbryncaled	105	Pont Faen	252
Pencelli	326	Pont Rhyd Goch	142
Penceulan	339	Pont y Carw	107
Pencraig	142	Porthgain	327
Pencraig	326	Porthlwyd	108
Pencware	326	Porth Treuddyn	167
Peniarth	251	Powis	304
Penlan	105	Pretoria	130
Penlan	326	Prince Llewelyn	108
Penllyn	57	Prince Llewelyn	142
Penllyn	105	Princess	142
Penmorfa	142	Prince of Wales	143

Pwll Deri	327	Tan y Bwlch	33
Pwll Fanog	75	Tan y Darren	231
Pwll Llong	328	Tan y Foel	305
Queens	218	Tan y Gader	231
Ratgoed	274	Tap Du	278
Rhaeadr	253	Tap Tŵr	231
Rhewl	305	Targwrmoel	253
Rhiwaedog	219	Tarran Cadlan	278
Rhiwbach	200	Tarren Hendre	254
Rhiwgoch	108	Teilo Vale	331
Rhiw Goch	305	Temple Druid	332
Rhiw'r Gwreiddyn	277	Trebenig	332
Rhiw Rhedyn Cochion	231	Trecastell	112
Rhos	109	Trefach	332
Rhosydd	168	Trefarthen	36
Rhyd Goch	111	Trefelyn	332
Rhyd y Sarn	203	Treflan	130
Rhyd yr Onnen	253	Treflodan	332
Ridgeway	328	Tre Hir	332
Rosebush	328	Troed y Rhiw	333
Rosehill	329	Trwynllwyd	333
Rowlyn	111	Tu Hwnt y Bwlch	144
Sarphle	305	Twll Coed	77
Sarn Helen	219	Twll Goch	57
Sealyham	329	Twll John Ffowc	77
Serw	219	Twll Llwyd	77
Siglen	111	Tyddyn Agnes	78
Singrig	75	Tyddyn Llwyn	144
South Pole	203	Tyddyn Mawr	144
Spite	331	Tyddyn Shieffre	232
Spring Hill	305	Tyddyn Uchaf	112
Summerton	330	Tyrch	333
Swch	111	Tŷ Cerrig	144
Tai Cynhauaf	219	Tŷ Draw	305
Tai Hirion	219	Tŷ Gwyn	305
Tai Newyddion	253	Tŷ Mawr Green	78
Taldrwst	75	Tŷ Mawr	219
Talmeuryn	253	Tŷ Mawr	254
Talmignedd	76	Tŷ Mawr West	78
Tal y Fan	112	Tŷ Nant	232
Tal y Llyn	112	Tŷ Nant	306
Tal y Sarn	76	Ty'n y Berth	278
Tanrallt	77	Ty'n y Bryn	112

Ty'n y Ceunant	278
Ty'n y Coed	219
Ty'n y Coed	232
Ty'n y Fach	254
Ty'n y Fallen	113
Ty'n y Ffridd	34
Ty'n y Ffordd	340
Ty'n y Garth	254
Ty'n y Graig	306
Ty'n y Llan	144
Ty'n Llwyn	78
Ty'n y Rhos	306
Ty'n y Rhyd	306
Ty'n y Weirglodd	79
Vaynol	57
Vagur	334
Vivian	57
Votty	203
Wenallt	279
Waen y Fedwen	113
Wernddu	306
Wernfawr	220
Wern Ifan	79
West Llangynog	306
Westminster	306
Windy Hall	334
Wrysgan	203
Wynne	307
Wynnstay	254
Y Cefn	220
Y Garnedd	220
Y Garth	34
Ymlych	145
Ynyscyngar	145
Ynystywyn	145
Ynysypandy	145
Ysgubor Gerrig	146
Ystumiau	113
Yr Horon	254
Yr Ogof	34